THE SCIENCE OF ART

Other Books by Robert E. Mueller

EYES IN SPACE
INVENTOR'S NOTEBOOK
INVENTIVITY

THE
SCIENCE
OF
ART

The Cybernetics
of Creative Communication

ROBERT E. MUELLER

with drawings by the author

THE JOHN DAY COMPANY
NEW YORK

TO HAROLD H. LANIER,
*a brilliant friend who conceived his own
theory of communication;
and to my children,*
ERIK THOMAS
and
RACHEL ANNE GEORGETTE
*May they generate an art awareness
sufficiently profound to comprehend
future science.*

Contents

TABLES

Preface

COMMUNICATION is the root idea of our age, just as evolution or relativity was for previous generations. Its theoretical considerations provide us with skeleton keys to unlock many modern mysteries. However, Professor Norbert Wiener's brainchild, cybernetics, which applied electrical communication concepts to analogous biological systems, has had only limited application to human communication problems. A more recent twist of this kaleidoscopic theory suggests that we have only begun to understand its potential, namely the more general studies of communication conducted by Marshall McLuhan and others.[1] I venture to suggest that even more spectacular results are in store for us as these communication ideas are deepened and scientific cybernetics is brought to bear on the more interesting problems of art communication and the establishment of human values.

Communication as an electric phenomenon is rather restricted and one-dimensional. When you consider art, however, you enter a domain of broad meanings, containing structures and human values whose complexity transcend the ciphers of simple electrical exchange systems. The question is to determine just how meanings are generated and communicated in the various media which comprise our present and potential art forms. The creativity of these communications becomes important and we are forced to evaluate how specific art systems can be humanly original and meaningful. If it can be shown that a creative communication is at the core of our most valuable human experiences, or if we can assay the extent to which all our intellectual activities—including the scientific—are dependent on them, we will approach an area of communication theory with tremendous implications. This book investigates the creative aspects of art communication, where *creative* means the origination or invention of an insight that is presented to our senses in the very elements by which a communication is made. The approach is both from the standpoint of cybernetics and general communication studies.

The initial impulse to write this book occurred four years ago. During the Seattle World's Fair the art critic of *The New York Times*, John Canaday, was more impressed by the shapes of the scientific satellites than by the artistic architectural structures. He wrote an article suggesting that the scientist is unwittingly creating the true artistic expressions of our age.[2] I was working as a scientist at the time, in the laboratory in which Tiros, one of the satellites that Canaday had admired, was designed and built. I had watched Tiros grow at RCA-Astro, and I was intimately familiar with the reasons behind its actual configuration—none of which was deliberately aesthetic. I wrote this to Canaday, indicating that scientists might be creating a "new nature" to which artists could react, arguing that the interesting shapes of scientific constructs were not art, although they might be impressive to artists.

Shortly thereafter Op art became the rage—the science of physiological optics began to have new meaning for artists, critics, and the public alike. I began to wonder if indeed I had overlooked an artistic possibility simmering beneath my nose. I visualized the most amazing science-as-art show of the century: three-dimensional, televised, computer-controlled, multicolored pictures and sculptures, set to the strains of stereophonic, electronic-synthesized music. But in reality I was committed to the traditional media: oil painting, drawings, etchings, and woodcuts. Moreover my feeling was that new media did not make the artist modern, although I could not deny the fascination of inventive techniques in art. This train of events led me to a reevaluation of modern art forms and media, and to a study of the uses and limitations of science as the source of serious art expressions.[3]

But the actual origin of this book goes back much further. I have been interested in the relationship between art and science since I first started to paint as an undergraduate at the Massachusetts Institute of Technology in 1946. Then I was in the Navy V-12 college training program studying electrical engineering, after having served as a radar technician in the Navy for a few years at sea. It was with great reluctance that my college advisor had allowed me to cross the discipline boundary to take an art course. It was my good fortune to take my first formal art course at M.I.T. with the artist-educator Gyorgy Kepes, a student of László Moholy-Nagy of the Bauhaus and the author or editor of many books relating art and science.[4] I was just beginning to think seriously about a career as an artist, and I barely recall the details of my first course with Kepes; but reading him now sounds many familiar chords.

At about the same time I met a brilliant student, Harold H. Lanier, who had conceived an idea several years previously which obsessed him. This idea had to do with communication, and whenever Harry had the chance he bent my ear about it. We heard a rumor that Professor Norbert Wiener was also working on communication theory, and we discussed it with him on occasion. Although Professor Wiener was encouraging to us he was necessarily vague about communication theory since the Second World War was in progress and his ideas were top secret. During that time Harry and I also considered some of the communication problems of art.

Later the epochal concepts of Norbert Wiener and his associate Claude Shannon were published,[5] and communication theory was presented to the world in a precise mathematical form which neither Harry nor I could have imagined. Communication, and its investigation, was just then becoming a part of the intellectual climate, and it is not surprising that it was anticipated by Harry. Harry and I also brainstormed inventions together, one of which the Navy patented for us.[6] This marked the beginning of my interest in the creative process; I gave the Stratton Paper on creativity during my senior year at M.I.T., and recently published several books on the subject.[7]

Upon graduation I went into industry, but I discovered that the creativity of science interested me less than the creativity of art. I decided to return to college to study art and to major in philosophy, having some remaining funds under the G.I. bill of rights. I went to New York University in Washington Square, where my most influential art teachers were Myrwyn Eaton and Samuel Adler; I studied aesthetics with the poet Delmore Schwartz and philosophy with William Barret and Albert Hofstadter. Professor Hofstadter, although he does not know it, influenced me profoundly. I also studied painting afterward with Gregorio Prestopino and printmaking with Antonio Frasconi.

About then I also wrote my first autobiographical novel. I have continued to make a periodic venture into novel writing, recently with the counsel and criticism of my novelist neighbor Benjamin Appel. I have supported myself as a scientist, science writer and illustrator since then (with occasional stints as a puppeteer with Diana, my wife), devoting my creative energies to art (visual primarily, but also literary). Only now and then would an invention idea come out in my work as a scientist. Periodically I left industry and painted, wrote or traveled. Financial reasons have constantly forced me back to science, and although I enjoy working as a scientist if the work is creative, I do not take it very seriously—a fact that many of my employers have sensed and understandably looked on with dissatisfaction. I was compelled to keep abreast of the developments of science, however. During this period I have never quite got communication theory out of my mind, and I have continually jotted down ideas of theoretical or sociological interest as I encountered various problems in the arts.

Books such as T. Munro's *Towards Science in Aesthetics*,[8] F. Kainz's *Aesthetics and Science*,[9] or W. B. Honey's *Science and the Creative Arts*[10] seemed to me to overlook what I felt to be the main issues. The poet hit closer when he investigated music and meter, as in J. P. Dabney's *The Musical Basis of Verse*[11] or in *The Science of English Verse*[12] by Sidney Lanier, a distant relative of my friend Harold Lanier. Abraham Moles's book *Information Theory and Esthetic Perception*[13] approaches the problem from the standpoint of the cyberneticist, recognizing that art entails complex encoding schemes which the traditional information theorist overlooks; but he fails, it seems to me, to understand how the deeper creative meanings are generated in art by its peculiar encoding system. *Science and the Creative Spirit*, a collection of four essays, has many relevant passages. Karl W. Deutsch, also a professor of mine when I was at M.I.T., explores the mutual resources and constraints of science and culture, in the same spirit as my Chapter 1.[14] David Hawkins recognizes that the mathematical theory of information provides "a theoretical perspective within which communication is seen as expression of the basic features of life, that it is able to maintain itself at a higher level of energy and organization than its organic environment,"[15] an idea which I pursue in detail at the end of Chapter 2.

It was once thought that the imaginative outlook of the artist was death for the scientist. And the logic of science seemed to spell doom to all possible artistic flights of fancy. The antagonism between science and art, between the logical and the aesthetic reaction to experience, seemed to me to resolve itself if they were both considered as communication phenomena. Each entails a structured communication between men: art for the purpose of *creating* a new reality, science for the purpose of *describing* the reality of nature. I began to see the need for a careful elaboration of what is meant by communication in art, in particular what is created and how it is made into a communicative package. The idea slowly took hold of me that man's consciousness was due to the building of creative communications in humanly perceptual forms. When we give a mechanistic explanation to a concept which has a vitalistic existential quality, we are always suspicious. Electricity, for instance, has been attributed to the flow of electrons, yet such an explanation does not seem sufficient to account for the mystery of lightning or electrical power. However, to be good, a theory need only describe the facts and lead to predictions which are borne out in practice. A theory that postulates the primacy of man's art over his science may seem farfetched, but the cogency of the conclusions that can be made from this assumption has led me to believe that it may be an example of a relatively simple concept hidden in historical prejudices which have tended to discredit it. The conclusions of this book, however, do not depend on this assumption, since I am primarily concerned with art and not science. A more difficult task would be to assemble the facts behind the generation of scientific ideas in order to substantiate this thesis, which I only present here in passing (formulated theoretically at the end of Chapter 2).

If indeed it is true that science presupposes art, it is a beautiful rationale for my own personal motivations which led me from creative activities in science into the realm of art. And here too is a way to help rectify the current discrepancies many thinkers have noted between science and art, leading perhaps to the marriage which C. P. Snow has argued was so important today,[16] or to the reemphasis of general knowledge, as E. H. Gombrich has suggested.[17] A demonstration of a basic art-science interdependence would help bring together the impersonal outlook of the scientist and the humanistic viewpoint of the artist—which is, I feel, greatly to be desired.

The Britton House   ROBERT E. MUELLER
Roosevelt, New Jersey
May, 1967

THE SCIENCE OF ART

1

Art and Science

1

THERE are many ways to compare art and science. Art usually suggests the humanities that emphasize the anxious, creative, irrational aspects of concrete experience; and science, the calm, systematic, rational formulation of general experience. Differing fundamentally in their modes of operating on experience, art and science could be so separate as to be independent, and any comparision would seem to be meaningless. Jacques Barzun puts them poles apart: science complicating with artificial absolutes, art elaborating with anthropomorphic reactions of man.[1] A more sympathetic relationship is suggested by Aldous Huxley in his *Literature and Science*. He concludes that "the sciences of life have need of the artist's intuition, and, conversely, the artist has need of all that these sciences can offer him in the way of new materials on which to exercise his creative powers."[2] In the past hundred years science has changed exceedingly rapidly, being matched only by the pace of art in the last ten years. It is not particularly meaningful to say that art envolves human tensions, because although the products of science are supposed to be objective, the scientist may be less than relaxed when he creates his calm productions.

There is agreement that art and science are two activities which share the same human creativity. They are "equal, but not identical, assertions of man's attempted mastery over what would subdue him," as David Hawkins writes.[3] This places science in the humanities, welds art and science into a single human discipline, although it is multifaceted or many-moded. Artists and scientists have expressed a similar view many times.

Goethe thought that the beautiful in art is a manifestation of the secret laws of nature which the artist discovers. Constable said, "Painting is a science, and should be pursued as an inquiry into the laws of nature." Wordsworth said that the poet should "follow in the steps of the Man of Science." Balzac and Zola considered themselves sociological scientists, and Flaubert wrote that poetry is as exact a science as geometry.[4] Scientists have again and again expressed their feeling that the most imaginative productions of science were close to the artistic. Einstein felt that his anxious searching for harmonious structures in the darkness of nature was not unlike the artist's quest for beauty.[5] A recent explanation of the most abstruse mathematics concludes that modern mathematicians, deeper in impractical research than ever before in the history of mathematics, were "trying to make precise the intuitions of poets."[6]

Although the Baconian antithesis between science and poetry as thinking versus feeling has gone out of fashion today because it is "simplistic," the cliché that both science and art are children of human creativity may also hide an important truth or so. It is not enough to emphasize the humanistic foundations of science, to show how the scientist is after all a human being with both creative and irrational impulses and limitations. Nor can an upgrading of the artist to an important cultural position suffice to clarify the issues involved. The problem is to make a basic reevaluation of what we generally mean by the disciplines of art and science in order to determine if we are in fact overlooking something meekly hiding beneath a dichotomy with no meaning.

The idea proposed by Martin Johnson, that science and art are antithetical, internecine as well, would be extremely valuable if it could be demonstrated to be true. He cites two examples as proof: first, the fact that the East did not develop a practical science, being prevented from doing so, according to Johnson, because of a preoccupation with an artistic-religious mystique; and second, Leonardo da Vinci's denial of science and eventual capitulation to the fantastic creatures and catastrophic drawings of his later period.[7] There may be other, more convincing explanations for these developments, however. Such a fundamental relationship as this, although a destructive one, is not a cliché, however, and it has the merit of bringing the issue of art versus science out in the open.

Recent media investigations indicate that man is considerably more dependent on his sensual experience for the logic of his thought than has been supposed. Marshall McLuhan notes that "any extension of the sensorium by technological dilation has a quite appreciable effect in setting up new ratios or proportions among our senses," and William Ivins, in discussing the Greek mathematical theories, writes that the tactile senses of the Greeks were too highly developed and that it limited their geometry to corresponding tactile concepts.[8] Had the visual world begun to dominate, a visual world in which parallel lines do obviously meet, the Greeks might have transcended purely Euclidian geometry. Since art obviously alters the "human sensorium" as does technology, we can only conclude that there is a circle of mutual interdependence between art and science. This may be one reason, as Stefan Toulimin and June Goodfield say in *The Discovery of Time*,[9] that throughout centuries of intellectual endeavor the growth of men's consciousness of many subjects, from theology and the historical sciences to the natural sciences, has taken closely parallel forms.

The historical fact remains that science is a much later development than art, but historical inference is often misleading. Man was making viable art when he was still in the cave; and science waited until the advent of the sophisticated cultures of Babylonia, Egypt, or Greece before it began to rear its modern head, and until the start of the Renaissance before it stood up and shook its wings in preparation for total flight. Without opening a philosophical Pandora's box we can safely suggest that art, unlike science, is less concerned with natural reality than with a created, imagined reality, almost a priori like mathematics. The caveman discovered spirits in the stars and made the gods to control his destiny; and he thought the cracks in cave walls resembled animals, and traced them with root juices to make them permanent. The primitive art-urge was expressed by forming the fantastic in tangible, physical shapes; and then the science-urge rushed in to suggest the practical value of the fantastic. Art aided early man in his hunting because the animal was as good as captured when it was drawn. We see mostly game animals in the great Cro-Magnon murals, and it was important that early man trained his artist, whose magic was the science of the time, for the practical reason of survival.

When early tools were developed the art forms could be made more elaborate; traced images could be transformed into carved forms. Sculpture is the picture- or image-making urge improved by technology. Down through the ages artists have appropriated technology whenever it helped them to make the jump from fantasy to fact with a greater ease. The discrepancy between a dream and its physical embodiment leads the artist to embrace technological improvements to help him close the gap. The sequence may not be immediate, as George Kubler says in *The Shape of Time*,[10] but it is implicit and potentially available for the artist in his development. Greek sculpture profited immediately from technical solutions to the bronze casting of complex structures, with a greater freedom of expressiveness in its forms. Renaissance painters seized on theories of perspective to improve their representation and on the development of oil paint and resins to increase the color possibilities of their palettes. The Impressionists derived their ideas on color and perception from the works of Herman von Helmholtz and Michel Chevreul.

Modern artists are so overwhelmed with science and technology that they are forced into a mad race through media and

methods. Every season seems to bear a new crop of artistic produce. Unless you keep carefully informed some succulent artistic
fare may pass you by, and, overripe, fade away before you know
of its existence. The solitary stream-of-consciousness is plural-
ized in the New Wave French novel; experimental film is taken
over by the painter seeking a more pliable medium; avant-garde
theater, also in the hands of painters, turns into "happenings";
dance gives up story and obscures the human figure in nonobjectivity, keyed to electronic music; Abstract Expressionism falls
to Action painting, is erased by Pop art, and then swamped by
Op art; atonal music becomes serial, then aleatoric, allowing the
preformer a choice in the composition, and the computer tries to
join the ensemble. Fad after fad, movement after movement, in
a confusing and rapid succession, challenge the serious art buff
and overwhelm the innocent bystander. As McLuhan writes, the
"wild broncos of technological culture have yet to find their
busters or masters. They have found only their P. T. Barn-
ums."[11] The "tradition of the new," to use Harold Rosenberg's
phrase,[12] has become the only modern tradition, and technology
is its logical father. But to what extent can we attribute this
assortment of art movements to modern science and technology
alone?

A larger view admits that the confusions of modern art are the
result of many forces: technological to be sure, but also economic, political, and social. Yet science and technology are unde-
niably influences of great import today; ours is essentially a
scientific culture. In *Science: The Glorious Entertainment*,
Jacques Barzun traces some of these myths and their meaning for
us due to our predominantly scientific culture.[13] The most powerful art form in the modern world in fact owes its existence
entirely to technology: the talking motion picture. We are too
close perhaps to other modern inventions and developments,
such as television, the tape recorder, the computer, drugs or electronic stimulus to the brain or supplements to our senses, to
begin to guess what fundamental art forms they might germinate.

But since Whitehead's *Science and the Modern World*,[14] we have realized the influence of science on cultural states of mind, and in turn the impact of science on art.

It is clear, but I think it must be emphasized, that art is more than a technological innovation like printing, the pianoforte, or photography. These three inventions have had tremendous influence on their respective arts: without photography painting would probably not be so abstract or nonobjective today; music would probably have remained untempered without the need to adjust a harpsichord for all key signatures, and as a result who knows how much less atonal today's music would be; and certain stories or poems, such as those by e. e. cummings, would not be possible without the typewriter. Most authors soon realize that there is a fundamental difference between handwritten and typewritten prose, and adapt their work habits accordingly. This accounts for Truman Capote's wry criticism that Jack Kerouac's prose is "typewritten" instead of "written," implying that it was unthinkingly run off on a mechanical device. One can conclude that however dependent on technology, the unique use of a new innovation appropriate for art gives it a certain ascendancy over the technology of its birth.

While technology influences art, art also has an important role to play for modern man, hopelessly enmeshed in technological achievements. The artist is singularly aware of the present, and, as Marshall McLuhan says in *Understanding Media: The Extensions of Man*: "The serious artist is the only person able to encounter technology with impunity, just because he is an expert aware of the changes in sense perception."[15] All science, all technology affects our sense perceptions, and those who understand this can read the future of our changing awareness of nature and of human life. The artist is a seer when he grasps the implications of a new medium and can guess how our perceptions will be altered by them, formulating an art which depends on this alteration for its comprehension. The artist may not be aware of what he is doing, but intuitively he may have grasped what the scientist has not yet begun to comprehend.

In general, then, there are four main ways in which science and technology influence art, as detailed in Table I.

TABLE I—WAYS SCIENCE AND TECHNOLOGY INFLUENCE ART

1. CHANGING MEDIA BY:
    a. Making new media (photography, motion pictures)
    b. Improving old media (oils, acrylics, electronic musical instruments)
    c. Combining media (talking motion pictures, television)
2. INSPIRING ARTISTS WITH:
    a. New revelations of nature (the new landscape, microscopic worlds, outer space)
    b. The effects of interesting new constructions (mathematical shapes, satellites)
    c. New world views (evolution, relativity, the unconscious, communications)
3. COMMUNICATING ART FORMS BY:
    a. Recording (film, printing, magnetic tape)
    b. Immediate exchange (radio, television, relay satellites)
4. IMPROVING HUMAN UNDERSTANDING OF:
    a. Human functions (psychology, psychoanalysis, sociology, drug experiments)
    b. Art processes (aesthetics, cybernetics, psychology, criticism)

2

The developments of photography and the motion picture are related examples of media that technology provided the artist for his exploitation. Erwin Panofsky suggests that this is the first time in the history of art that something other than the urge to expression motivated the creation of an art form.[16] Here was an automatic image maker, and it had immediate repercussions for the painter, heretofore the dominant producer of images. As a result, the technique of the virtuoso brush stroke and the craft and techniques of painting, became the preoccupations of the painter. But scientists, as well as painters, Maurice Grosser suggests in *The Painter's Eye*,[17] were interested in the optics of the world of the eye. The pictures of Manet, Sargent, and Whistler, although quite painterly and devoted to techniques, held the eye up as a criterion. They emulated instead of opposed the camera, admiring Velasquez, whom they considered as having an almost "scientific" detachment; or Ingres, who created realistic black-and-white positives and tinted them like a photograph. The camera was an ideal to be emulated, actually an ideal which had been anticipated years before by the Renaissance painters. Then Leone Alberti had conceived of painting as a window through which to look at the visible world, and Leonardo da Vinci, Dürer, and Brunelleschi had advanced the theory of artistic perspective that *tracing* objects of the visual world on the plane of a sheet of glass is how the eye sees, and accordingly how art should present reality.

The motion picture can be seen as an extension of the puppet theater in mechanical form. Its first step was the comic strip, invented in 1845 by the Swiss humorist and draftsman Rodolphe Töpffer.[18] With the discovery by Peter Mark Roget (of *Thesaurus* fame) that the eye maintained an image and persisted in its vision for a short time after the exposure to a picture, the frame-by-frame artificial motion of Töpffer's picture-novels was quickly transformed into action motion pictures. The first instrument to present the illusion of motion was the Zoëtrope, invented by the Frenchman Pierre Désvignes, and it immediately became a popular toy.[19] Dancing clowns, somersaulting puppet-like figures, barely acceptable as serious, indicate the vast gap which can exist between the early and the final form of a potential art media. Technology had at last returned the sculpturesques puppet back to its original two-dimensional surface from which early man had derived it.*

Once invented, once the ideas of Roget were connected with

---

* The almost total lack of popular support of serious puppetry in movie-oriented America substantiates the idea that motion pictures supplant puppetry as art.

the inventions of Joseph Niepce, Louis Daguerre, and William Henry Fox Talbot and improved by Thomas Edison and his assistant William Dickson, to produce the first, practical movie instruments, it was taken up by the artists who knew that the illusion of motion had a vast potential for them. They showed the technicians what could be done with their toy. The magical qualities of the new medium intrigued the magician Georges Méliès, who saw that here was an illusion-producing machine par excellence; but he soon discovered that the narrative quality was its true métier. His theatrical background, however, bound him too closely to the tradition of the set and actor, and it was destined for Americans like Edwin S. Porter, Mack Sennett, and D. W. Griffith, the father of modern film technique, to realize the true potential of the motion picture medium.[20]

The motion picture also had important effects on other art forms. Alex Comfort suggests in *The Novel and Our Time*[21] that novelists got the idea that they could describe a locale as if flying down on a movie boom; the sensual viewpoint could be shifted at will and turned into multitudinous views as in the movies. The movies began to usurp the narrative function of the theater and the novel, and this actually paved the way for modern literary and theatrical experimentation, some of which are just coming to fruition today.

We see, however, a later development which is affecting the movies in turn: the image exchanger we call television. This new medium forced a revival of three-dimensionality in the movies: the 3-D and wide-screen curiosities of which we have probably not seen the end. Television also exerts its influence on the other arts in many unpredictable ways. McLuhan notes that the addition of sound to film detracted from the importance of tactility, mime, and kinesthesis.[22] Television on the other hand is more tactile, having a small screen with a rough-looking interlined screen texture that you can actually touch. The texture of the television screen is of course due to an electronic compromise made by engineers faced with the problem of allocating space in the radio frequency spectrum: the more lines, the wider the band-

width of the signal, permitting only so many television channels to fit into a given band of frequencies. The 525-line interlaced television picture is acceptable in America, but the French, who are closer to traditional visual forms and more visually oriented than we Americans, require a 1000-line picture that is less tactile. The tactile return would be complete if electronic specialists solved the problem of a textured or a true dimensional display, the media returning to a kind of miniature puppet theater.

When Edison invented the phonograph and applied it to the films he began a train of events which culminated in Warner Brothers' Jolson film, *The Jazz Singer*. This was quite a shock to audiences, used to the solo piano player as the only sound; but it was quite easily accepted and was an immediate success. The radio was just beginning to become popular, and if a small wooden box could talk, it was to be expected that the images of people could talk also. Faced with an economic problem then, because of radio, similar to the one they face today with the competition of television, the entrepreneurs immediately exploited sound. The artist of course realized that three decades of learning how to use a new medium were being thrown to the winds. As Edmund Carpenter indicates, the silent film had given artists a new opportunity to develop the artistic use of gestures and facial expressions, and if the medium had been given a few more decades to do so, we cannot guess how it would have ultimately developed.[23] Stage-trained Charlie Chaplin and Laurel and Hardy survived the transition to sound because they knew how to use talk, but pure silent movie artists like Buster Keaton, Harold Lloyd, and Harry Langdon did not.

Technology is continually throwing obstacles in the path of the movie medium: first sound, then color, and today wide-screens and television, requiring that artists learn new techniques and that audiences develop new sets of responses every few years. The cinematographic artist must feel as did the tribal chronicler of old when writing became popular, or the manuscript illuminator when printing was developed. Socrates, uttering the classic grievance of the artist whose medium is evolving out of his grasp, complains in Plato's *Phaedrus* that the spread of writing weakens the importance of memory. Yet technology is not to be blamed for inventing and "improving" media, any more than is the artist whose inspiration forces him into new syntheses of media. When Jacopo Peri and Count Bardi contrived the merger of musical instruments with the Greek recitative in 1600, giving birth to the opera, they did so out of a need to make a richer form than they knew; Richard Wagner's conclave of all the arts in his *gesamtkunstwerk* was an artistic necessity to him. Today artists who graft abstract images to electronic music in dance or film, or painters who try to bring their visual images to life in "happenings" or other devices, are motivated, not by the desire to confuse or shock an anxious audience, but by the need to enrich artistic media, however successful their attempts may be.

The technical innovation which most interests an artist is one which is potentially sense-impressive, but it must also permit combinatorial comparisons and structural articulations before an artist can put it to work. *Haute cuisine* or sexual imaginativeness fail as serious art forms because they lack these structural requirements (except perhaps only as performing arts, as practiced by fabulous chefs like La Varenne or Escoffier, or famous lovers like Cleopatra or her modern equivalents). Drugs or LSD are sense-impressive, and so is electronic stimulus to the brain, but until it is possible to control them they will remain outside art (except conceivably as a stimulus to the imagination). We might imagine, however, drugs packaged as pills whose successive layers dissolve in our stomach and cause predetermined hallucinatory experiences, or prerecorded stimulus tracks which can be played directly into our brains. "Feelies" are fantastic, but we cannot rule them out as potential art experiences.

Man's limiting senses and his potential for sensitivity are essentially incommensurate. The difficulty of determining the information-receiving abilities of the human is due to the remarkable ability of the brain to adapt to new complexes of inputs. If we could take an adult Cro-Magnon man into the psychological laboratory and compare him with a modern adult, he would no doubt be found to lack, most of all, sufficient perceptual sophistication to cope with modern reality. Any modern child would have an advantage over him, traceable to basic attitudes, words, concepts, images, and intrinsic art consciousnesses which had subliminally crept into his brain. The vestigial art-consciousness we inherit is a cumulative thing, and the nature of its communication package is such that it becomes more efficiently arranged by each generation of artists, although it probably remains relatively constant for a given era. The natural mind, however, seems to expand to include greater and greater sensitivities to the experiences which the limiting senses gather.

Apart from the discovery of new, hidden powers of the brain, such as ESP or DOP (Dermal-Optical Perception), it seems fair to assume that science will not surprise us with radical innovations for exploitation in art. It is certain on the other hand that the artist *will* surprise us, and he will do so using the most antique media in the most incredible new ways—this is his wont. Our humanness limits the effects of science and technology on art; it is art's virtue that it absorbs technology only to the extent that it can be assimilated into its frame by a human. Art is not limiting in the usual sense of the word because it has the potential for building utterly new and surprising experiences out of even the most commonplace science.

3

Shortly after man conceived science he began to realize that he would have to find out how to transcend his human frame if he wanted to understand nature. He needed a new objectivity which could only be obtained by an artificial device, an instrument not as frail or as inaccurate as was the human body and its senses. He began to develop better eyes to see with, better sensors to test nature with, better means to move about in the universe. Once outside his frame, he found himself wandering lonely in an amazing new world. We all know that the great mobility of modern science has given us startling new glimpses of nature, from the most invisibly minute particles or animals to the views of the infinite reaches of space. Here is a "new landscape," as Gyorgy Kepes calls it, a landscape that comes out of magnified images, intensified views and sensations, expanded or compressed time-or-space experiences, and visual conversions of electrical signals.[24]

To what extent is this new landscape inspirational for modern artists? Most of the new images of science are complex variations on the theme of order in nature: symmetries within symmetries; elegant solutions to the problem of pleasing arrangement—all of which give us an aesthetic reaction. We can imagine that this reaction is how a scientist must feel who evolves some complex mathematical description of nature. The new landscape is a visual mathematics of nature, and it is artistic only insofar as all art is ordered. G. H. Hardy said of mathematics that it is always beautiful; so is nature. Order in nature is extremely impressive, and it gives us a feeling akin to music; but in and of itself, or as revealed by a mechanism, order cannot be called art, mainly because art is never *given*, but always humanly *caused* to exist.

As a source of inspiration, order in nature has always impressed the artist. Yet in his hands there is always a new quality added to the order of nature; a transformation takes place when the artist appropriates order in nature which puts it on a new level of communicative experience. The method whereby the artist transforms the orders of nature into art is the main problem of art communication, to which the remainder of this book addresses itself.

What artists are directly inspired by this unnatural nature: the new landscape of modern science? The influence is most obvious on a group of individuals seldom accorded the compliment of being called artists: the science fiction writers. When C. S. Lewis turns his hand to the creation of uncommonly novel and beautiful other worlds, as in his interplanetary trilogy, he is obviously taking some inspiration from the new landscape of science; and Ray Bradbury or Arthur Clarke, in their most poetic moods, often succeed admirably in transforming the modern science spirit into art. In his analysis of science fiction, *Future Perfect*, H. Bruce

Franklin indicates that most American authors had their science fiction phases, namely Hawthorne, Poe, Melville, Bellamy, and Twain. The sciences, as Huxley suggests, order public human experience, and whether literature is carried to a positive Utopia, as in many H. G. Wells novels or as in Norman O. Brown's recent *Love's Body*,[26] or rendered pessimistically, as in Huxley's *Brave New World*[27] or George Orwell's *1984*,[28] it is a reaction of artistic sensitivities to some or many phases of modern science or technology.

The climate of science at the turn of the present century encouraged a view of nature which defied common sense. Space was thought to be curved, time was dependent on velocity, and the tiniest atom harbored tremendous energies. Einstein's theory of relativity was beginning to be grasped by the world, and it started the upheavals in world thinking which we still feel today. It is not surprising that the doctrine of art for art's sake then came into being. Braque and Picasso conceived their cubistic

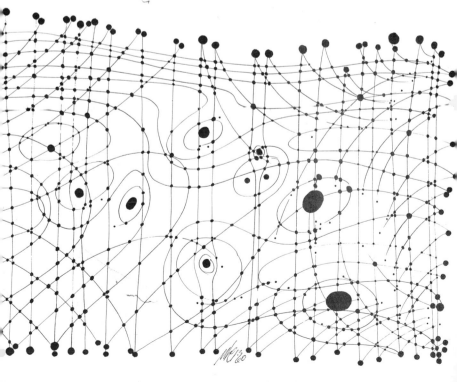

expression which was a multiplication of images similar to the multiplication of ideas that was sweeping the scientific world. Their friend Gertrude Stein, beginning with an idea suggested by her scientist teacher William James, wrote compositions in which words were associated almost at random—the stream-of-consciousness writing which James Joyce and the recent New Wave French novelists have carried to an ultimate. The Futurists extolled the mechanical world over the artistic (a speeding car was more impressive than the Victory of Samothrace); The fact that matter and energy and movement were related led them to the use of multiple images. There was a new emphasis on form, the syntax of art was broken up, and the traditional "message" began to disappear. Inspired by the broken, irrational shape of modern information, and deriving many ideas from the symbolists in poetry led by Mallarmé who was inspired in turn by the front page of the daily newspaper with its discontinuity of ideas and startling juxtapositions of feelings,[29] the position of the artist began to evolve. Picabia, Duchamp, Man Ray, and Max Ernst used geometric surfaces and optical illusions right out of the textbooks—more than current art seasons have given us to date, and this back in the 1900's.[30] *

The more impressive tools of modern science which have human use and influence are often meaningful inspirations for the modern artist. Constructions such as the gigantic radio telescopes, the fascinating forms of the satellites and radar antennas, rockets poised and fired toward the heavens—these physical forms can sometimes spur an artist into action. Superficially—in the direct physical terms of their craft—the architect and the sculptor will most readily employ current scientific instrumentalities since they both deal directly in physical constructions. John Canaday wrote: "If we ever have to reject the painter (and even the

---

* When you realize that the surrealists and Dadaists used *objet trouvé*, optical and movement illusions, pseudoscientific gimmicks, and many other Pop art ideas, you realize how sterile the equivalent modern movements actually are. I think that our galactic-oriented, atomic-powered, biologically controlled age deserves more originality from its artists.

sculptor) for the scientist-technician as the expressive artist of our time, the architect may hold alone the position of the man who combines pure art with scientific knowledge to keep humanistic values, along with new scientific ones, as the controlling ones of our lives."[31] Frank Lloyd Wright or Le Corbusier have left few scientific innovations in the area of structure and materials alone until they had yielded some artistic architectural expression. Although the architect traditionally converts technology for human use and appreciation, I do not accept the idea that he may be the only contemporary artist to exploit the artistic meaning of science.

In any age the artist of genius usually finds his proper materials. Contemporary American sculpture leans heavily on technology, particularly, I think, because American know-how and mechanical ingenuity readily lend themselves to typical American images: stainless steel, plastics, automobiles, locomotion, and electronics. If you see much contemporary American sculpture you are impressed by the total control over the most intractable materials.

In the other arts too, technological or theoretical innovations can sometimes provide the structural material for art expression. Electronic waveforms and the geometric or mathematical curves which the professional scientist hides in his books and journals can be the source of a new visual experience for the artist. A book like Jahnke and Emde's *Table of Functions*[32] contains many different curves plotted in three-dimensional charts, transcendental and harmonic functions that are degrees of order derived purely from the human-originated and tautological discipline of mathematics. This book itself could be stimulating to an artist, much as exotic primitive sculpture was to Picasso; it has been a favorite of mine since I first opened it as a student at M.I.T. In fact these mathematical plots, plus Picasso's own visual introduction to Balzac's *Unknown Masterpiece*[33] inspired me to a form which I call the "schema," a visual music of lines and dots which has attracted my creative energies for nearly twenty years. A group of my schema illustrate this book.

Naturally all ideas suggested by science or by theory or by mathematics, and appropriated by art in one way or another, succeed as art only insofar as they are creative artistically. The criterion is not whether the origin of art is interesting or well-ordered, but whether or not the result has artistic validity. To this extent science only serves as a source, and it may be lost in the work of art, as nature is sometimes lost in a work of art which it inspires.

The more fundamental problem of the relationship of the imagination of science to the artistic and cultural heritage from which it springs depends on a careful analysis of the unconscious effect of media on man, and on a discovery of how the artistic perception and its manifestation in form change or affect our consciousness. Man is not such an isolated and impersonal thinker as scientists would like us to believe. Our view of nature from the mysterious mansion of our consciousness is through a fenestration of remarkable complexity, one which I feel is considerably altered by the artistic vision we have inherited. Pascal said that man is both an artist and a scientist at heart, defining the artistic attitude as that part which reaches truth by a spirit of finesse that grasps total relationships, and the scientific part as that part which breaks down experience into rigid, emotionless geometries.[34] This dichotomy of mind restricts the potential of man too severely, I think, because history suggests that man has been able to range through more inexplicable modes of knowing and feeling and guessing than this would imply.

The credo of science excludes the subjective, and therefore it seems to exclude art. There is a danger that the denial of the artistic vision of man could fundamentally affect the creative vision of science. This is not the case because art is an emotional concomitant which coddles the human being and disposes him to scientific creativity. Instead art may be a necessary condition for constructing the new consciousness from which future science gets its structural realities to match with nature, in which case it is more important than we generally admit. The question remains to determine just how art builds its perceptual framework and how it affects science.

4

Science has invented and developed all of our modern communication media, improving means for duplicating, reproducing, exchanging art across both short and long distances. No other modern scientific or technological contribution has influenced art so profoundly as that of electromagnetic communication with all of its practical inventions. Part of the difficulty with modern art is the assumption, made by the artist and critic and public alike, that art is the same now as before this series of inventions. The ever-changing awareness of our world due to communication has altered our response to all art forms. The artist, perhaps more urgently than his audience, is forced to understand the effects of communication if he is to continue to create art with meaning in our mass-communication age.

As mentioned previously, Marshall McLuhan and others[35] have made an excellent beginning to a general study of communication effects on mankind. They have noted that we are as changed in our awareness of and attitude to reality, due to the telegraph, radio, television, and automation, as was early man when he captured the spoken word in writing, and again medieval man when he crystalized writing in movable type. I would add to McLuhan's list every great and influential work of art which man creates, for reasons that I will try to make clear in this book.

Certainly the artist has been influenced by accurate, multi-colored printing, by the hi-fi and stereophonic reproduction of music, by the tape recorder and by television and worldwide instantaneous news coverage. As André Malraux wrote in *Voices of Silence,*[36] the painter today can have his own private museum-without-walls, and the musician also can have his auditorium-without-performers. This puts the modern artist in a unique position in the history of art, one that can be as overwhelming as it can be useful. This super-artistic awareness perhaps partially accounts for the fact that fads multiply so easily today. Every country on the globe can respond immediately to the newest New York or Paris innovation, much as they do to the current dance craze or woman's fashion change. If you attend an international art exhibition today you are likely as not to find Pop art from Zambia.

The artist is a human being like the rest of us, but he is often more passionately engaged in the current scene for one reason or another. The paradox of the artist is that a comprehensive awareness of current trends and events and also of historic art forms often consumes or clouds his abilities to discover his own artistic vision. He is sometimes forced to rush off to the woods, to seal himself up in an ivory tower, in order to develop the necessary perspective to work. This is usually not done by an artist in order to encourage his own idiosyncrasies, but rather to develop the calm and remoteness necessary for the creative vision.

Few artists are able to assimilate new movements as quickly as the communication media make them available today. Just the same, it is incumbent on artists, I think, to be aware of as much modernity as the communication trade allows. It is essential for successful creation in art to have a wealth of current and vital ideas from which to draw. Of course it is not certain that such ideas have to come by means of the communication media. Some artists without even trying seem to arrive at great art-knowledge and sufficient current sensitivity to provide them with all the information and inspiration they need. Communications may speed up the process, but it does not necessarily make the situation any easier for the artist—and in fact it may confuse it in certain cases. To hope so is to be like the psychiatrist who thinks that hypnosis or drugs will give him a quicker inroad to his patient's unconscious, but who discovers that he still cannot move his patient to a quick cure.

We are approaching a world consciousness in which everyone shares all ideas, including those throughout the entire history of man. Alfred Korzybski noted[37] that man is a time-binding animal, but I think that man is more truly a sense-stretching animal. When our senses are stretched and new technological means are found for communicating or recording them, the demands we put on society increase. We *need* the awareness of distant lands and peoples of other walks of life; we *have* to experience the exotic and remote. Town meetings of the world become a necessity in a modern technological society; world art becomes a compulsive need on the part of every individual who is in tune with life.

Therefore art is forced to be creative today in a broader sense than in the past, not only as a form of childish perversity or eccentricity in reaction to a conservative world, but as a serious expression of an overt reaction to an increased awareness. The mechanical, electronic, or chemical ability of the machine to imitate throws artistic creativity into a new mode. The merely imitative or reproductive in art becomes banal, to say the least; Polaroid cameras, Xerox machines, transistor tape recorders, force art to be unusual or extraordinary in order to attract attention at all. In our communication-doped world, art sometimes gives us kicks to startle us into recognition of its value—which is often why some artists use mad humor, the macabre, tricks of illusion and perception, the esoterica of science—anything that is unusual and attention-getting. The deeper meaning of creativity in art is often lost sight of; it resides not in any superficial effect, but rather in the composition of new artistic experiences which build the human consciousness.

5

The workings of the human mind will probably be the last bastion to fall beneath the onslaught of insatiable modern science, if indeed fall it does. It would be unrealistic, however, to assume that biochemistry, combined with the insights of physiology, psychology, and cybernetics, will not amass considerable knowledge of the workings of the human nervous-control system. The question is not how completely science will enable us to understand the workings of the human mind, but rather how success will spoil the artist.

When psychology or psychoanalysis first became popular many artists feared that it would supplant the artistic intuition. But as the limitations of these new disciplines became obvious, a more relaxed attitude set in, allowing artists to exploit Sigmund Freud's discoveries. Marcel Proust and James Joyce in particular used the unconscious. Of course we do not know whether or not, like Dostoevski or Tolstoi, they could have arrived at their insights independently of Freud. Nevertheless, literature has not been the same since Freud. And since we have only begun to understand, the extent to which psychoanalytic insights can be applied to man and to his art we cannot begin to evaluate the influence of scientific psychiatry on art. But as Norman O. Brown indicated in *Life Against Death*: "Psychoanalytic formulations seem like scrannel pipe of wretched straw when set beside [the insights of an artist like] Rilke,"[38] whose utterances on art often cut to the core of its human meaning and illuminate like a brilliant light.

I am optimistic, however, that clarifications of the creative methods and purposes of art, even those made in the name of science, are important for the artist and the public alike. I think that it is essential for the artist to try to discover the details of his method, and also for man to learn as much about human action as possible. This is necessary today so that we will be in a more knowledgeable position in the complex world of our own creation—which means asking what some people think are either impossible or embarrassing questions. That which is truly mysterious and unique cannot be embarrassed by science. We must assume that art is a serious human endeavor, and that the final and most astute analysis of art will reveal its profound human importance for mankind. It is arguing out of a position of strength to assume that knowing how art functions will not destroy its meaning for man.

Usually the scientist does not take the artist very seriously, whereas the artist often takes the scientist too seriously. If the scientist is forced to find out, by his own logic, that art has great human meaning, he will have to relax his prejudices. The practical man, either the scientist or the businessman, thinks that art is play or at most beauty—enjoyable, perhaps, but only after-hours. When the modern man realizes that he is capable of using his mind "in many modes," as Barzun suggests, only then will he be equipped to survive in our increasingly complex society. Barzun writes that man must learn to use his mind in "all modes of use, from the analysis of the scientist to the synthesis of the historian, from the art of the poet or the musician to the study of man's superstitions, and thence upward to the intuitions of mystics and religious men."[39]

The modern aesthetician must be as much a scientist as the sociologist, although this does not mean that his techniques will ever supplant artistic creativity. There is a danger that a science of art can mislead the artist into the treason of which Barzun speaks, promoting a competition between science and art for "The Truth." The artist who feels that his art is science, the purist or the experimenter whose artistico-scientific studio-laboratory gives rise to a group art, amalgamated art-experiences that derive from the Bauhaus experiments in education, are heading for the perfect, computerized, and automatic art, which is, actually, I think, a human resignation because it is not humanness-building.

Nevertheless there are very basic reasons, I feel, which make it necessary to try to discover what, other than the clichés of science, govern both science and the urge to art. We must go beyond the clichés of faith in the regularity of nature, a consuming desire to call all nature to account, a love of the beautiful and the ordered. Both the scientist and the artist fail man when they embrace and turn man himself out of the picture. The modern apotheosis of science, art, and culture with its obvious pitfalls indicates that our basic problem is to give man a human center from which all artificial methodologies radiate.

After all is said and done, when the artist or the scientist has served his apprenticeship to whatever methodology or school is most personally congenial to him, or to his age, he must range off into the mysterious world of his own private intuition and vision, if he wants to be creative. The upbringing of every artist and scientist should serve as a springboard for the jump into the inchoate world of intuition, because to be shackled by theories is to prevent soaring. Science must be a liberating force when it theorizes about art, before the artist will accept it and profit. A science of art, properly understood, tries to aim, I think, not at verities which elicit the response of a routine to be followed like a formula or a catechism, but rather at a basic understanding of the human as a producer and creator of moral values. If successful, the resulting science of art would deepen our understanding of man, and increase man's potential for developing the volume of his humanness.

2

Cybernetics and Art

Communication and Control in Art

1

IN HONORÉ de Balzac's short story "Unknown Master-piece" the old master Frenhoefer painted for ten years on a single canvas, his "Belle Noiseuse," dedicated to celestial feminine beauty. He hid it away in his studio, insisting that it was incomplete, until two young friends chanced to see it. To their surprise this mysterious work of art was a total chaos of color, with only the barest trace of a delicate ankle showing through. This perceptive story suggests that there is an exchange between an artist and his work, and if the artist is mad, it is to be expected that his work will appear mad to anyone normal who looks at it; it also suggests that a work of art is limited to something this side of chaos if it is to be considered valuable by society.

It seems reasonable to assume that the art exchange is a transmission of some nature, but if this transmission entails some significant response and is not just a signal perceived by a person, how is a humanly meaningful exchange actually made? I propose to bring to bear on this problem cybernetics and information theory, heretofore used by some physicists or theorists only as a curiosity. J. R. Pierce, for instance, has a chapter on art in his book *Symbols, Signals and Noise*,[1] because everyone agrees that art is clearly a communication phenomenon. A more relevant book is Abraham Moles' *Information Theory and Esthetic Perception*,[2] an excellent beginning to the science of art communication. In his autobiography, *I Am a Mathematician*,[3] Norbert Wiener grudgingly admits that sociology and anthropology are primarily sciences of communication, and he agrees that cybernetics theoretically should have a good bit to say about them. The overwhelming task of calling them to mathematical account led him to believe, however, that even with our powerful modern mathematical tools it would be almost impossible to construct good theoretical models that would apply. No doubt Wiener would have felt the same about art. Nevertheless, he speculated, in *God and Golem, Inc.*,[4] about the implications of cybernetics for religion. To paraphrase Wiener: it is necessary to forget for the moment that art is a hallowed ground where transgression is frowned upon. Certain ideas which seem clear in the brilliant clinical light of science may at first appear disagreeable, if not entirely mistaken, from an artistic standpoint. For the moment such ideas will be entertained without squeamishness even though they may be counter to the current artistic precedence and even too vague for scientific theorizing. At the same time it is necessary to be cautious of using scientific theories out of context. Northrop Frye attacks the forceful conversion of science to mythical applications, but he extols the integration of science and myth.[5] Can science, especially cybernetics, somehow be used as an integrating factor for the many near mythical attitudes we have about art?

First, it is necessary to review briefly the cybernetic sciences dealing with communication and control in animals and mechanisms as they have so far advanced. Wiener's important book *Cybernetics*[6] is a lucid introduction to the science. Control theory in this science hinges on a principle first suggested by James Watt, which he used to regulate accurately the speed of his steam engine. Called *feedback*, it describes the means of sending back an error to the primary source of control so that it may correct itself. When you reach for a glass of water, your eye estimates the distance your hand must go, and it feeds back the information to the brain, which enables you to correct your hand motion so that it will pick up the glass. A rocket homing on a comet has a sensor that detects any directional error, which is fed back to readjust the direction of the propulsion jet guiding it toward the comet. Cybernetics has shown that this special approach to control links much knowledge gained by engineers in their communicative sciences, with the understanding of living animals that biologists, physiologists, and psychologists have obtained.

Control is also obviously important when you consider art, as with all human operations and productions. Feedback principles operate at many levels in the production of a typical work of art. The particular feedback loops in the production of an individual work of art may be traced in this way: an artist begins with a vague idea and an untouched medium like a blank piece of paper or a canvas. He begins to initiate an exchange—for the moment let us call it a communicative exchange—between himself and his medium, going through a series of choices that are governed both by his own attitude about his art and by the medium, until he slowly builds up a work of art. Countless feedback loops are traced out as he originates, corrects, adds, interprets, and changes, until he finally reaches a situation of stasis with his medium. When the creative act is complete, there is an absence of motivation to feed back any more choices.

Next, the work of art is published or read, viewed or heard. It is removed momentarily from the personal artist-communication cycle, existing now as a communicative link of some nature between a physical object and another person. The art object somehow represents the artist's choices, and it comprises elements that are in some way meaningful to a second person.

The second person in the art-exchange cycle reacts to what he experiences. Although he does not necessarily create art as a result of this reaction, he may communicate back to the artist in subtle or obvious ways. He may, for instance, speak up, write a letter, or simply make a purchase which indicates a tacit assent, or he may give a lengthy criticism or explanation of his reactions. The artist may profess to be oblivious to all such secondary feedbacks, and in some cases, as when he is a recluse, he may never learn about them. Generally, however, the artist has a sensitive nature and adsorbs these communicative feedbacks to greater or lesser degrees. Perhaps the artist is disturbed or amused; perhaps he ignores the feedbacks; in any case he receives them, and they can and probably do affect his next creative act. This extended communication cycle is particulary rapid and powerful, as I have suggested, in our modern instant-communication world. The very act of formulating a work of art is another important feedback influence on the artist since it represents a manifestation which itself can be sensed at a later time.

The internal neural-physiological feedback processes within an artist are very complex because they are intermingled with his total psychological makeup, and in addition, the external feedbacks are colored by current attitudes toward art and artists. All these factors tend to inhibit or reinforce the various feedback loops of art, sometimes causing it to slow almost to a halt or to magnify so greatly that the art world goes into a type of oscillation similar to that which we are observing on the current art scene.*

This simple restatement of the control cycle of art in cybernetic terms is limited principally by a lack of detailed knowledge of the physiological-psychological systems within the human being and the resulting social interactions of man. Man is extremely complex as a control system, and it is difficult to comprehend the various loops and checks internal to the human nervous system, much less its interactions with the environment and with many

---

* A sociological analysis, striving to arrive at the frequency of this oscillation in the art fads of our time, is conceivable since this suggests a ready analogy to feedback in an electrical oscillator. The parameters for oscillation in social systems are less readily determined, but the communicative interchanges provided by the mass media clearly serve as the feedback path. The oscillation of social systems, once they are begun, may be dampened by society, by some technological change, or by individual members such as the artist himself, or they may naturally exhaust themselves.

other similar systems in a society. The construction of small mechanical and electronic animals which exhibit extremely bug-like behavior illustrates the complexities which are possible in more advanced creatures. Circuits composed of the simplest electronic components have a surprisingly rich behavior pattern. In 1915, B. F. Miessner, working with J. H. Hammond (who later invented the electric organ), built a remarkable mechanical dog that could seek out light or sound.[7] More sophisticated but simpler devices have been recently constructed by W. R. Ashby, W. Grey Walter, and Claude Shannon.[8] All these devices have shown that the barest minimum of elements (Ashby's Homeo-stat has four variables; Walter's, two) is capable of exceedingly complex conditions and patterns of operation. If W. Grey Walter's bug is allowed to roam around in an unpredictable environment, it does many things which would be indistinguishable from the actions of a real bug. Since the human nervous network contains many more such systems, with many more variables, imagine how many more complicated states are possible. These devices also suggest that acts which seem to be vitalistic can be supported by relatively simple mechanistic functions. It would be important if we could find a simple rationale for man's nervous action, enabling us to predict, if not the letter, then the spirit of every human action or motivation. The effort in this area has the help of the modern computer, approaching the subject in either of two principal ways: by analysis of human actions, or by the synthesis of neural components or their actions in an attempt to build them up until they duplicate human actions. Chapter 8 investigates the success that computer specialists have in simulating the art operation in particular; it also considers the potential of the computer as a robot apprentice artist.

2

It is obvious that ordering in the sense of influencing nature occurs when an artist creates a work of art (even if it is a *dis*-ordering, as Morse Peckham insists in *Man's Rage for Chaos*[9]). The English mathematician and physicist James Clerk Maxwell conceived the general mathematical expressions for the ordering of closed physical thermodynamic systems, and he was followed by Ludwig Boltzman and the great American mathematician Josiah Willard Gibbs, who reduced thermodynamics to statistical mechanics. A closed thermodynamic system is one which, like a vessel containing a gas at a certain temperature and pressure, is completely isolated from its surroundings by insulating means. Satellites in space are isolated by thermal shields to prevent extraneous radiation from affecting them; the coffee in a Thermos bottle is a simple closed thermodynamic system. The change from thermodynamics, which concerns heat and temperature, to statistical mechanics is from a system that is thought of as a single dynamical system (a container or object being heated or cooled) to one in which there is a statistical distribution of many dynamical systems (the individual atoms being agitated). The development of scientific thought from the statistics of heat engines to the mathematical model which applies to living mechanisms is traced in detail by Wiener in *Cybernetics*.[10] Further, its application to communication systems in general is described by Shannon[11] and Leon Brillouin.[12] But to what extent is it applicable to art?

Maxwell suggested a concept that has considerable theoretical importance in cybernetic considerations of communication systems which may lead us a little closer to art productions. The dreamer's hope for a perpetual-motion heat engine could only be realized if he had the cooperation of a microscopic demon. The demon's function would be to sit at a small port between two connected chambers containing a gas in statistical equilibrium for a given temperature. He would allow molecules of gas that are faster to go into one of the chambers and those that are slower to go into the other. The one chamber would get hotter as a result and the other cooler; this could finally provide sufficient energy difference to drive a steam engine. The demon must have knowledge (information) about the velocity of all molecules which come at him in order to influence or direct them into the correct chamber. Despite many serious or crackpot attempts to do so, perpetual motion, of course, has never been realized physically, so a Maxwell demon is therefore practically inconceivable. But living organisms seem to exhibit characteristics for internal self-organization which suggest that indeed something like this anthropomorphic mechanism does exist within them.

It is possible at this point in theory to connect information (a communication idea) with entropy (a statistical mechanical concept), a connection first made by L. Szilard in 1929.[13] Szilard was interested in the problem of the Maxwell demon as a manifestation of an observer of an experiment. It was suggested by Werner Heisenberg before him that all experimenters in physics introduce a minute amount of disturbance into any experiment they make, a disturbance that is particularly annoying to the experimental results when the objects being investigated are small like molecules or electrons.[14] This is a concept biologists or surgeons have always taken for granted because any attempt to investigate organisms, or medical operations on the human body, obviously greatly influence them. Szilard wondered why this so-called Heisenberg's Uncertainty Principle was true and thought that perhaps the concept of the Maxwell demon might provide a clue. He indicated that the entropy lost by the gas owing to the demon's separating the high and low energy particles had to be exactly balanced by the information gained by the demon itself, since information had to be carried by some physical process—say, in the form of radiation passed on to the observer of the experiment.

The concept of entropy is used to describe the degree of disorder in a closed statistical mechanical system. Such systems usually tend to get more disordered if they are left alone. There is a definite condition of maximum disorder for every gas at a certain pressure in a closed container insulated from its surroundings: all containers of gas at a definite pressure will have a certain temperature. If we change that temperature by heating or cooling the container and leave it alone, it will of itself go back to the original entropy state—which is its maximum entropy state. The theoretical condition of infinite entropy is when the molecules of a gas are infinitely disordered, and zero entropy when they are perfectly ordered. In the above example of a perpetual-motion device, the Maxwell demon would therefore be causing one container to tend to its maximum entropy and the other to zero entropy. When all the molecules are resting on the bottom of the one container, it is perfectly ordered and has zero entropy.

It is useful to keep the following in mind when thinking about entropy and order:

DISORDER $\longleftarrow$ $\dfrac{\text{Increasing}}{\text{to infinity}}$ ENTROPY $\dfrac{\text{Decreasing}}{\text{to zero}}$ $\longrightarrow$ ORDER

It was Wiener who said that it may be possible to regard living organisms, including man himself, as having Maxwell demons at their core since there is indeed an inexplicable tendency in man to reverse physical processes and cause their entropies to decrease.[15] Care must be exercised, however, in making generalizations between entropy and organization on the part of man, since, as Cherry has shown, it often leads to misleading results.[16]

It has been rigorously demonstrated by Leon Brillouin and others[17] that the communication problem of the Maxwell demon, as well as the similarities of the mathematical expressions of entropy in a thermodynamic system to the mathematics of ordering in a communication system, justifies the use of the term *entropy* to describe the degree of disorder of any physical choice-order system. In arbitrary but restricted domains in the physical world we can measure the probabilities that newly received elements in the same domain will have less or more order than previously known elements. Thus, language can be subjected to analysis since it is a restricted symbol system; or music whose elements are always tone, and so on. It seems clear then that, as physical facts, works of art can be considered as ordered systems, and it is possible, by means of a statistical analysis, to assign an entropy figure to each individual work with respect to other works of art of the same genre. How to preform such a statistical analysis for many domains in communication and art is clear, and has actually been done for word formation in many languages[18] and for many examples of music,[19] and in theory it could be done for all the arts as physical productions.

The experiential art productions of man exhibit a measurable statistical property in terms of their choice-order domains which seems to reflect some desire on the part of man to bring his universe into order. This is not yet to insist either on the probability that this ordering will be toward certainty, as when G. K. Zipf suggests that man strives toward the "simplest structure," his Principle of Least Effort,[20] or that man desires to push nature towards chaos, as Morse Peckham suggests.[21] It appears that some kind of well-orderliness motivates man, but well-orderliness with respect to what? Taking a very general look at art and human productions, we might ask what the entropy boundaries are for all possible things man would make, and then perhaps it would be possible to determine the significance of particular physical productions.

One can assume that man can communicate nothing or absolutely everything, an absence of exchange or an impressive maximum of infinite exchange. Practically, man does not have world or time enough to arrive at these theoretical upper limits. Time and the medium restrict the amount of information we can exchange—the medium because a sufficiently broad medium would allow us to communicate as much as we want in an instant of time. On the other hand, it is also clear that the human mind must have some limit on the amount of information it can receive; for instance, we can comprehend only so many words per minute, so much data in a given time span. Thus, for human communication we are limited by time, the medium, and the human brain. This is not taking into account any possible interference which may be disturbing the theoretical exchange of information, such as distracting noises, fatigue, poor quality of the medium, and so on. Art appears to fall within this range of human communication, since we must assume that its communication entails choices less than infinite and more than zero.

The painter Frenhoefer was trying so hard to order that he

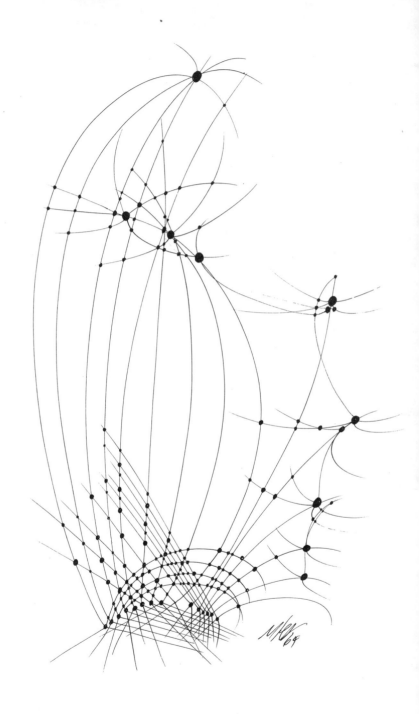

approached one of the limits of his art: either the infinity of chaos or the zero of wasted choices. The musician John Cage managed to do the same when he composed his piano composition "Four Minutes and Thirty-Three Seconds," all of them silent. Rudolph Arnheim suggests that strong order is exemplified at one pole in art by simple styles like the Byzantine icon, and the empty pole by the blank patterns of the schizophrenic. He indicates that the order-seeking artist is faced with the adventure of reconciling these sterile extremes, drawing the lifeblood from one—the pure order of perfect classicism—and the wisdom from the other—the pure randomness of the ideal romantic styles.[22] This polarity can also be expressed, as Nietzsche did, by the Apollonian perfection and the chaotic Dionysian sensual life. Gyorgy Kepes opposes them in a cosmos-chaos, stasis-kinesis, two morphological archetypes behind all art, in his estimation.[23] Northrop Frye opposes the pure convention of folk and popular art, using invariable plots and character types, with the pure variability of novelty and unfamiliar archetypes.[24] And Kenneth Clarke uses the blot and the diagram as metaphors for these extremes.[25] More to the point, however, is the idea that Ben Shahn suggested to me (in a 1955 conversation); it indicates that perhaps a masterwork, like Lorenzetti's series of frescoes on government in the Palazzo Pubblico of Siena, would be a more reasonable upper limit of maximum human artistic information.

It would be possible then, but of questionable meaning, to go through each of the arts and discover the two basic extremes (in literature, for example, *Webster's Unabridged Dictionary* or the complete works of Shakespeare might bound the list; in architecture, perhaps the Great Pyramid of Cheops versus a tepee or a cave, the zero house given by nature, and so on). More meaningful, however, would be to determine where a given physical work of art lies in a spectrum of choices from chaos to perfect order. Can there be discovered a mathematical model which would allow us to make such a computation for all works of art? If so, and if it is possible to calculate the order or disorder of a given work of art, would there be any actual significance to this measure? Do the theoretical considerations of statistical mechanics, carried into the cybernetic theory of communication, provide us with any answers to these questions that are meaningful?

3

The mathematical theory of information proposed by Claude Shannon[26] adapts the idea of entropy measure to communication systems, although the root idea for him was not thermodynamics, but rather telegraphy. Samuel F. B. Morse, who invented telegraphy in 1832, felt that there was a limit to how much or how fast signals could be transmitted over his system. He realized from experiment that signals were corrupted when sent distantly, in comparison to those sent short distances but just as quickly. He also knew that only one message could be sent at a time over his original system, and he felt this was a basic limitation. The mathematical statement of these limitations was formulated by a Bell Telephone engineer, Harry Nyquist, from 1924 to 1928.[27] As mentioned before, the concept of information was first used by Szilard to try to explain Heisenberg's Uncertainty Principle, but it was not immediately realized that entropy and information were related. Nyquist and his associate R. V. L. Hartley considered the problem of the rate of information transmission of signals over a telegraph or radio channel,[28] and Hartley gave a mathematical credence to Morse's intuitive encoding scheme in which he assigned the simplest telegraphic encoding to the most frequent letter (the dot to the letter e) and the most complicated code to the least frequent letter (the dot-dot-dot-space-dot to the letter z), and so on. It waited, however, for the generalization of communication theory by Shannon, supported by the mathematical work of Wiener and the Russian A. N. Kolmogoroff,[29] to uncover the true relationship of communication to statistical systems. Wiener was concerned primarily with the difficulties of interpreting or predicting signals hidden within noise and other electrical interference; Shannon studied the problems of efficiently formulating and transmitting encoded messages, pure signals, as well as signals in the presence of noise.

Given a group of symbols out of which a message is to be sent (like the twenty-six letters of the alphabet), it is possible to calculate the entropy of any given message using them. A completely random string of letters has a maximum of entropy since it is highly disordered. The redundancy of certain letters lessens this entropy, tending toward order, until at the other extreme of zero entropy and perfect order, a single letter is repeated again and again. Intuitively we may expect that a more efficient encoding of language could be obtained if we could take these concepts into account when building it. A little reflection indicates that this is indeed the case with natural languages. If the probable frequency of occurrence and the degree of redundancy of letters are known for a particular language, it would be possible to make certain predictions about future messages, given only parts of past messages in that language. This is true, and recent attempts to reconstruct obliterated passages of the Dead Sea Scrolls, for instance, have taken advantage of this fact.[30] The actual information measure of a particular message is made by taking a statistical count of the repetitions of the symbols being sent, compared with the total amount of symbols possible in the language, considering their total probabilities of occurrence. In an English text, for example, the letters or words occur with a certain frequency, as Edgar Allan Poe suggested in his introduction to cryptology, "The Gold Bug." Gaps are filled in by placing in the most probably redundant letters, words, or ideas.

We also choose words with a certain frequency when we write or talk, owing to the structural restrictions of syntax, but whatever the reason, it is the statistic that counts in an analysis of language. Structure demands that certain words and ideas call forth others. A person receiving a message can sometimes tell what the next word will be, or if he cannot actually predict the word, he can say that it may be an adjective, a verb, or a noun. Certain individual letters call forth others, as when *i* precedes *e*, or *q* precedes *u*, and so on. Too much structural redundancy in a language makes it too well ordered to transmit any significant new information, and too little makes it too random to transmit information without losing much of that information, especially if it occurs in the presence of other normal interference. This redundancy in English, for instance, is about two to one, and it is therefore possible to construct crossword puzzles in which a two-dimensional matrix of words is used. Were a language redundant three to one, where three times more letters could be predicted than not, three-dimensional puzzles could be made. Shannon and others have made detailed statistical counts of many languages which are useful in these types of communication analyses.[31]

The uncertainty about the actual next word in a message is resolved only on its receipt. The amount of information in a given message, according to Shannon's formulation, is a measure of the amount it reduces the uncertainty about what is being sent. Information is measured in binary digits, called *bits*. When the choice made reduces the number of alternatives one-half, one bit of information is gained about the possible future choices. Any given message is said to have an information content of so many bits per second; time is introduced since all messages are usually sequential at a certain rate of transmission.

The maximum information which a perfect electrical communication channel can transmit is called *gaussian noise*, a statistical concept which applies to perfectly random strings, suggested by the German mathematician Karl Gauss. But most electrical channels are not perfect, having instead a limiting bandwidth, and as a result, the gaussian noise is limited to a frequency defined by the maximum of the summation of the frequencies it can pass. All electrical communication channels can be assigned a measure of their channel capacity to describe the limits of information which they can pass. Channel capacity can be illustrated by considering that some information-handling devices, such as a telephone, can pass less information than others, such as a hi-fi system. If you listen to a voice over a telephone, it is considerably more stilted than when it is heard over a hi-fi system. However, it is a well-known fact that a difficult and broad-band signal, like the video signal of television, can be transmitted over a narrow-band channel like a telephone link if time is of no importance.

On these premises then, the information theorist has been able to solve many complex electrical coding and decoding problems for physical transmission systems. Information theory has created an entire new approach to the communication of electrical signals, to an intrepretation of electrical signals disturbed or hidden in noises owing to their being weak or distant; it has suggested many new pulsed-coding methods, and countless improvements in the qualities of signals transmitted over given radio-frequency devices. Most important, however, has been the fact that information theory has improved our understanding of all communication systems. How can we then apply it to art?

4

The statistical nature of art, when considered devoid of the meanings we generally associate with each art form, suggests that it too might be understood in some way by information theory. Abraham Moles made the first serious attempt to approach this problem.[32] That which is left when you subtract meaning or content from art is the form, and this form represents a physical choice-order system which lends itself readily to a statistical analysis. By use of an informational analysis and a statistical tabulation it is easy to break down a physical body of art from its formal standpoint into a ranking of the probabilities of each of its elements deviating from certain recurring norms established from similar analyses of past arts in the same domain. For instance, as Richard Pinkerton showed, it is possible to analyze simple melodies such as folk songs by counting the frequency of occurrence of the notes, as well as the probabilities of different intervals following one another.[33] In this way all melodies can be ranked and assigned an entropy measure. A group at the Physics Institute of Aachen, Germany, ranked and assigned an entropy measure to many works of literature and classical music.[34] The most important conclusion of this group to date is that with respect to the interval of consecutive tones in classical music there has been a logical increase in the informational content of music since 1500 (considering music solely as an ordered statistical system), up to Prokofiev, Hindemith, Bartók, and Shostakovich. A radical decrease in information—a sudden jump back to greater statistical order—occurs, however, for Schoenberg and his followers.

In other words, the trend of music since Palestrina's day has been from a rather pure order to a state of complexity or disorder in music, the most complex composer being Bartók. But these studies note that suddenly with the serial school of composition there is a return again to a rather pure statistical order, so that it is possible to say that Webern and Bach are closer statistically than Beethoven and Bach, from the standpoint of the entropy of their musical outputs. In a given domain of music, in a given tonal system like the classic modality, we see that music tends from a pure order to a more random and higher informational content. This agrees with our intuitive feeling that Bach is more ordered than Beethoven, or vice versa, that Beethoven is more complex and intricate structurally than Bach. Now when there is a completely new system of making music, a shift into a new logic, as when we enter the serial duodecaphonic domain, we have a sudden jump to a new ordered system, when considering their statistics. The tone-row idea, carried out strictly and logically, is a highly ordered mathematical system.[35] The same reasoning would obviously also apply to the other arts, although an actual measurement would be more difficult. Paintings would have to be ruled off like a television screen; their elements from area to area—the object, its color and shape, and so on—would have to be tabulated and compared with the same elements in other similar paintings. In a given genre of painting—for instance, the domain of colored rectangles conceived by Piet Mondrian—we would probably find that the order has tended to decrease in the current equivalents to this style—namely, the Op artists (considering also the probabilities of color transition from rectangle to adjacent rectangle).

The order or disorder of a work of art then must tell us something about the design or abstract form of art. Whether a minimal form is the most beautiful, as George Birkhoff suggests[36] or a complex form is the higher art, as Hans Tischler writes,[37] is a moot question. We know that the earlier music is extremely formal and simple, as is the highly logical music of Schoenberg (although they sound radically different to the ear, for reasons I give in Chapter 5). The simple order in art is analogous to the redundant letter in a language communication, whose entropy is low or zero. As design grows more and more complex, so does the entropy measure, extending, as previously indicated, toward a gaussian random statistic—the chaos of the upper limit in which there is no meaning but a maximum of possibility of choice. This means that radically different arts, in the same or different media domains, can have an identical entropy measure. Which then is the more beautiful?

It becomes clear in this point in the reasoning that the design of art is very much different from the meaning or from the human significance of art. Beauty cannot be measured by the entropy of the formal communication means. Also, it becomes clear that the communication of art forms is somehow more than

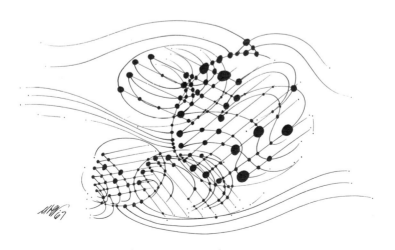

just the building of designed or ordered forms, whose aspect is exchanged from person to person. Further, it is possible to conclude that there must be something beyond the communication of this formal type of statistical meaning which makes art creative and uniquely meaningful for humans.

In sum then, cybernetic theories suggest that structured choice-order communication systems can be tagged; that some systems are more organized than others; that the uncertainty of all new messages is their virtue, the resolution of which we define as communication; and that the receptor channel has a certain limitation in its capacity to receive information. Now if we can believe the psychologist who suggests that the mind desires the simplest system—Zipf's Principle of Least Effort—indicating that at its naïve best the human gives a perception the simplest interpretation possible, we generate two opposing attitudes in man. These attitudes are: first, the desire for uncertainty necessary for man to conceive contingencies and therefore to strive for a potentially maximum of meaning in his world (a physical necessity for communication); and second, this psychological desire of man to seek only the clearest and least disorganized system of perception in order to be grounded in fact and certainty. Man is therefore caught between two poles: uncertain nature, on the one hand, and his human desire for organization, on the other. Out of this dialectic comes the control mankind has developed over all experience, emerging as an organization of uncertainties within which our humanness is structured. For the artist, it is a striving to bring his small artistic worlds of chaotic choices into the temporary equilibrium of well-ordered, closed systems, which he hatches like eggs, and his then being dashed back again and again to a fundamental state of chaos, from which he must again work his way to some degree of order. The rewards of the artist are those momentary joyous periods when the forces of nature, as reflected in his agitated body and confused psyche, are denied and overcome in tangible works of physical production. This idea is the opposite of Plotinus' theory that pure intelligence suffers a loss when embodied in material form; it suggests that *only* embodied intelligence is truly meaningful and capable of maintaining human values.

The important question remains, however: how do we attach any significance to art, if not through its formal, designed structure? Going back to the elementary communication system, we see that we have forgotten from the start that a message is more than just letters, chosen according to a certain statistic. Letters build words, and words have "meaning." Shannon begins his classic paper with the disclaimer that semantic meaning has nothing whatsoever to do with his definition of information; the choice of the word "information" is unfortunate since it has commonly applied to semantic meaning, whereas Shannon means it to signify simply a choice out of an ensemble of choices. The significance, or meaning, of the choices made is beside the point of the mathematics of information theory. Information, the quality which is assumed to be exchanged, is like time: it does not exist as a physical quality, only as a sequence, a part of our mental apparatus for grasping the world. This abstract mental concept is obviously not some kind of a fluid or field which can be contained and conserved like its thermodynamic ancestor, heat.*

Whether or not a single bit of information represents a single letter of the alphabet or stands for the complete works of Shakespeare is beside the point of information theory. A bit can signify an event in and of itself, or it can signify events with a long history, triggering off a train suggesting many past experiences or ideas upon its reception. Clearly certain concepts have more possibility of evoking a larger volume of ideas than others. Nevertheless, all choices in information theory have an identical entropy measure if they are equally probable, regardless of this human meaning-volume. To hunt for a small quantity when the semantic meaning is restrictive and for a larger quantity when

* Harold H. Lanier's theory of information, alluded to in the Preface, makes this mistake, if I remember correctly.

the semantic meaning is expansive is to misunderstand the nature of the mathematical theory of information. This also underestimates the potential for symbols to carry meaning.

The crux of the matter is that an electrical signal can encode meaning, as can all other kinds of human signals. The information capacity is shifted from the formal means of communication, the signal itself, to other forces which are not accountable by the statistical model called information theory. Encoding then is the most important of the considerations which give all signals their unique human meaning, and the communication considerations provide the framework for this encoding.

Despite all impressive arguments to the contrary, I feel that no theory to date, much less a mathematical one, has succeeded in capturing the meaning of meaning.[38] The complexities of mathematics, physical theories, languages, and all types of artistic encoding allow us to build structures out of the simplest of communicative elements, to which it is possible for us to assign an indescribable gamut of humanly significant meanings. All that is required of a communication channel is that it be capable of passing but two single elements—an 0 and a 1—and with many yes-no's we can fabricate and communicate all of our human mental productions, including the artistic. The most complex series of choices can always be simplified by encoding them into new, single-choice systems, discharging the communication of the higher meaning. If a meta-description, or higher-level description, is used somehow to preserve these replaced meanings, the very symbols which constitute this meta-description must be detracting from the new symbol by exactly the information content it tries to eliminate.

Yet when the actual meanings which we attach to our various communication means, in particular artistic ones, are considered, we find that complexities seem to merge into simplicities and still somehow preserve the essence of the original complexities. Physical theories grow simpler, yet become more comprehensive; ideas are united into purer and more inclusive thoughts; emotions merge in metaphors and carry greater feelings. How is this possible, considering the encoding factors which the human mind assigns to its communicative elements? It represents a jump from disorder to order, a reversal of the normal process of nature which thermodynamic theory has described. Somehow it must be possible for the human mind to take a communication having a certain meaning, merge it with another communication, and come up with a new communication that is formally simpler but which unites the two original meanings.

It is like the action of the Maxwell demon in a way, but instead of being a demon that operates on molecules of gas, the art demon operates on particles of information, and instead of sorting high and low energy particles, he correlates meanings. The art demon must act on information so that the physical symbols associated with a given element of communication decrease their entropy, while the meanings associated with them seem to increase their entropy. All we have to discover is how to measure the entropy of meaning. Since this has to do with the various ways in which encoding is accomplished, an approach to this very difficult problem is to study the ways specific human transmissions encode their meanings.

An attempt is made in this book to determine what meanings are encoded in each art form and how relationships between these meanings can be set up and reduced to simpler versions without destroying their greater values. The intermixing of different artistic techniques, the invention of new media, and the stratification of an old art medium into several new ones unendingly proliferate the encoding possibilities of human art communication. The actual value of this proliferation for man is to cause discontinuities toward order in the entropic trend of the cumulative physical arts, saving man from the pit of communication chaos.

Before continuing, however, I propose to make the following epistemological speculation about how man functions in his communicative choice-order world and what meanings are possible in his total existence. This is without scientific validation at present, although I suggest a few tests to make it so, but the rest of this

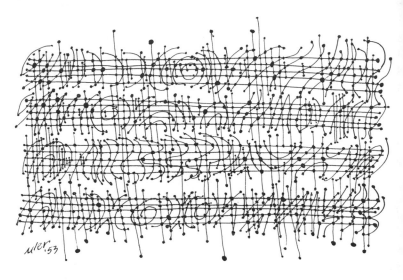

book in no way depends on an acceptance of these ideas. The only justification for going beyond this point in the present discussion is that some very interesting perplexities of philosophy and science resolve themselves and a few interesting psychological predictions can be made when the ideas of creative communication are generalized.

5

It is assumed that man's mind begins to function humanly when sensations are communicated in through the body's sensors, an assumption which sensory-deprivation experiments reinforce. At birth the human brain is highly disorganized, a maze of new neurons whose intertwining is random and whose electrical hookup has not yet begun to be organized. Except for extremely limited experiences gained *in utero*, experience which the embryo can begin to assimilate at a certain point in its development, the electrical organization of the human mind seems to begin at birth. When man is isolated or suspended in a warm fluid and deprived of all possible sensory inputs, his mind begins to stagnate, and he loses orientation and falls into a torpor, at first hallucinatory, and then more and more static until he even begins to lose the memory of experience.[39]

The random and near chaotic material of the brain is ideal for communication since, as we have seen, it is through uncertainty that all differentiation is possible and in contrast takes on its meaning. From the standpoint of a communication receptor we can think of the virgin brain as having a very high entropy, being a highly disorganized physical array of neurons, none of which is electrically connected. In this respect the mind at birth is a *tabula rasa*, as John Locke suggested, or more strictly a grand network like a telephone system where no numbers have yet been dialed. But the mind is not just passive, appearing to have the potential, as Immanuel Kant suggested, for actively coordinating new inputs which it receives through its sensors. As a meaningful communication, the elementary act of reason is one of discovering correspondences, be they correspondences between simultaneous or contiguous sensory inputs, between a new input and a remembered one, between remembered ones called out in the mind by some external stimulus, or between two or more remembered inputs not suggested by an external stimulus.

The acts of making communicative correlations must be attributed to a theoretical demon, who probably resides somewhere within the reticular formation of the brain stem, where most neural activity is said to be governed. The reticular formation of the brain is like a way station; from it, man's sensory input system is regulated, and his neural activity is inhibited or enhanced.[40] The demon acts like a miniature conductor who is directing an electrical symphony up and down man's neuraxis, keeping him in perpetual emotion. If a person's sensors are imperfect or severely limited, the demon gorges himself on the experience derived from the remaining ones. There is no basic reason to assume that an aesthetic experience in the blind or deaf is any different from that of the normal person. G. Révész shows us that blind artists can create sculpture which satisfies even the seeing person's visual aesthetic.[41] And of course, a person like Helen Keller illustrates how far even the most restricted inputs can carry the human spirit. Without this active agent correlating inputs, the mind is merely a recording device, jotting down what it experiences, but not acting on it, allowing no change in the communicative organization within the brain.

When man encounters his first physical phenomenon, the various human sensors provide different inputs to the mind, and this redundant information is the elementary communicative material which the demon correlates. The interdependence of the human sensors is a well-known fact; one sensation often has an equivalent form for two or more sensors, as sound and touch, visual form and tactile shape, taste and smell, etc.[42] As soon as there is one initial correlation, the mind has increased its ability to interpret experience one more degree. Any slight order in the electrical hookup of neurons is the beginning of a primitive repertory of elements which can be used for comparing with new inputs to help discover more order.

We come to know experience only as we order our minds since there exist at birth no a priori concepts, no preestablished innate knowledge, only the potential for building concepts. This was suggested previously by the Gestalt psychologists, notably Max Wertheimer.[43] The very agent of selection and direction in the brain, our art demon, is a growing agent, whose ability to select and direct depends on the particular experiences he has already perceived, so that we cannot say that either space or time or relations or sequences are the dominating organizing factors of the mind. What we can say is that the given human sense perceptors do direct man toward building certain perceptions of the natural world, which every man shares. There is no a priori knowledge by this view, no a priori knowledge determined by the structure of the brain or by the structure of experience. Instead, knowledge is built up as a result of the particular inbuilt human communicative sensors, which determine the kind and quality of the communicative inputs to the human brain. Instruments serve the role of communication enhancers and increase the perceived inputs to the brain as if they were artificial supplements for human sensors. Until we can tap new perceptors into the brain directly, however, man is confined to the restrictions of the normal input-output devices of the human body, the so-called five senses.[44] We can hazard the guess that what fundamentally affects human sensors and the form of sensations also fundamentally affects man's growing sense of structural knowledge. In other words, it is suggested that what we commonly call art has a profound influence on our abilities to build logic and in turn the scientific reasoning which follows from it. But how does art articulate perceptual experiences?

The brain of man acts as if it were an information reservoir, draining off orders detected in the outside world through the communicative link of its sensors, under the guidance of the brain's demon, who must recognize correlations in the communications it receives in order to try to keep the entropy of the brain's electrical organization as low as it can. Slowly the mind fills up with order. It is an ordering which begins as an electrical, communicative ordering, but probably in time it becomes a physical thing, which, as some physiologists and biochemists have suggested, settles into the structures of the brain's protein molecules. For this reason mental order may even become a physically cumulative thing which the DNA molecule, the design storehouse of the human gene, is able to pass along from generation to generation.[45] Slowly then, the primitive man (or child) reaches a certain equilibrium with his communicative surroundings; man's internal mental ordering comes into approximate agreement with the detected orders he derives from nature, and soon there are few surprises in nature.

But man can also operate on nature to affect objects and to change phenomena, and those concerning perceptions are particularly important at this elementary level since they establish human communication and mental meanings. By this view, art is the attempt to reorder sensations in an external form or to articulate and correlate the structures standing for sensations that have been previously accepted in this role by the mind. To make a structure or a particular sensation stand for another is an identical act to the primitive one of correlating sense inputs from one human sensor with another. The demon makes arbitrary structures, like the curlicues of letters, stand for particular sensations—namely, for the sounds of words or for objects—and both in turn have more complex correspondents. The results of words sensed are to let flow an extremely involved fabric of internal messages with perceptual equivalents, including objects, relationships, actions, involvements, and so on, subject to the same correlation of sense inputs made at the most elementary level of communication (although they can become extremely complex).

Science in this framework may be thought of as the communicative recording of nature's organization. All such records must obviously be carried out in terms of the meanings which the mind has already built up, especially the most elementary ones. Science then depends on the repertory of elements man develops from his sensory experience. The structures they exhibit already exist in their physical equivalent in nature, as far as we can determine, and in the equivalent form in our mind by which we make this determination. Science is nature redundant in the mind; art is nature's perception revised by the mind.

Prediction or empirical verification is essential to science, and it serves to indicate if the mental theoretical formulation in the mind is in fact a true redundancy of nature, at least as far as we can determine with respect to communication. A new empirical fact which cannot be fit into a theory does not disorganize uniformities, either in the mind or in nature; it instead suggests the relevance or irrelevance of a theory or the limits of some coherent formulation of nature. The recordings of small events in short periods of time might be called the physical or psychological sciences; the recordings of large events over long time spans, the historical or social sciences. Each has its own set of meaningful terms correlated at the primeval level, individual communicative domains which represent meaningful orders and structures.

A physical operation on the world may lead to the uncovering of previously undetected phenomena, new levels of entropy previously untapped. A new construction such as a telescope, cyclotron, or laser can be considered to be essentially a device which matches the entropy of the human communication system with the entropy of new domains in nature. They serve to open new channels of communication between man and his natural surroundings, and this is important, not only because it reveals new hidden secrets in nature, but also becauses it enlarges man's sensual world and provides new perceptual material for further organization.

The assimilation of new physical information derived from nature through instruments perforce depends on an adequate repository of structures in man's mental system so that he is able to encompass them, able to correlate them with his previous knowledge. The order figure of any new scientific record, the statistical measure of the elements of a particular record system in science, such as those of a given particular theory or mathematical system used for some theory (calculable by the methods described by Brillouin),[46] must be greater in entropy content than, or at most equal to, those similar systems residing in the mind of the person who comprehends them, measured by the structure of the previous art systems which constitute them (calculable by the methods described by Shannon and others).[47] This is essentially another formulation of a remarkable mathematical proof devised by Kurt Gödel.[48] Gödel's theorem applies to consistent mathematical or logical systems. He developed a formula which was unprovable in a consistent system. A second theorem showed that it was impossible to prove in a consistent system that it *is* consistent. This may sound like circular reasoning, but if we think of the various domains of mathematical thought, like geometry or algebra, we can begin to understand its significance. It used to be assumed that in any of these domains any new proposition which was correctly deducted in them *had* to be true. Each branch of mathematics was thought to be perfectly consistent, and all new propositions were considered to be self-evidently or tautologically true. But Gödel showed that this was not necessarily the case. The axiomatic method was proved to have limitations, and no final systematization was attainable in even the more sophisticated mathematical logics. It is not possible to guarantee the complete systematization of an area of mathematical thought, even though carrying it out as far as possible reveals no inconsistencies. Gödel's theorem confronts this human limitation mathematically and shows that if we augment any mathematical domain by an indefinite number of new elements, there are always more true mathematical statements which we cannot derive from even this augmented mathematics. This is because of the fact that any given mathematical domain which is rich enough to develop simple arithmetic—that is to say, a domain which is humanly useful or meaningful—must have the potential to generate a low entropic figure or a high informational order with respect to previous human logics. Such a domain turns out to be one that is never complete, one which can never be brought to a lower entropy state by manipulation than the total internal organization statistic of the particular mathematician (or mechanism such as a computer) who performs the operations. If man had an infinite intuition into mathematical forms, Gödel's theorem would be meaningless.

The present reasoning explains these conclusions by suggesting that it is humanly meaningless to expect an abstract system to be consistent without actually carrying out every possible manipulation in that system. This is an impossibility because a rich mathematical system is endless and does not exhaust its manipulative possibilities after so many finite operations. The information content of any mathematical domain is therefore not infinite, as Brillouin suggests,[49] but calculable on the basis of the actual operations that mathematicians have actually carried out. Like the statistic associated with the organization of music,[50] a statistic associated with the organization of a particular domain of mathematics must demonstrate an increase in entropy as mathematicians elucidate new proofs year after year. A newly conceived formal mathematics begins this statistic all over again at a point near zero entropy or perfect order. A computer could be programmed to perform mathematical manipulation and thus help increase the information figure for a given mathematical domain. However, the contributions of a computer in this respect will probably be as trivial for mathematics as they have been for compositional originality in music.[51] The reason for this is the obvious inability of the present-day or conceivable future hybrid mass-memory computer to make the more significant and highly complex informational orderings which are commonplace for the human mind.

The cumulative effect of art and science as they develop is to flood the mind of man with a communicative order of an increasing degree of complexity. A paradox now begins to emerge: the orders which man first desired, extremely low entropy orders that are perfect and simple, begin to grow into orders which have increasingly higher and higher entropies, since they become complicated, with many new facets emerging and new interlinkages being constantly evolved by man. This is an intolerable situation for the demon we have proposed, a demon who has a rage for order, a need to keep the neural electrical system of the human brain in good order. Man is forced to find ways to clean out the mind, and as a housekeeping function he is forced to devise new structures, communicative orders which are pure and low in entropy. But before he can do this, he must possess the wherewithal to do so, and lacking a basic structure that is simple

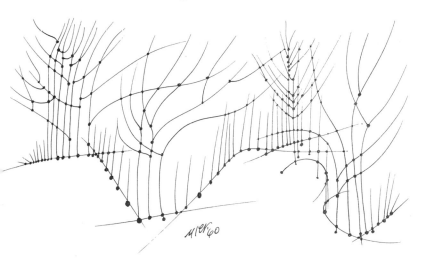

enough, he cannot begin to reorder his mental records. He is forced then to look for or to create a new art system that is extremely simple from the standpoint of his perceptions—not for the reason of reordering the records of experience, but for the reason of uncluttering the complexities in his mind. This is a way to explain parsimony, the desire to couch physical theories in the simplest possible form.

Epistemologically then, knowledge is a stepwise progression, beginning with man's elementary mental organization exhausting the entropy he perceives in the organization of natural phenomena through his sensors, arriving at a lower level of mental entropy owing to an artistic ordering of perceptions, some of which can cause a drastic jump in the entropy since they are extremely novel organizations, and making a record of that experience in the lowest entropic terms he has generated.

Science follows perceptions which art has articulated deepest. For instance, if man's art experiences are primarily tactile, arrived at through a preoccupation with the tactile sensory perception channels, he will concentrate on tactile experience in his sciences, since this is the perceptual area given the greatest entropy boost—as with the Greeks and their scientific organization. In this sense then, Newton's theories began with the Greek artistic preoccupation with linear kinesthetic movement and harmonious symmetry.

The characteristics of art organization depend on the physical media of the arts and how they are perceived by man. More than one ordering is possible for a given art medium, as we have seen. Painting, for instance, can organize recognizable form or pure color and line, or music can organize pure tonality or pure form that is atonal. Each new art form which man builds has, in summation, an overall physical communicative order organization. When a person tries to grasp the order of any work of art, the entropy figure of his mental neurological organization system intermingles with or interferes with the entropy of the art source, like noise in a radio receiver, corrupting the incoming signal and limiting the extent to which a person reacts to art. These internal disturbing sources affect the person, but naturally they do not affect art because it is external and permanent—that is, art is like the smell of flowers which communicate but cannot be communicated with. The individual is also limited in his perception of art systems by the information-handling capacity of his sensors and by the total capacity of his mental information reservoir. But with enough time, as we have seen, this limitation is unimportant; man exposed to a new art form long enough and seriously trying to grasp its order ultimately reaches an understanding, which is a way of saying that a man's brain adsorbs the order of new art and decreases the entropy of man's mental organization thereby. Since art is a perceptual organization, the order can be appreciated in time without preparation, whereas a logical order of the kind basic to mathematics requires a foreknowledge of the assumptions and conventions. No matter how long one studies the scratches of a quadratic equation, without knowing the rules of exponents or radicals it would be impossible to grasp the order envolved.

When exposed to a given work of art whose entropy figure is a constant, its entropy in the mentally reflected domain of the human mind is decreasing. We listen again and again to music, and the repetition decreases the entropy of our internal sense of the order of music. When it gets to the point that we can predict an entire work of art, or even before (for instance, if we can predict Beethoven's First Symphony, given the first single sforzando, or an old Hollywood movie from one familiar scene), the physical work of art no longer has any entropy meaning to be communicated to us.

An exposure to art causes a gradual decrease in the entropy of the mentally reflected art, owing to man's becoming more and more familiar with it and able to predict the experience more and more accurately. Man is essentially bored with this art from the standpoint of information exchange, and he is always looking for new experiences, which he needs to feed his insatiable demon and which he can no longer find in old art. But since he is human, man finds that he must keep exposing himself to old art, probably because his memory is not perfect and is always corrupting remembered experience. His personal mental agitation and the impact of new, incoming entropies are tending to corrupt the stored information in his mind. Paradoxically, then, man must experience art again and again, to maintain himself at a high state of boredom. But this situation is intolerable, and it demands that something truly new be experienced. Man is therefore forced to search for new art or to create new art himself, with its concomitant revitalizing statistic. This is the motivation of the creator, and it forces him to look to those aspects of perceptual experience which he can manipulate.

There are two main components in perceptual experience which man manipulates to make art: the units and the structures. He can make different sensual forms, or he can make different sensual connections between old forms. Making different forms is a use of natural perceptions in basically new ways; making different connections between old forms is a discovery of new organizations in old forms which significantly reduce the entropy of their configurations. Sometimes the new discoveries of sensual media also influence the old forms by helping the artist organize their communication into tighter systems with a higher order. This means that the artist can decrease the entropy of art constructions by: (1) finding new or unused physical qualities of man's perceptual environment that can be organized anew; (2) organizing old qualities into tighter forms; and (3) using newly discovered sensual qualities to affect the organization of old qualities. An example of the first is the motion picture, a new physical and technological development; the second, the typical case of art whose organization is being increased, as classical music has done since Palestrina's day. The third has two typical examples: first, when one art is added to another to affect its total organization, as when the opera was conceived to join the instrumental music with the human voice or when electronic music was welded to dance; and second, when it is found that the typical qualities of an art form hide other qualities which can be equally significantly organized, but in a radically new way, as when Schoenberg found that music could be arranged to create a new logic of tones or when Kandinsky left behind recognizability and concentrated on abstract visual shapes. There is actually no comparison between new art organizations and the old ones to which they seem to be related, since they represent a radical new communicative ordering and are therefore always capable of displaying a new entropy figure.

The manipulative order of mechanisms such as the computer can be coupled to man's communication system to expand the total volume of the neural network. The limitation is the link between man and the computer, although sufficient available time can expand the information passable through even those computer output-input systems operating at a slow rate. The basic problem with computers and making them available for human use is one of entropy exchange, from the standpoint of the entropy of the signals within the computer and those organized in the human mind used to grasp their significance. No computer program with a total organizational entropy higher than that of the applicable symbol system conceived by the person who uses it can be constructed and ultimately utilized by man. This is a variation of Gödel's theorem for a computer.*

A variation of Gödel's theorem also suggests itself for art forms. Music, for example, was considered to be as basically wedded to classical combinatorial tone rules as geometry was to Euclid's axioms. The advent of a new compositional convention, of course, showed the validity of other tone combination rules, much as when Euclid's parallel axiom was replaced in geometry

---

* A super computer conceivably could cumulate an order in its circuitry and memories which exceeds that of man, putting it in a position to grasp a structural order in nature that man could not detect, if it were provided with adequate in-built sensors and told to try. If it succeeded, however, it could never communicate its success to man, nor could the computer appreciate its own abilities as if it had a consciousness. If this were accomplished, it might be appreciated by man vicariously even though he did not understand the details. By instructing the computer with this knowledge to make predictions, man might be able to verify the computer's understanding without being able to understand it directly himself.

to give the unexpected new world of non-Euclidian geometries. We can predict that many basic compositional possibilities exist in music, since it is obviously rich enough from a standpoint of elements in an information system to support them (as a cursory look at the unusual modes that exist in the history of music confirms). An art system of any richness, one with sufficient perceptual elements to allow the generation at least of a folk idiom, can never be exhausted of basic new art systems, and yet we cannot guarantee them always to be meaningful. It is the proper business of an artist to derive new compositional systems from postulated rules, and it is not his concern to decide whether his postulated rules can be validated by other means. That is, if a new art does not strike the senses as people would like it to, this does not invalidate the art's basic novelty and final human value. We cannot guarantee all new art systems to be meaningful, however, at least to everybody, because of the communication requirements which must be brought to bear before there is a significant exchange to the person sensing them. It should be theoretically possible to develop a classically correct tone cluster which, when played, seems incorrect, much as Gödel did for mathematics. This is obviously a test of the richness of classical music which original composers acting in the spirit of Gödel have made again and again. Any new system can take on meaning only when the mind of the perceiver is prepared with a sufficiently low mental entropy in the communicative orderings of his experience—in this example, his awareness of musical form—so that he can grasp its entropy content. The human value of a particular form domain is this very richness which cannot be predicted to be humanly meaningful a priori and which cannot be quickly exhausted.

The effect of art is to build the human potential for perceiving larger entropies which exist in various isolated domains in the natural world. Thermodynamics suggests that the total order of this natural world is tending toward an infinite entropy, becoming increasingly disordered; that the natural evolution of any physical system is to lose information, increasing its entropy.

How do we know, however, that our feeling that the universe is running down is not just the effect of our perceptual apparatus' running down, losing orders because of memory corruptions and other perturbations? We cannot assume that any definite entropy or change of entropy is actually a part of some domain of nature because we always make the observation or calculation by a human mechanism or mental system which may in itself establish that entropy or entropy change. The entropy of some empirical evidence or experiment is due to the communicative means whereby we arrive at the data, whether limited by an instrumental or a mental structure.

By this view limitations of nature or constants of calculation like those of Einstein or Planck or Boltzmann are not necessarily actual facts of nature outside man, but instead a feature of human logics and sensory mechanisms and instrumentalities whereby man gains his knowledge of nature. If man were to develop a suprahuman mechanism for building new communication links to nature, he might see these constants broken down, giving way to other constants and limitations resulting from these new links. The mysterious goings-on at extremely small lengths within the atom and the unfathomable happenings at galactic distances represent the two extremes of man's perceptual understanding, the entropy limits both of his instruments and of his mental apparatus. More comprehensive nature communication devices, such as bigger particle accelerators to probe the extremely short distances, or grander deep-space sensing instruments on satellites, or more powerful mental structurings to explain what we already know but cannot fit into theory, may force us to alter our attitude toward the so-called constants of the universe.

When there is an unexplained natural phenomenon, some new fact of nature which we know but cannot explain or which our instruments detect but which we cannot understand, it is due to the lack of a sufficiently great entropy figure in any mental structure to allow for an adequate recording theory. In these cases the human perceptual system has not yet been raised to a sufficiently high entropy level by art to enable it to rationalize the natural phenomenon in question. This can be used to explain Szilard's interpretation of Maxwell's demon trying to overcome the Heisenberg Uncertainty Principle, which was described in detail earlier. Szilard's idea, that the entropy lost by nature (in a gas) is balanced by the information gained by the demon and passed on to the observer, can be restated: the mental information of the observer, the information of the communicative means by which he interprets nature, must be greater than the entropy communicated from an area of nature before he can expect to encompass and comprehend its significance, since no communication is otherwise possible. This is what we mean by meaning.

The organization statistic of the art media of which a given era of scientists is aware has to have a greater entropy than the scientific theories they conceive to describe natural phenomena. It is not always obvious how to determine which art media are relevant, since our perceptual apparatuses do not always give a clear indication of the natural phenomena being manipulated by our mind. For instance, that motion accompanies vision is not obvious, nor is the fact that time can be measured by both aural and visual sequences. The particular historical art forms of which an era of scientists is aware could serve as an indication of what perceptual phenomena are relevant to the theoretical building of their particular theoretical sciences. As David Hawkins suggests, it is easier to see in retrospect the ways habitual patterns of thought have inhibited or supported the growth of knowledge. Elementary mathematics, for instance, can be disentangled from empiricism, yet the experiences which let us develop mathematics may have been, psychologically speaking, established through subtle, primitive, self-evident foundations. Our ordinary experience of spatial relations is in a sense implicit in the everyday language by which we describe them.[52]

The question of whether or not nature is infinitely amenable to the forms artists invent, unconsciously used by scientists for theories of nature, turns into the question of whether or not the human mind is infinitely potent as a creator of perceptual form. Nature obviously exists, as we all naïvely assume it does, and it is certainly complex beyond all understanding; but the human mind exists too, and it also has a corresponding incomprehensible complexity, which can at least approach, if not match, that of nature. There does not seem to be an intrinsic bond to scientific inquiry, and at the same time no scientific inquiry can ever exhaust the infinite variety of the human mind. This is because the human mind is defined, articulated, given substance itself, by the ever-growing heritage of perception articulations that we call art.

3

The Creativity of Art

New Human Awarenesses

1

THE CREATIVE aspects of art, like the truth of art, seem to escape precise scientific analysis. If science concentrates on art as it does on other phenomena, everything seems to fall apart: meaningful experiences turn into colored shapes, scratches on paper, simple harmonic motions. Science only tolerates unobservables or intangibles when they serve a useful function for explanation, like time or electromagnetic radiation. And creativity, that is a phenomenon of the mind—of interest only to the philosopher, or perhaps to the psychologist when he considers aberrations or idiosyncracies of man. Art is grouped by science into curious but unapproachable human regions, like metaphysics or faith, and artists encourage this grouping since it adds to their own specialness and increases the mystery. The desire of more causally oriented people to understand the meaning of art, something which they usually admire and wish to assimilate even more—an artistic desire at heart—is met with ridicule by the scientist and scorn by the artist. It is the human nature of art which places the aesthetician in his unenviable position, the particularly volatile meaning and transfiguring essence of art through which mankind draws some mysterious lifeblood akin to a religious experience. Inspiration must guide the true artist, and faith is the only requirement for the pure art lover.

The truth and creativity of art are obviously closely bound to the human condition. But if that condition is ever to go beyond certain rather restricted limits, I think it is man's duty to try to explain the most intimate details of art. The very drive toward mysticism, toward the mysterious and awe-inspiring; the need to expand our psychic world and to cast off mental bonds through drug experiences, are but disguised attempts to penetrate the mysteries of life. In the past all mysteries unmasked, however much vested interests or dedicated practitioners have resisted them, have led mankind toward different human experiences, often at a higher spiritual level and certainly with a broader intellectual understanding.

Art is a mysterious experience on the one hand, but it is tangible and existential, and it deserves to be thought about as a phenomenon. A Rossini overture or a Debussy sonata or an Eliot Carter string quartet is more than just sounds; it also has a quality you might call beauty or even profundity. A poem is more than just words, spoken or written according to a certain rhyme or rhythm. The indescribable vitality of art must come from somewhere and you have to somehow attach its significance to the original experience. Traditionally it has been called the *aesthetic* experience, derived from the Greek word to perceive, especially by feeling. Is the truth of art then but a feeling? Is the creativity of art the presentation of feeling for our perception?

Art is a perception which is experienced as a sensation at the level of input, and simultaneously as a mental event at the level of brain reception. In addition to this perception there is a vitality which makes it somehow linger to establish itself within our brains, and even to influence us. It might be admitted generally that art is something that one man makes for the experience and perception of another man, although it may not reach him; art only becomes meaningful when the cycle of creator to perceiver transpires (although the making of art alone seems to suffice for some men). When the perception of art is consummated by being exposed to another person, there is a transference by some as yet unknown mechanism, of an as yet unknown quality—a transference which also seems to have a special meaning. Susanne Langer of course insists that art is above all the communication of "feeling," but she gives such a broad definition of feeling—everything that may be felt—that we are right back where we started from, unable to tie down exactly what is exchanged.[1] We must admit that some exchange does exist when a work of art is experienced by us—but whether or not it is an exchange of feeling, in the sense of emotions, or otherwise, and what is the extent of this exchange, are things yet to be determined.

Is this then a communication? If we mean by communication merely the exchange mentioned, art is at least this much—but it might be something more. What is this something more in art, and how does it actually bring about a value in this world? Any perception by one man is a passive communication in a way because it is a reception of something from the outside world. When that communication is more than passive; when there is an effect on the person who perceives the phenomenon, then we can say that the communication is more than just an exchange. It also has the potential of being called a *creative* communication if it does something more than merely exchange something— but it remains to be discovered just how it can be called creative.

· Langer also suggests that art is good expression, attributing to art the ability to formalize our feelings in such a way that we can appreciate them best.[2] Benedetto Croce felt that this expressiveness must also be creative, however, by which he meant that it must be personal and original in the sense of novel or fresh. But Albert Hofstadter, in his book *Truth and Art*,[3] indicates that the theory that art is the expression of feeling is an isolated phenomenon in the history of aesthetics, occurring in our times because of an excess of feeling due to a reaction to the violence of wars, to the automatism of the machine, and to the inhumanity of thought control. The expressionists, be they traditional or abstract, are throwbacks to a subjective, post-romantic attitude, hoping to raise art to a more universal level of feeling, probably even to help compensate for human alienation in the modern world. The expressionistic theories which explain this limited art are inadequate, especially in the light of a long history of works of art which are not always expressive in this sense.

Seeking a more universal theory of art truth and creativity, Hofstadter indicates that art not only expresses, but that it actually articulates our humanness in the act of artistic creation. He maintains (in the tradition of Kant) that our very conscious existence, our emotional and human beingness, is due to the creation of art, a result of the manner in which we make and perceive art. The actual creation of forms, the organization of artistic elements, is the act whereby we create the truth of our human existence. As the linguist Benjamin Whorf and the social psychologist G. H. Mead had suggested earlier, the fact that the mind operates primarily linguistically means that the prime being of man, his intelligibility and subjective meaning, is linguistic.[4] This is an ancient idea, actually, since the Greek Sophists taught that there is no differentiation between words and wisdom. The Ciceronian claim that eloquence was training for practical life is an early harbinger of Hofstadter's theory which maintains that art helps man build his being (and my extension which claims that art predisposes man to science by ordering his mental structure). Articulated being, man's manifestation in art, is, in Hofstadter's sense, not a copying of nature, but a building anew. The illusions of art are more meaningful than we suspect since we owe our actual human *being* to their articulation; and I would add that we even owe our human *consciousness* to art, for reasons which I will try to make clear.

Hofstadter says that we intuit, for instance, a cry of pain as being grief or suffering, much as anything we perceive, like a color or a person's face we know—it is an immediate and intuitive recognition; grief and suffering are, according to him, identical with the cry. He does not distinguish between reception and mental event. What holds for the cry also holds for language and art. Edvard Munch's painting "The Cry" is also identical with a cry or with the lonely suffering of a destitute little girl—and it is perceived in a direct way that is immediately intuited, without recourse to other experience. We directly experience these complex emotive ideas when we experience them in language or in art; but they come across to us, according to Hofstadter, in a more complex way than that of a simple communication, dependent rather on a reaction to a shared situation which is itself understood intuitively.

Communication, Hofstadter maintains, is present in advice, command, or conceivably even in prayer, but is insufficient to explain the truth or creativity of art. He insists that the meaning of art is not carried in communication alone because it is a building operation, which functions to bring our human being into a new existence; that communication occurs only when one person addresses another, and poems and pictures or music are not necessarily addressed to anyone in particular.

Up to this point I agree with Hofstadter, and I think that his fundamental insight into the creative building potential of art is extremely profound and useful, but I still wonder how we get to *know* a particular articulation of human being; how we perceive the fabric of beingness which is our human estate and which we all share and by which our collective humanness grows. And further, how does art actually hold a creative experience in store for us? Art may be a kind of bubbling over of our humanness, and it may not be aimed at other people in particular; but if anyone *does* pick it up and perceive it, sense it, I think that it has to be the communicative act which carries meaning across the gulf.

The quality of our human being grows by means of a feedback from object to person, from generation to generation, regenerating into new meanings which bloom into our greater awareness of ourselves as human beings. This includes an awareness of ourselves in nature and in the surroundings of our artistic and scientific creations as well. The carriers of these new insights and meanings are the results of science and the embodiments of art, but they are communicative, I feel, in the elemental sense of an exchange. They are a building phenomenon, it is true, and in this sense they are more than the simple communication of a given idea. Before relativity we did not conceive that time had any special meaning other than insistent regularity; before Liszt we did not realize that music could be so personal and romantic and literal; before the motion picture we could not conceive of things in very slow motion, or imagine the motion of such slow things as plants, sped up by stop-motion photography.

Man's reality is changed by art, although it is his perceptual reality and not his physical reality which is the province of science. Teilhard de Chardin calls this cumulative growth of the mind a "noogenesis," which he insists is an evolutionary process—a bettering and "hominisation," or making more human, of mankind.[5] At this level science and art are not distinguished, and they seem very much related, although one deals with the outer world and the other with the inner world of man. But are there more fundamental differences between art and science?

2

Science is true or false; art is meaningful or insignificant (swell or lousy, as a friend of mine remembers that Heywood Broun once wrote).[6] Science constantly compares the guesses that the mind makes with the reality it tries to probe; art builds new ideas on old ones without rejecting them. Science becomes outdated because it finds that it overlooked part of the reality it thought it understood; art is constantly renewing itself. Ancient science is a historic curiosity with little or no contemporary validity, and need not be taught as a foundation to modern science; ancient art is as valuable today as is our own modern art, especially for the person just becoming aware of art. While the ideas of science may be as vague as those of art, as much a result of intuition or creativity, they are rejected if they do not work. Art that is vague or spurious is rejected too, but the criterion is not whether or not it works, but whether or not it succeeds in raising us to some new undefined level of appreciation. The insights of art are not scientific because this level of appreciation cannot be closely defined; and the insights of art are not scientific because they are not psychological insights into human nature. Rather the insights of art are enlargements of inner human perception, a soul-building phenomenon. Art articulates our soul, or, to be more scientific, art articulates our consciousness of what it is to be human. Art creates our humanness.

The fundamental discovery of early man that he could elicit an inner world—when before he was only aware, like an animal, of the outside world—is when man became both a human being and an artist. Then man's inner world could somehow reflect itself in the outer world. When this was a successful and meaningful reflection, when the outer world could be shaped to have a significance for man, he perceived himself for the very first time, like Narcissus first discovering his own image in a pond. The primary creative act of making art was in the forging of an outside illusion that communicated itself back to man as a part of his previously private inner world. This seems so commonplace today, and we take it for granted and consider it trivial to find our inner world manifest in an outer reality, but it was what initially distinguished man as a human being from all other animals, I think.

How this creative construction of our humanness originally came about can only be guessed; it was obviously some higher level of the evolving awareness of itself which matter has constantly been striving to obtain. Much can be said, however, about how this creativity is actually manifest. The very idea of creativity must first be considered, because the mere mouthing of that word conjures up too many hopes and confusions. Art is creative, but so is science—why is the one any different from the other?

Does science try to comprehend or assimilate a more permanent world than that of art? Is the reality outside of man any more permanent than the inner? The recent difficulties of physical theories to tie down matter suggest that the outside reality is just as inchoate, when the chips are down, as the inner world of man's psyche. The recourse of the scientist has been to take up the Kantian idea that we are limited by our subjectivity—by our measuring devices—the Uncertainty Principle suggested by Heisenberg. We seem to get in the way of all measurements of nature, especially when we are trying to look at the most minute sectors of nature. What about our inner reality? If you are a physiologist or a psychoanalyst you come to the same point: we cannot probe man's innermost physiological or psychological secrets because they stop or change when we interrupt them or probe them.

If the outer reality is just as inchoate as the inner (as recent physical science seems to suggest), then the question arises: why is art more permanent than science? Perhaps our inability to find a good answer to this question is enough of a reason to reject the idea that art is a reflection of a psychic inner reality in man, as science is the reflection of the outside physical reality. How can we replace the theory that man makes art out of an urge to express or explain his inner human beingness; or out of a desire to articulate the humanness he detects within himself, in order to capture it in the act and formulate for his own and someone else's edification? Hofstadter's conception would answer this, but for the fact that it does not explain how the articulation of humanness created by art is exchanged, and that it does not develop the actual workings of that creativity.

Let us go back and review the cycle through which the artist goes in order to make art, and hope that we might get a new clue to a more complete answer to this question. At birth man is an unfilled ensemble of possible communicative elements from which his exchange of ideas and feelings could be fabricated. The child discovers slowly, by means of perceptions of the outside world—and of his own inner world—that there are various relationships and structures which seem to have meaning to him, and the finds "media" in which to build them. Due to a "communication" between himself and these probable sense data, man conceives a structure which he begins to formulate—and he slowly becomes aware of himself and of the outside world: a person with feelings and attitudes, located in a world of many experiences. The act of becoming aware of the world and of oneself

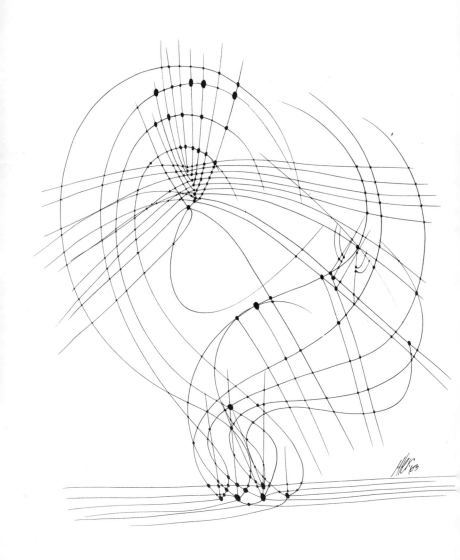

is the act of building communicative forms and attitudes, at the most elemental level written in the medium of flesh, the neural system of the human body, in whatever else chemically or physically that is involved in building the communicative potential within man, and reflected in all possible external means at his disposal.

Here is a suggestion, taken from the workings of the human body (its chemico-neural system), as to how reality can be concretized: by placing it in some potentially communicative physical form. We overcome the uncertainty involved in a communicative relationship with the reality of our experiences in nature, because the act builds a new reality in and of itself due to the exchange and the storage. It is structurally organized in a physical form before it can be called potentially creative. This establishment of our communicative reality works sometimes, other times it fails. When it works it does so because there is a *creative* extention of our past awareness into some new dimension of beingness—into a further expansion of what we mean by our *human* beingness.

As a result the art act must be a making of something that is communicative; but more, it must be something that is enriching, broadening, deepening of the experience of a human being. This is near to Benedetto Croce's idea that art is expressive insight, but I think that there is a further elaboration in the idea that the true essence of humanness is a result of communication, thus explaining Croce's idea of intuition. The act of formulating the insights of art in a communicative form is essential before they can be reacted to, adjudged, or appropriated to complement the humanness of the self or another being. After the formulation of art, if it is successful, the sharing of it with another person, through the communicative act, builds onto man's perceptual and conscious world. Linking creativity and communication reconciles the romantic urge for newness (creativity) with the classic need of tradition and style (order), because the new can only be communicated when it is almost classically ordered. Beauty is art that is a creative communication. A correspondence of meaning and form may be associated with a creative communication, but it is not its raison d'être. When meaning and form are split, what is lost is not beauty, but the communication, as will be seen. Consciousness is manifest because we build our own consciousness by a similar self-communication from the physical world to our own brains.

Art by this conception is not merely a means to move information; art is instead a technique that expands our lives and our consciousness—the awareness and beingness of our lives—through the creative encodings in a communicative form that persists in a permanent physicality. In this sense art may have less to do with the exchange of emotions and feelings than has been supposed. What is communicated in art cannot rightly be called just an emotion—certainly artists do not try to communicate specific emotions which they have felt and desire to pass on to us. This confusion is perhaps why some aestheticians have been loath to call art communication. Artists grow their emotions in the organic means of their art, providing vessels into which we can pour similar emotions if we desire—but the original emotive origin may not always be pure or necessary (which means that other emotional possibilities exist for an identical art form). If something like this was not the case an artist would only have to name an emotion to communicate it, and we would easily get the idea because of our common shared ideas about feelings. Instead, what is actually communicated in art is a sensual and creative enlargement of our perception of human existence, morally and intellectually, both emotional and otherwise. It derives its communication from conventional meanings to which we respond by virtue of our human makeup and experience; it derives its creativity from the artist's ability to find or build meaningful encodings of perceptual phenomena we have not recognized before.

The young Mozart could compose music, to which we respond as if it were the product of emotions exceeding his immature years, because the manipulative genius required for the creation of music is such that, like mathematics or chess, the prodigy can rise to it. It simply does not require a deep emotional creativity to build good music. Since music is sensual we call it art; it is felt and we react to it emotionally; but music is not a communicative exchange of emotions experienced by the young Mozart and passed on to us in an accurate analogous form. This is how art is more than simple communication, why it is not only the expression of emotions, and why it is instead a creative communication of new perceptual possibilities.

At one stage art is a display of the creative possibilities of a medium in a communicative form. At a different stage, however, the prodigy is at a loss, as in literature or painting. The manipulation of the communicative means of these latter arts exceeds the abilities of the young because they do not have sufficiently broad human emotional experiences to comprehend their encoding means.*

The encoding of literature, for example, extends out of the purely technical into the adult world of human experience, which is not to say that it is more or less profound or humanly meaningful than music or any other art. Whether the one or the other art is humanly richer or more important is a matter of one's mood or viewpoint. The simple perceptual creativity of music fits some moods and satisfies some viewpoints; and the complex emotional encodings of literature or painting (when literal) are required by others. Together, all the stages of artistic communication build the perceptual broadening of our experience into the fabric we call our humanity. Human experience is actually extended out in many directions in the virtual volumes of art—to borrow Langer's phrase. The extent to which a person can respond to all of these broad communicative enrichments indicates how far a person is able to partake of the richness of the human condition. One might expand Benjamin Whorf's proposition that the way a person perceives the world is determined by his language (it pays to increase your word power) to include

---

* It can be predicted that nonobjective painting could have its prodigies, because it is a direct medium like music or mathematics that requires less human experience for its comprehension and formulation.

the arts of which he is sensitive (it pays to increase your art power).

3

The creativity of art can perhaps result from three possibilities: (1) the formulation of new communicative forms with new creative possibilities for encoding, (2) the deepening of the encoding possibilities of old art forms by new creative insights, and (3) the revelation of new perceptual meanings hidden within the accepted communication media of art (Table II).

The way art gives rise to new, creative meanings can best be appreciated by realizing that a creative insight is in general the

TABLE II—CREATIVE COMMUNICATIVE POSSIBILITIES OF ART

1. NEW ARTISTIC FORMS
    a. Entirely new (oil painting, motion pictures) with resulting new human perceptual experiences
    b. Combination of old forms in a new basic way (mobiles, nonobjective movies, electronic music) with resulting new insights into the possibilities of form
2. NEW ENCODING POSSIBILITIES
    a. New significant human meanings (tone poem, surrealistic use of dreams, Theater of the Absurd, etc.) with resulting new insights into meaning
    b. New technical refinements (development of perspective, inner space of sculpture) and resulting original perceptual experiences
3. NEW PERCEPTUAL MEANINGS
    a. Within one level of encoding (most restricted media, "pure music") with insights into perceptual, structural possibilities (space, color, time)
    b. Between two or more levels of encoding in a single form (most literary and visual arts) with resulting insights into human experience

bringing together of two or more old ideas or forms in such a way that we recognize the originality and revelation of their combination. This is an old idea, and the literal meaning of the Greek word for symbol, according to McLuhan,[7] is the putting together of two unconnected things. It is specifically the symbolist technique as conceived by Mallarmé. Arthur Koestler developed it most fully in *The Act of Creation*.[8] His idea of the "bisociative" act, a joining of two "matrices" of thought to give a creative union, is extremely important. The matrix is, in my view, an encoded package, and the relationship is creative when it enlarges our humanity. A creative insight results in art when the encoding of one form is related to the encoding of another form in a way we recognize as being *inventively* meaningful. I feel that the union of encoded ideas is not like an optical illusion, however, since it is not ambiguous any longer if it is creative. A pun or a metaphor is not ambiguous because it presents both meanings as well as the relationship between them simultaneously. Ambiguity sometimes only resolves in our unconscious, and though we may not be able to focus on the elements consciously, we somehow sense—intuit—that they are indeed birds of a feather. It is a mistake, I think, to insist as Gombrich does[9] that the ambiguity of a cubist's rendering of a vase simultaneously in two planes is unresolved. The various images come together not in our eyes but in our minds, and they are resolved in their creative relationships. Abraham Moles's interpretation of multiple meaning misses the point, because he fails to consider the importance of their synthesis, calling them unstable, tending to dissociate in time.[10] Even the ambiguities of tone in music must resolve in time before we can comprehend them, as L. B. Meyer says in his important book *Emotion and Meaning in Music*;[11] but I think it is also a mistake to equate ambiguity resolved with creativity, as he does. William Empson in his *Seven Types of Ambiguity* makes many important distinctions about the use of ambiguity in poetic language, and shows how it can have a creatively meaningful application.[12]

We must assume that creativity in art is more than the simple association of mental states. Otherwise we would, like Pavlov's dog, accept any repetition of mental states or coincidences of ideas as being creative. Dr. W. Grey Walter suggests that, "when two series of events are perceived together they form the warp and pattern of the probability that two events are significantly related."[13] This turns causality into creativity. We are mentally disposed perhaps to the recognition of a creative relationship due to a coincidence of association, but the simple coexistence does not seem to me to be sufficient to define creativity—there must be something else to justify their relationship. The test of justness, of imaginativeness in the new relationship, is whether there is a new awareness derivative from the connection. When there is an ambiguous relationship, we feel that it is creative when it resolves itself into something newly meaningful; the poetical habit of uniting disparate objects by metaphor is a spontaneous expression of creative communication in this sense, because opposites have a way of canceling or modifying and pushing or pulling you into a new grasp of reality. In his book *Productive Thinking*,[14] Max Wertheimer stresses that creativity arises out of a comprehensive structural knowledge. Creativity is an illogical operation of the mind which breaks down rigid classes and ignores the rules of logic and past conditioning. But a purely random trial-and-error of combinatorial permutations (which I suggest in Chapter 8 is the most fruitful aid a good computer can give the artist), without concern for structural or wholistic concepts, is insufficient to be deemed creative.

Of course, true, fundamental, and profoundly creative works of art are as rare in art as startling new theories are in science. But those which do occur (whose artistic value is as revolutionary to artists as perhaps Einstein's theories were to scientists) allow countless lesser artistic insights to follow them; great art paves the way for lesser art insights, which are nevertheless important because they are always deeper complications of an originally simple discovery.

To hold the criteria of creativity up to *all* art productions or experiences is of course rather meaningless. Usually we have to expose ourselves to all innovations in art, to all truly original art inventions, for some time before we can begin to grasp their insights. Also, each generation must absorb the cumulative art insights they historically inherit. This means that a great deal of merely reproductive art is very important, be it an honest attempt toward versimilitude, as in a preformance of traditional music or past theatrical fare; an inspired but unoriginal influence coming out in the style of an artist; or a purely reproductive duplication of another's innovation. This duplication carries art to all of us; it is necessary to sustain past art in our minds, to maintain us at a sufficiently high level of awareness of previous art, so that we may be prepared to appreciate the truly novel when it comes along. Reproductive art is boring only if our memory is perfect (or if we happen to be a practitioner in some special art form and are sated with its history and form, as are artists and perhaps critics), but being human, we can always use it. Yet the greater meanings which an original work of art conceives for us is the fruit of our long preparation by exposure to past "high" art and also to past art that is not so high. Although each art is investigated here to determine just how it is possible for it to rise to a creative insight, it must be emphasized that this is not being done to the detriment of lesser art or other manifestations of the communication of art.

The creative potential of each art form depends to a large extent on its encoding abilities, and on its potential to relate different artistic codes, at the same level or at different levels. The level of a creative artistic meaning, considered out of context, is often confusing, as when phases of an optical illusion come and go despite our attempts to control them; but once it is related and welded to another level of encoding in a significant way so that we recognize a true creative relationship there is no longer a clash or a separation of meaning in our mind.

This extra significance and vividness which is discovered by the mind when two or more artistic levels of encoding are creatively related is analogous perhaps to the startling quality which occurs when slightly displaced views of an object are presented to both the eyes. The added third dimension of a stereoptical picture could barely have been anticipated from the original two pictures, yet there before our eyes is an utterly new phenomenon of the mind's eye, a vital phenomenon out of a mechanical one. As the mind establishes its intelligence by following the multipathed road of art existence, so all art achieves its vitality through a multileveled series of meanings. Art unites the material of its articulation with the illusions of its encoded communications, to give us a meaningful creative experience which actually enlarges our awareness. The various possibilities for encoding are discussed in greater detail in the next chapter, and for all of the individual arts in the chapters following that. In the later chapters I have tried to confine my remarks to those basic elements in each art from which a creative communication is fabricated, with but a few examples and suggestions as to how artists have put them to use in the past. Beyond this, specific reference must be made by the reader to exhaustive and traditional studies of each of the various arts, hopefully to be read with a renewed insight into the function of each element in the formulation of a creative communication.

A creative insight is an almost gestalt mosaic concept, indicating that only by looking at the ideas is it possible to determine if they do in fact build a creative newness. Creativity in art, as invention in science, is not a mystical thing. It cannot be predicted, however, although usually it can be analyzed after the fact; we recognize it because it provides us with an advancement, an improvement in our humanness which we so badly need. Since the list of the creative areas in which art can operate includes some which science can also influence (the creation of new art media, or the combining of old media), it appears that science *can* have a directly creative influence on art. Artists need not rely on science for this creativity, however, and in most cases new or combined art media have resulted from an artistic need

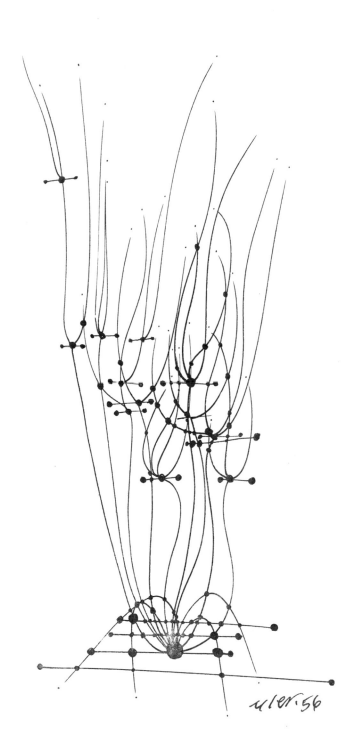

uler.56

for creativeness. If the artist has the energy and the motivation he can duplicate the originality of the scientist, even in the latter's own province.

4

The fact that artists have taken natural or commonplace objects and called them art—the Dada *objet trouvé* or the "ready-mades" of Picasso—pose some serious theoretical problems. "The Venus of the Gas Stove," a mounted gas burner that suggests a nude, does in fact seem to be significant and creative to us; the burner, which we may have overlooked for years, does resemble a lovely nude, and when viewed in a museum, we are amazed at its originality. What Picasso is doing here is suggesting similarities which he saw but which we did not: he is drawing visual metaphors between our mechanical world and our natural world; he is refocusing our awareness of the world to give us a new creative communication in the process.

The possible variations of this artistic mode are four: (1) to recognize analogies or metaphors which already exist in nature and isolate them as art; (2) to take nature or natural objects and employ them directly in art with fabricated art elements; (3) and (4) the same, substituting "man-made" for "natural." The Japanese formal gardener places stones in significant places in his garden, and these "found-natures" can become as creative when the flowers bloom and the sand is smooth, as a symphony of Mozart. The value of isolating, say, a can of Campbell's soup in a museum is in refocusing our attention on something so commonplace that it has nearly lost all of its illusion even as an object. This act is not as creative as Picasso's when he isolated the more intrinsically beautiful stove shape, but it can be refreshing under certain conditions. Our common, mass-produced objects have lost their truth for us, become mere labels of a reality we have forgotten. The same applies to our ads in the mass media, which, as McLuhan notes in *The Mechanical Bride*, hold meanings for us we have forgotten.[15] Isolating common popular phenomena like mass-produced objects or comic strips, and calling them art, refocuses our attention on the unseen and forgotten. In this case it might move us to realize how impossibly thin are the objects of our experience (in comparison to the more graceful design of Picasso's gas burner), making us realize that they *should* remain invisible!

The artistic value of isolating objects per se could be possible only in an age like ours which is devoted to the annihilation of object meaning through mass production. Perhaps one reason printmaking is so popular in America is that here is a pseudo-mass-produced object which is also artistically rare and individual. Only in an age in which communication is overblown could packages of soap have any artistic significance. We amplify even the trivial to such an extent that we are forced to take notice of it. Junk art, assemblages, myriads of weird concoctions, can take on an almost mystical meaning as part of the cult of reproductivity and mass production which we idolize. Not only does the public get snared with these meanings, but museum directors and critics also catch the fever.

Illusion and also our subjective ideas of reality are never comparable; we cannot be sure, for example, that red is the same for everybody; and this is part of the reason man strives to check up on what everyone else is perceiving. It is also why the scientist excludes illusion from his consideration. It would be conceivable perhaps that science could probe into the brain with a super-sensitive television pickup and learn how to reassemble the visual cortex on a screen. Until science invents a means to tap into another person's consciousness the scientist will leave it up to the artist to judge just how objective is our subjectivity. But until this far-fetched scientific gadgetry is built we will have to content ourselves with the clues of less explicit forms of communication for our reassurance of the continuity of human consciousness. What we value, we must assume, other men will value; and what ages have valued, all ages will continue to value. Creative art, as illusive and as changeable as it is, is the best measure of our subjective objectivity. What we subjectively intuit as being creative is usually beyond objective analysis. The artist is he who has the measure of this subjective creativity; the artist actually objectifies his subjectivity, and the act is called creative art when it is an original subjectivity.

5

Man's strange sense of wonder enables him to find beauty in everything living or in nature, even in the grotesque. All nature is beautiful. Man's wonder also enables him to appreciate and value the most seemingly artificial things. It is felt to be a highly sophisticated thing to learn to listen to four stringed instruments playing together, sounds which many people hear as thin and screechy; but actually it is only a more developed primitive sense of wonder at the possibilities of life in the outside world. A composer like Beethoven or Bach, or Webern or Wolf, builds a kind of life in his conclave of four stringed instruments, sometimes sweet, sometimes horrendous, which is amazing when sensed and appreciated. The illusion that there is a kind of fragile vitality in the wisps of tone is what fascinates the music lover trained to the delicate sounds of chamber music. It is only the learning process applied with rigor which transforms the vague and illusionary manipulation of art forms into the means for communicating creative lifelike processes.

The supreme truth artists are called on to create, or which they sometimes feel motivated to work up into a tangible form, is the complete vitality of another living being. The lifelike processes of the arts are one answer to a need to reflect the ego in the world. As Freud suggested, art is the transformation of the unconscious of the artist so that it is made public and given a reality which other people can perceive. The ego manifestation in art is an approach to sublimating, that is, realizing some part of the human vitality in a tangible form. In *Life Against Death*[16] Norman O. Brown says that Freud relates the desire for conscious control and intelligibility on the part of the artist with the demand for communication. The third person is indispensable, although he must have experienced the same vitality or repression of vitality which leads an artist to make the original fabrication of life in form, which would seem to make the communication meaningless because it is redundant. Life is always redundant, but it must always be relived just the same. The truth of art is in its struggle for the instinctual liberation of our unconscious desires, the psychoanalytic viewpoint maintains. This seems to me to leave out originality and creativity, however. Brown holds to Freud's early formulation when discussing wit and the unconscious, rather than that of the older Freud who formulated art as a substitute-gratification akin to dreams and neurosis; according to these theories art is a conscious play which has the gratifying effect of communicating pleasure, and also showing us the ego or unconscious workings of another person in play. We are therefore enjoined to struggle against our own repressions and partake of the vitality of a more sensitive observer, who has managed to place his observations and struggles in a form which we can understand.

If we add to this formulation that the artist reaches into his own unconscious to discover his own being, and that the discovery amounts to a creative formulation when it is put in an artistic form, then we can understand how we can become bound to it since we all share the same desire to liberate our own instinctual and repressed selves. In this way the artist binds us to his vision in a partnership which we cannot deny. This is a good reason why human images fascinate us in art, however literal they are, however descriptive or scientifically true they have been made. The "profounder roots of the dark unconscious," as Brown calls them, are always interesting even if they are not creative in the sense mentioned before; they can lead to the feeling that we too have shared in a creative revelation within ourselves if the artist has succeeded in embodying them in an artistic media. And the insights proliferate as the artist commingles his internal discoveries with the creative discoveries he makes in an artistic media formulation.

There is a limit of course, and carrying the vitality of one's being to the point of communication within a passive framework is the necessary and sufficient condition of art. The humanness which a humanistic artist desires to contain in his art—usually employing some type of a literal man image, or dealing directly with the human condition in society—is not always as creative a way to use art as would be desired, therefore becoming less than humanly meaningful and defeating the original purpose. To show a man, to describe a human situation, to restrict art to something directly and obviously related to man in a literal way, may not always be the way to give human vitality its needed boost for perceptual enlargement of its own humanness. The Marxian view of art is admirable, but it may not accomplish its stated goal. That which is obviously human is not always a creative presentation, though it may be touching or profoundly moving. Since the true nature of man is not so easily presented or formulated, it is not always possible to decide just what has the most human meaning. Abstractions can sometimes touch a chord within us more profound than concrete realities. Music, for instance, can sometimes suggest a humanity greater than all the photographs in the "Family of Man," because it can be more vital than the stillness of deathlike images.

Man images are used in painting, theater, and the movies; and psychologically motivated people fill novels. In all these cases, however, the human vitality presented must breathe with a limited artistic life. The goal of art would be to create automatons as real as those of Jaquet-Droz, Von Kempelen, or Walt Disney if art had as its purpose the creation of man in his literal vitality. The communication of such a person could be best done by creating that person again in a different form. Such a trick is obviously not art, and the truth of humanity is actually demeaned when the literal, human image is stretched too far. There must be an aesthetic distance between us and the art employing literal humans, and a slight depersonalization must occur which puts it on a slightly greater-than-life plane of existence, before we can truly appreciate it as a human contribution.

Paradoxically, then, art must creatively communicate the vitality of truth in nature and in reality and in man, but at the distance of objectivity that is this side of the creation of that lit-

eral truth itself. Art articulates our human being in such a way
that perceiving it causes *us* to be more human. Art is a growing
of our human being in an objective form that not only communicates to us just how we have formulated the truth of reality
through the ages; it also establishes our human reality in the act
of communication. In this way man builds up his sensitivities to
the world, and also he enlarges the materials by which he can
grasp more and more realities—art sense-stretches, perception-
proliferates, and soul-builds. The techniques of art are thus
extremely important since they establish the elements needed to
reveal the creative relationships that can enlarge our humanness.
The actual means of establishing this communication depend on
the medium and the artistic techniques of encoding in a creative
way.

3 ways in whic

4

The Communication
of Art

Encoding Artistic Meaning

1

FLETCHER PRATT tells a fascinating story in his classic book on cryptology, *Secret and Urgent*,[1] about an indecipherable manuscript written by Roger Bacon. Discovered by an Italian rare book dealer in 1912, it reached the United States where many scholars attempted to decipher the meticulous and mysterious scrawl. The manuscript also contained a series of unusual pictures which did not contribute much to the solution. Finally a medieval scholar of the University of Pennsylvania, Dr. William Newbold, acquired the manuscript and turned his hand to the problem. He worked long and hard, absorbing the difficult text and trying to determine the connection of the illustrations. At last he began to have success, but the decipherment was too amazing to be true! Roger Bacon had evidently invented the microscope back in the thirteenth century, well before its official invention in 1677, and also the telescope long before Galileo! Dr. Newbold felt that the accompanying drawings could be nothing other than spiral nebulae or one-celled animals! After carefully checking his method Dr. Newbold published his findings, much to the amazement and skepticism of the learned community. But cryptologists who checked out his method could find no error. Finally a brilliant English astronomer named Proctor took up the problem, and he showed that using Dr. Newbold's method it was possible to take Shakespeare and decipher it to practically any meaning desired! In all innocence Dr. Newbold had actually manipulated the indecipherable manuscript of Roger Bacon to satisfy his own unconscious wish for particular facts!

Art is sometimes such indecipherable material into which it is possible to read anything you desire. Is such art uncommunicative? Art sometimes seems to be private or a hoax; you have to have superhuman abilities and wide knowledge and some talent as a cryptologist to understand the message of certain schools of art. Is this a failure on the part of the creator, or on our part? Was Roger Bacon really fooling us and making a massive hoax by dreaming up utter nonsense, complete with fantastically imaginative pictures, realizing that the brains for all eternity would attempt to unravel their mystery?*

If you have a fertile imagination, or if you are sufficiently motivated as was Dr. Newbold, you can see things in cloud shapes or in random art, much as if you were looking at a Rorschach inkblot in which you can see faces or animals in the rolling clouds. Leonardo knew the value of the random, and he suggested that the throw of a sponge charged with paint would give many interesting shapes to an area. His idea of *sfumato*, a method of creating an ambiguity by blurring,[2] like the Japanese idea called *shibuyi* which allows for a resolution of an order behind a rough confusing exterior, is a useful method for an artist in search of original form, and it was pursued methodically by the English painter Alexander Cozzens who actually set it up as a principle of creativity.[3]

But after the fact, when you look at a finished work of art, you expect it to have more value and more independence than that which require the complete application of your private imagination. There must be some suggestions of form in randomness which the artist somehow calls to our attention, in order to

* His manuscript is still not deciphered, to my knowledge.

transcend the purely accidental. If we have to read all the meaning into a work of art ourselves, why do we need the work in the first place since anything ought to do as well? What communication is possible for random art, if not this limited reflected opportunity for our own imagination to work? What if an artist probes into his own inner randomness—his own mental-physiological entropy—and tries to manifest it directly in an art form? Are there not degrees of randomness? The communication theorist who applies the cybernetic methods developed by Wiener, which are called auto-correlation techniques, is able to discover order beneath impossible confusion, like those caused by radio noise that cover radar signals, or the confusions caused by cryptologists hiding their secrets beneath difficult ciphers. Dr. Newbold would have envied these modern cryptological and decipherment techniques which make it possible to rank even noise.

As mentioned previously, purely perfect randomness is called gaussian, and it is only achievable by mechanical means, like the throwing of a die, the tossing of a penny, or the amplification of electronic shot-effect randomnesses due to the motion of electrons in a vacuum tube. We humans, on the other hand, always create something this side of perfectly random when we are left to our own devices—we cannot escape our own entropy figure. Theoretically, at least, we see that something of ourselves is always communicated, even in our most haphazard productions—the Maxwell demon is never idle in us, and even our most chaotic moments exhibit our particular entropy figure. Try as we may, we cannot transcend a certain minuscule order which is somehow characteristic of each of us, even if we do the random walk.

Now if an artist probes into his own inner randomness and tries to put himself into a shot-effect mode, in which he is externalizing his psychophysical randomness in some artistic form, he usually still creates some kind of order in his act, due to his Maxwell-demon soul. The so-called Action painters who go at their canvas with pure motor movements dominating, or the surrealists who capture dreams, are not as arbitrary as they think; in the first case the lines often suggest the pivot points of an arm, and in the second a dreamlike logic with symbolic content comes forth. Aleatoric music that leaves freedom of choice to the performing artist, for instance, adds not accident, but the statistic of the performer to the statistic of the composer. This is similar to the baroque composers who left ornamentation up to the performers. It is not as easy to transcend the intrinsic organizing abilities of the mind as many people think, especially if an artist has been trained for years, or has inherited a strong tradition.

The modern schools that try to put randomness into their art do so only with limited results—they are less chaotic than they think (although certainly more than we desire). The time of confusion in which we live forces some artists who think that art should reflect their age to turn to the random in art instead of recreating a new degree of confusion that could have meaning. They imply, as Ben Shahn suggests in *The Shape of Content*,[4] that they have an affinity for the unknown; that they are "revealing the mystical paroxysms of nature," and are in touch with the great unconscious sea of unknowns which engulfs us all. But, as Shahn suggests, they are only communicating their romantic desires to be associated with the unknown (and also building certain orders of randomness). Their art becomes but an imitative thing, albeit imitating something chaotic. Modern science seems to corroborate or enhance artistic effort toward randomness by suggesting the essential randomness of nature and its limitations as far as causal certainty is concerned. One is reminded, however, of Einstein's famous remark that he believed that God does not play dice with us, which can be changed in this case to read that our unconscious probably does not play dice with our imagination; and if we allow it to do so, we are missing the point of artistic meaning.

There is a certain respect we must always pay to chaos as the source of all order, however. Too much emphasis on order and perfection can lead to sterility—the impulse to destroy an old art form can be a healthy impulse if it leads toward a new creative vision. Ben Shahn recently gave a talk to a group of architects in

Aspen, Colorado, who were planning a new art center to perfection, and in it he emphasized the importance of a little chaos.[5] He reminded them of the Babylonian creation myth in which the original god of the universe Chaos, the monster Tiamat, was slain by the younger god Marduk, the magician artist, who split Chaos in half and hung one part on high to make the heavens, and the other spread out under his feet to form the earth and all its creations.[6] That this applies to our scientific theorizing also becomes patently obvious in time because we begin to accumulate new facts which cannot be ordered by our old theories. Art is not so lucky as science in this respect. Science looks to explain the orders of nature, and when chaos rears its ugly head it must begin to take it into account; art can deny chaos by keeping attention focused on the ordered creations of the past. But chaos makes its secret entry through the imagination of man, and appears in new artistic productions. The fact remains, however, that this chaos is but a disguised brother to previous orders, unrecognizable because of man's unfamiliarity with its strange costume, that is if it has any final creative meaning for man.

2

The extra-art information, arising when the title, name, or caption of a work of art carries important communicative suggestions about the work of art, can be more meaningful than we suspect. Given a near-random work of art—even one as inchoate as the mad Professor Frenhoefer could create—the title can actually define it. Countless meanings can therefore be communicated by virtue of a simple title, and the meanings actually arise due to the work of art and its being given a "name." Consider for instance an entirely black canvas called "Death Riding a Black Horse on a Moonless Night." Most people who read the title and then looked at the picture would think they actually saw a creature lurking there in the blackness, and perhaps even imagine it. It is possible to conjure the entire image up in our minds—it is easy to see the figure in the carpet, as Henry James called it, and to think that the artist actually put it there. This is one degree less than a hallucination, however, because it is a controllable mode of the brain, like a hypnotic suggestion. We are not carried away into an unreality of image despite our better judgment, as in hallucination, but even though we are firmly anchored in our own reality, we find that the caption pulls us into a new imagined reality. Max Ernst took this idea to its logical but ridiculous extreme when he gave poetic and lengthy titles to some of his pictures. One amusing title is "The Transfiguration of the Chameleon on Mount Tabor Takes Place in an Elegant Limousine while the Angels and Halcyon Fly from the Houses of Men and While the Very Holy Costume of Our Lord Exclaims *de Profundis* Three Times Before Whipping The Exhibitionist's Flesh."[7]

The power of the extra-art clue is very strong because it actually *assigns* communicative meaning to a work of art. This applies both to nonobjective art and to realistic art, although we most easily accept the suggestion when the picture is vague or random or surrealistic. This is perhaps the best sense in which the word "symbol" can be applied to art, because the caption defines the symbolic intent of art—which is the meaning we generally attach to the idea of symbolization today. I have purposely avoided using the word "symbol" because I feel that art is more complex than the symbolic assignment of meaning or the symbolization of emotions through an analogous morphological correspondence. Symbolism in poetry or symbolization of form in Langer's sense is but part of the story, and the actual art act is more properly called encoding because it partakes of that for which it stands. If we are familiar with an artist's body of work and know his past symbolic assignments through captions or a familiarity with his subject matter, we can guess about any new work of his we see. We continue to appreciate this symbolic meaning without really experiencing the work of art at any deeper level—which seems to me to demand a separation from the more important meanings which are contained in successful new works.

This extra-art meaning can be quite relevant to us as humans if, for instance, it concerns some cause or idea which is important to us. Such causes obviously affect our humanness, but they do so as simple messages which describe themselves, not as perceptual communications whose insights are built out of the actual communicative elements, as is art. Such causes and ideas are important, but art is not the only way to communicate ideas which are important, nor is it the only way in which we build our humanness; science, both as description of conjectured facts and as the revelation of natural forces, also influences us profoundly.

Captions or titles may or may not always coincide with the image which the artist has tried to capture in his art, but they most certainly change our response to art. We react differently toward a canvas whose title we know-than toward one which we do not, and the captions deserve more care in their assignment than most gallery directors or artists give them. Biblical titles given to banal novels often shift them into a more profound mode of communication than they deserve. In a sense the caption or title of a work tells you something about the artist, if you care to study it as a symptom or hint as to the philosophical orientation of the artist.

In the last analysis—and this should be our concern when we approach art—we must accept the title de facto as part of the active communication situation of all art. When an artist gives a title to a picture, a name to a book, and so on, we must assume that he does so for a very specific purpose, although he himself may not understand what he is doing, nor how it affects the communication situation. He must realize, however, that someone will read the caption or the title and be influenced throughout the time that he is considering the entire work of art. If a purist whose canvas is two squares of different shades of chartreuse calls his picture "Glory Arising," he must realize that two out of three museum-goers will actually see images of women on high, or God apotheosized, or lofty images of some sort. If the picture is close to the title in some literal way—if, for instance, the picture is random and it conjures up images like cloud shapes

and is called "Chaos Apotheosized"—there is a good chance
that people will actually see what the artist thought he saw, however indefinite his title, much as we recognize the profile of Lincoln if someone points it out in a cloud shape. The artist may
have chosen his title because he himself thought he saw something in his canvas, after the fact of its production, which we too
can see because of our common experience. We must recognize
that this is part of the communication situation of art, although it
is not necessarily part of the *creativity* of art.

This may seem trivial, but it is actually at the heart of the
confusion that everyone should react to a work of art in the same
way, and that art should be universal and always be reacted to
by man in a constant fashion. When there is a discrepancy
between the communication clues in the extra-art meaning of the
title or the caption and the work of art itself, the viewer or audience is confused. They suspect the artist of false motives, when
it was only sloppy naming. This suggests that there are different
levels of meaning going on in the art situation—that which is
called out by the title, and that which is suggested by the work
of art itself—which may be in conflict, sometimes to the detriment of the art.

Obviously there are many possible levels of meaning in a work
of art, and these can all confuse (or enhance) the general communicative situation of art. A story can be understood at one
level by say a child, and at another by an adult, as is *Gulliver's
Travels*. Some people react to art at one level, and others at
another level, depending on their information and knowledge of
the intent and the various suggestions and success of the artist.
People feel cheated when they learn that they have missed some
part of the communication in a multi-meaning work of art; or
they feel snobbishly self-satisfied if they can detect some new
level which has escaped everyone's attention. A recent analysis
of Edward Albee's *Who's Afraid of Virginia Woolf*[8] by Paul
Tannenbaum[9] shows how far it is sometimes possible to hide
meanings in art, or to what extremes meanings can be read into
art. Whether or not Albee consciously thought all of these mean-

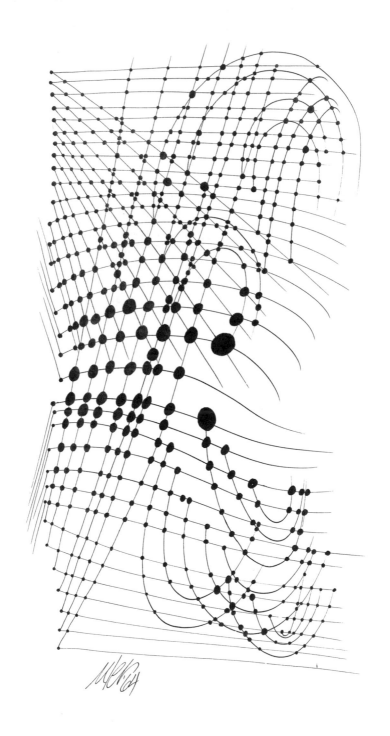

ings through, to the extent that Tannenbaum suggests, is unimportant, but their marriage to well-characterized people is one of the sources of the play's creative success. The main characters are named George and Martha (parents of our nation), and the play is set in New Carthage University (built on the ruins of the Old World), and their imaginary child plays an important role (the American Dream). Martha (crass materialistic society) is wedded to George (intellectual democratic liberalism), and their friends, a young scientist (who is seduced by Martha, the commercial establishment) and his mousy wife, inheritor of the church and its money (full of a fear that gives her a false pregnancy) are educated by them. The use of the name Virginia Woolf, herself a critic of the English upper classes, is another symbol of the American Dream.

The various art forms have developed different ways of generating these levels of meaning, and for the encoding of them in the different communication situations of each art. These meanings are important considerations which are more than just by-products of art; more than accidental facts of art which can be used or not, depending on the whim of the artist, and his desire to "hide" things in his art. As suggested in the previous chapter the true creative meaning of art arises when the various encoded levels relate in a new way to cause the revelation of a newly communicated perception, and this is due to the particular media and its possibilities for multilevel encoding. But before actually considering how all the arts achieve their encoding, we must go back to the problem of how, in skirting on the edge of randomness or the unfamiliar in art, the artist can successfully forge art which does in fact communicate beyond that randomness—although not necessarily creatively.

3

The desire to define a new work of art or a new artistic vision, at first glance appearing random or so unfamiliar that we are lost, is the reason why some artists (as, for instance, Picasso) always include something known, something recognizable in their art. Unconsciously artists often feel adrift if their current work does not have a continuity with their previous art, with reality, or with some predetermined logic (which includes a socially accepted logic). They feel that they must define what they are now doing, when they make a new departure, right in the work itself, by including some of the old ideas, the easily communicated and well-understood elements. Picasso suggested that this vague contact leads the viewer more easily into the realm of the unknown.[10] This informs the viewer that a departure is occurring, but that it is a connected departure in the way shown—this is like including a cipher in art by which to decode the entire work. The recognizable form defines the artist's style and provides a gateway into his new imaginings, and it allows the artist to deviate the more extremely at the same time. Even the vaguest suggestion of a past idea is sufficient to tie a work of art down to something familiar; and this is liberating in some instances, permitting an artist to be the more radical and abstract or bizarre if he desires. He must do so in some consistent way, however, but that is an easy matter for an artist who can easily hide inconsistencies in stylistic devices. Picasso's epochal "Les Demoiselles d'Avignon" does this by including the new and radical heads of exotic African sculpture on his recognizable cubistically influenced nudes. We accept the canvas because we recognize the conventional nude bodies, but the heads jar us; in addition, Picasso calls our attention to his knowledge of what he was doing by making the heads thick impasto, as opposed to the bodies thinly painted, symbolically justifying the joint representation in the same canvas.

Calling a work by a number gets around the difficulties of the extra-art meaning of the caption or title, and it makes it the more important that the work of art itself have its own significance. Opus numbers for string quartets or numbers for painting shift the communication back to the art. Now pure randomness palls, and something more than nothing must get across.

In Jackson Pollock we realize that the dripping motion of his technique becomes obvious, suggesting his stance and modus operandi, and indicating that brushwork has become unimportant. Pollock's shift from the centuries on centuries of easel painting, using brushes, to dripping is refreshing, if you are a painter and can appreciate the novelty of the act—taken seriously. This is one of the most esoteric of communications, however, as are all acts which give some artists the distinction of being called "painter's painters," or "artist's artists." When a society raises its artistic appreciation to that of the cognoscenti, it has done so by becoming aware of the subtleties of encoding in a given art form.

Some art forms, such as music in a classical mode, present their encodings in easily understood modes, especially in a society which has encouraged music for centuries. Surprises or radical new departures are not welcome because they are not understood. (Neither can we appreciate the subtleties of a primitive culture unless we have exposed ourselves to its art for considerable time.) When a painter uses lines and dots, endlessly varying images in a completely nonobjective but inventive way, as I have with the illustrations of this book, it takes a slow exposure to them, a gradual appreciation of their formal qualities—which should occur by the time you have read this book in its entirety—before it is possible to sense their perceptual meaning and creative communication. It is all a matter of form, and lines and dots communicate, among other things, the endless possibilities for so simple a medium to give rise to the new and beautiful. I think that, for instance, the creativity of an unaccompanied Bach sonata is most appreciated by string players, not so much for the variety of emotions or even the articulation of multifarious humanness, as for the endless imaginative complexities to which so simple a means can be subjected.

Recently, for instance, Milton Babbit announced that the public for electronic music is nil, and he suggested that the various composers working with electronic sounds should content themselves with composing for each other.[11] This "ivory tower" attitude has the merit of lifting the artist from the competitive realm of the mass-communication media, which is apt to distort their motives or destroy their values anyway; but it has the disadvantage of forcing art into more and more esoteric and sterile areas. It also deprives the general public of the almost forced necessity to learn how to perceive this new music. The deeper discoveries of creative communications are such that they can be appreciated on a larger scale than many of the practitioners suppose. Babbit underestimates the general audience for electronic music, perhaps drawing his conclusions from audience reaction to poor electronic musical clichés—which I think his own compositions are. We hear electronic music on television commercials and do not know it; our children hear it as the sound effects of their kiddie programs. That we cannot react to electronic music is probably due to the fact that it is essentially a young art form, and also one which even the artists do not yet know how to make truly meaningful. But I can imagine more interesting compositions now being created by some gadget-musician perhaps still in his teens, fiddling away in his basement; and when such a composer begins to have an opportunity to present his findings to a more responsive audience, then the world will see a new art form come to fruition.

4

The most elementary reaction to a work of art, the fundamental element in a work of art, is the medium—the message is the medium, as McLuhan suggests; at least the *first message of art is the medium*. The sonority of sound, the texture of oils, the syntax or sense of sentences, the fact of humans dancing, the structure of materials in a building—these are what is initially communicated when first perceiving a work of art. The reason we like to see-hear a symphony orchestra is because considerable meaning lies in seeing the conductor, the musicians, and the total visual display in the actuality of the concert hall—and most of all in detecting the fact of live performers in action—meanings which are all lost on records. Perhaps the reason many performing musicians are horrified by the idea of electronic music is not so much that they are worried about being replaced by automated musicians, as because it eliminates what is to them one of the most meaningful communicative facts of music: the presence of the human performer with all of his imperfections and possible greatness.[12]

The problem becomes one of determining to what extent one sense communication can substitute for another when we try to translate old terms like music to new ones like electronic music. If we see a musician playing we are not actually experiencing the tactile qualities of his touching the instrument, but we are directly aware of the kinesthesia of the act. McLuhan suggests[13] that the taped hi-fi (stereo?) recording system meets the tactile challenge of television because it restores the "depth" which the old scratchy record lost. He mistakes, I think, a broadening of the aural channel for the inclusion of the tactile communication; but no amount of stereo, however "sculpturesque" the sound appears to our two ears, can make up for not seeing the musicians at work. The eye's vision which gives a sense of kinesthesia is entirely lost on any record, and a broadening or a deepening of the sound of music through stereo can never restore the lost information. You could almost make the axiom that a symbol of a sense datum does not substitute for the experience of a sensation in art. The second axiom you could make would be that new sensations always give rise to new arts. The so-called hotness or coolness of the media, by which McLuhan means media with wide bandwidths as opposed to those with narrow bandwidths (telephone: cool; television: hot), only has the effect of tightening the human involvement, because it decreases the possibility of extraneous disturbing effects, improving the communication, making the requirements of encoding less complex.

There is another important meaning which our first impression of a work of art communicates to us, even if that art is either unintelligible to us or perhaps extremely poor. The work of art is realized as being a link between us and another personality. We are more impressed by the art if that personality has something special to offer us—even though it may not be carried in this particular work. The productions of people who have been lionized by society, deemed great, or flattered by the designation "genius," have a magical communicative quality. It is most powerfully carried by the name, or when the name is a signature, in the actual form of the signed letters on the canvas or handwritten on paper. We attach so much opprobrium to forgery in art when the artist goes to the extent of forging the signature because there is a mystical importance which resides in this signature itself, so much so that even the courts recognize it. Plagiarism, although it is, as Northrop Fry suggests, one of the fundamental elements of all literary creations, is frowned on because the communication of one person's essence is being confused with another's.[14] Man Ray carried the idea of the importance of the signature in a painting to the end point when he made a picture that was actually composed of the letters and numbers: MAN RAY 1914.[15] And anonymous art, such as the medieval sculpture that adorns the cathedrals of Europe, puts us in contact with an entire era.

A fragment of the essence of greatness is somehow embodied in art done by great people, and we react to it for this reason, whether we are prepared to admit it to ourselves or not. Even before we get a glimpse of the actual work of art, before we hear the poem or read the story or see the play, we are disposed in a certain way to accept it favorably. We treasure every scrap of the art of the recognized great, almost as if it were a fetish. Picasso can get away with murder in his art—and he sometimes does—and the world buys it and even reveres it; his buffoonery is a healthy reaction to the world's blindly accepting his art. The greater the artist—at least the greater the *myth* of the artist— the greater we value his productions, whatever they may be, and the more excited we become at the prospect of any art communication from him.

This is why success breeds success in art; why, as Picasso realized quite early in his career, the myth of the artist is actually quite important for the communication of art; why some artists concentrate more on creating a personality than they do on creating meaningful works of art. Death too is often the neces-

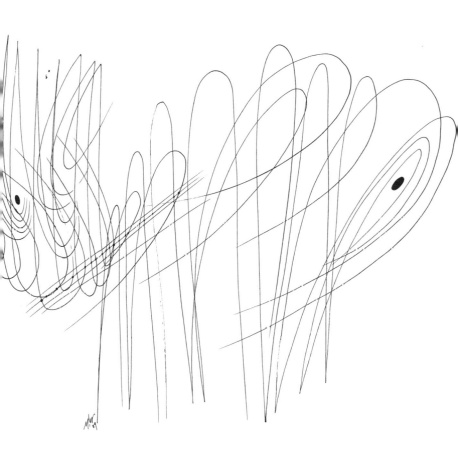

sary condition for placing the artist into this extra-human mode
we call the mythical genius. The true modern tragedy is this
death of our most valuable individual, and when a young artist with potential dies, we feel as Shakespeare's contemporaries
must have felt when a young prince died.

The physical and social problems which notoriety entails have
compelled some artists to lead anonymous lives. For instance the
novelist B. Traven (Traven Torsven?), who wrote *The Treas-*

ure of *Sierra Madre*, has managed to preserve his anonymity all of these years, and J. D. Salinger, author of *Catcher in the Rye*, avoids interviews and publicity. The personal reasons for an avoidance of the public eye may be psychological, but the fact is that such an attitude extols the art and diminishes the personality of the artist, who remains invisible and completely independent of his work (unless he has managed to work himself into his art).

The reasons the world accepts an artist are many, but acceptance paradoxically gives him license to communicate in new and more powerful ways. Works of art which might normally be overlooked are then given great attention in the world art market. Success gives the artist license to communicate in high gear, with full knowledge that he will get across. This overwhelms some artists and renders them impotent as creators, but it may be because their creative abilities were quite poor in the first place; or it may be that they have, like a kind of nouveau riche, lost their abilities to cash in on vital art. It may also be that an artist has a sufficient body of work left over from a creative youth to keep his art going, even after notoriety descends on his head. Or, optimistically, he could be that rare artist who manages to maintain and deepen his artistic vision in the face of fame, recognition, or fortune; then our hopes for the all-powerful artistic genius are truly justified, and mankind is rewarded with great art.

5

Short of chaos, this side of the extra-communicative suggestions mentioned thus far, how are the bulk of the important meanings built in art for the edification of mankind? The various media have manipulative possibilities which provide for artistic encoding to carry the human meaning of art. To assume that the encoding of art is just the literal use of artistic elements that express corresponding ideas—as rough-textured reds might convey aggression—is to miss the point of art communication, and to vastly underestimate the communicative possibilities of art, not to mention leaving out its creative potential.

The encoding of meaning in art is always formal, that is, establish through conventions. The conventions of a particular art encoding are usually so familiar that we forget that we have learned them, but in all cases they have been constructed in our minds by our normal perceptual development or built-up during a new and intimate association with a given work of art. Although the conventions are formal, they are not arbitrary, and they are not extra-communicative like the rules of mathematics either; we learn the conventions of art by an exposure to art, although help can be given to facilitate this learning process. The sensuousness of the conventions of art encoding usually allows us to detect them at the same time we sense the art itself.

The various possibilities of encoding different levels of meaning in a given media compound the problem and test the abilities of an artist to invent meanings within meanings that are significantly and creatively related. Nature is the experience with which all artists have had the longest acquaintance, and all the more so since there is a long history of artists who also have used nature directly in their work. The gamut of art which artists employ begins with nature itself and extends through all human experience including the psychic inner worlds of man; it also embraces the communicative art media itself, with all of the theoretical possibilities for encoding the relations of form which it may present. Problems of society, human redemption, the evolution of psyches, and the entire range of intellectual ideas also become an integral part of the encoding of art. This is important because communication allows the encoding not only of natural phenomena, but also of the phenomena of other art.

That which art encodes in the various media is not static, because as man lives and grows, as he experiences more and more art, as he learns to respond to art more meaningfully, he influences it. We all contribute to the establishment of new meanings in works of art after they have entered the art market, partially by our acceptance or rejection, but mainly by our absorption of its essence for transmission to the next generation. Sometimes a rejection of an art experience is overlooked or denied, and a succeeding generation will take it up and attach new meaning to it. As previously mentioned, an artist can sometimes anticipate the changing sensitivities of our awareness to a media, and take advantage of this by creating a new art which will only have meaning when it is understood—sometimes once removed a generation in the future. The artist is predicting how future generations will react to an art encoding means. It is necessary, in fact, that every artist have complete faith that the encoding means he employs will be perfectly grasped by someone, and perhaps such an understanding can only be reached in the future. The fact that art derives its basic form from a convention forces some artists to try and deny communication in their art; but they do not realize that even this denial will some day be understood and that their art too will be comprehensible, if only for its perversity.

Since the encoding of art meaning is a question of formal conventions and not an inherent, immutable physical quality of the media, it is reasonable to assume that the meaning of art will change. Not only do the conventions of art change, but the interpretation which successive generations put on them change. This is counter to the idea that art is ageless, but not counter to the idea that art is forever human. As a work of art or a school raises our humanness to a new level of awareness we can react to this art the more quickly and immediately. Those who have not as yet grasped the meaning of a given art form, the uninitiated and also the young, still have an opportunity to grow through a contact with old art. Music, for instance, if considered out of the context of a culture, illustrates the difficulty of comprehending the unfamiliar, as when Eastern tonalities escape the Western ear and vice versa.

One of the functions of the critic is to sharpen the awareness of a culture to the encoding schemes of its artists. Through an educational process which leads to a better knowledge of the aims and operations of the artist, and an understanding of the formal communicative means he uses, the critic helps us to respond to the creative communication of art. He cannot of course do other than indicate; the rest is up to us. Since this is a problem of an actual perceptual reaction, we must have the necessary psychophysical tools at our mental disposal before we can react to art—and this sometimes requires a lot of experiential conditioning: looking at art, listening to music, plays, movies, reading books, poetry, and so on. The theoretician can help too by pointing out what the artist is up to from a technical standpoint, how he actually brings meaning to full bloom in his art—which is one of the aims of this book.

The actual evaluation of a work of art cannot be made immediately on its perception since it is the function of great art to affect us in a creative way. Only after art has had its cumulative effect on us by repeated audiences; sometimes only after generations have had an opportunity to drink from the creative springs and assimilate the effects; only then can great art be grasped in all of its significance. The entire act can be sped up, perhaps, in our age, through the prudent use of the mass media. At this point, however, art sometimes has arrived at the exact point where it has lost its force and value as a source for the formation of mankind's creative awareness.

The advice of the critic is not like the extra-art meanings communicated by the title or signature or the personality associations of the artist. The critic can only indicate what may have escaped attention; he cannot perform the art experience by proxy for us and pass on his veneration with no justification. Once we begin to explore into the jungle of a work of art we are entirely on our own, although an understanding derived from the critic can serve us like a map. Experience obviously aids the art explorer as it does the African explorer, but maps save considerable time—although they do not indicate the ferocious animals or the exotic flowers. Teachers of art and critics emphasize that a person must venture into the art jungle and grapple single-handed with the beasts lurking there, and whiff the essences of all creative blooms.

This concept of the function of the critic and teacher is considerably less than the suggestions of some art historians who, like Panofsky, feel that a total historical-human-social knowledge is necessary to understand art. I do not think that it is possible to say categorically that all art must be approached only in the terms of the art itself, excluding all historical or psychological insights which might be gotten from a study of the culture of the time or a knowledge of the personality of the artist. D. H. Lawrence is, for instance, ubiquitously present in most of his novels, and the life of the man can enlighten us about the personal search of his characters, to give us many important clues about his encoding motifs and also to enlighten us as to his creativity. On the other hand James Joyce is the opposite, and we can easily apply the statement he made in *A Portrait of the Artist as a Young Man:* "The personality of the artist, at first a cry or a cadence or a mood and then a fluid and lambent narrative, finally refines itself out of existence, impersonalizes itself, so to speak.... The artist, like the God of the creation, remains within or behind or beyond or above his handiwork, invisible, refined out of existence, indifferent, paring his fingernails."[16]

The improved reaction of succeeding generations is due to the fact that the conditioning to art becomes more and more spontaneous as it becomes a more integral part of our perceptual apparatus. Since man desires to bind himself to previous generations, he will usually approach art approved by previous generations more favorably than he will new and unfamiliar art. As the freshman physics student today easily understands the complex ideas of the theory of relativity, once grasped only by a few men in the world, so very sophisticated art of the past can be comprehended because of a generally higher level of art awareness. My seven-year-old son Erik endlessly plays a recording of one of Beethoven's most difficult major works, his Choral Symphony, and it can even be heard briefly as a musical introduction to the daily Huntley-Brinkley nationwide news program. The broader environment for our children today actually speeds up our awareness of art, due both to the communication media and to the modern education process, allowing us a greater potential for future fulfillment. Sensestretching profits from time-binding.

7

It is a sad fact that the economics of art is connected with the extra-meanings of art, rather than with the more fundamental creativity of art. The price of a work of art unfortunately often matches the value we attach to the name of the artist—not unfortunately for him, of course. Works of art which are dependent on extra-artistic meaning have a more difficult course than those which are not. The decline of any fad, like the recent decline of Abstract Expressionism (which may also be more than a fad) always has its casualties, artists who were once riding on the crest of a profitable wave but who now are sinking in the trough of inattention and financial disaster. Works of art for which one generation pays thousands of dollars because they were done by those considered famous are put into the vaults of museums and often left to rot there. Composers one age thought were important are dropped from the concert list—(there is a difference here, because the dead composer does not depend on the commissions and royalties any longer).

When an art form is one that can be transmitted or multiplied, as, for instance, movies or plays or literature or music, the producing artist can suffer the most embarrassment financially—his presence is not required for the reproduction or performance of his art. The manual dexterity or the physical quality is not required to be present during the consumption of these arts, as with all the performing arts and also with the arts of painting and sculpture. You cannot replace an actor by some mechanism (except by a movie of him), nor can you reproduce a painting satisfactorily. Music can be performed from scores, books can be read in the cheapest printings, but you must always have the virtuoso or even the poet in the flesh if you want his personal readings. Although the poet is about the lowest man on the economic totem pole, if he becomes even slightly popular he is in a better position to earn his keep than even a well-printed novelist, for instance. John Ciardi, an important and well-known American poet makes a good living as a lecturer to clubs. People do not realize how little money an author gets for a printing of his book, especially a paperback edition—pennies a copy is usual, so if there is an edition of, say, ten thousand, the author gets all of a few weeks food money—one hundred dollars, barely enough to feed a small family.

The various modern methods of selling art to an unsuspecting and culture-hungry public have confused the art scene no end. It is possible, as Maurice Grosser suggests in *The Painter's Eye*,[17] to high-pressure an esoteric art form on the public—one they are not prepared to accept—simply because they are mad for the new or the startling. A few significant galleries or museums jumping on the bandwagon, a few important collectors starting a rumor, a slightly curious personality publicized effectively, is often sufficient to start a new movement and break the art bank. In writing, music, or the theater, there is a similar phenomenon, but the establishment is a little more conservative, requiring more artistry in their frauds. It is perhaps too harsh to suggest that all avant-guarde-ly advertised art is fraud, because it is often well-intended, or obviously business-motivated. The serious seeker after fame can always be found by the money-grubber, and hand-in-hand they can shock a willing audience and make a pretty hula-hoop penny. It has to be admitted, however, that if the publicity drive has unwittingly supported an art form with a powerful creative force, the world more quickly learns to accept something from which it can profit—although it takes considerable time for them to realize what they have bought. This is one favorable argument for the current culture craze in America—we end up with a heritage of art, regardless of the motivations which brought it about.

The point is that serious creative communications in art are usually so difficult to grasp that they are seldom rewarded financially. Creative communication in art creeps up slowly on our souls, taking us unawares. The masses respond not to such slow forces, taking rather to the splashy art, the bombastic, the unusual. Perhaps, optimistically, we have to conclude that the masses do accept the truly creative in time, because they somehow sense that vital art enables them to grow; mankind comes to live with and to expand its humanness through great art, because of a voracious appetite for all experience, especially the deepest.

8

The various artistic means to encode demand most of our attention when trying to understand the actual ways in which creative communications are fabricated. It must be emphasized that this knowledge does not provide an artist, no more than an audience, with all that is required to make or detect great art. That is a question of talent and of experience—as are all acts of true creation. Sunday painters, the Thursday night string quartet, the amateur poet, all dilettanti and culture lovers, however serious their motives, however high their aspirations, often get trapped by a static view of their art, which prevents growth. The Sunday painter paints only what his eye sees over and over, never giving his mind or soul or even his heart a chance; the amateur string quartets play only Mozart or the simplest standard works, saying that the moderns are too difficult technically; the poetaster makes maudlin sonnets that imitate some admired master. The usual in art is what becomes accepted by the most "serious culture lovers," and they often disdain a more creative fad or fashion which the uninformed masses will accept. The informed view of the "serious culture lover," however, has allowed them to go only so far—forcing them to err on the side of conservatism and poor taste, rather than on the side of overenthusiasm.

The reason it is not possible to set up standards for art production, or to derive practical methods from theories such as the present, is that the situation always changes, the practical situation of art is always different from the theoretical basis which might explain it. We do not necessarily always respond to certain artistic elements in one way, and to others in a different way. For example, blues can be thought of as being cools, and reds as warms; rumbles as fears, bearded men as prophets; established conventions can be accepted as being important elements for future artistic encoding only to a limited extent. Artists have a way of taking up the wrong notions and using them in incorrect but powerful new ways; this is the very nature of artistic creativity. Familiar elements, the well-known contents of past art, are given new twists and taken to surprising extremes, in all new, creative art which deserves our respect. The painter loves to push reds back and to bring blues forward; and a musician can use a rumble as he might use a flute; and a writer might make a wise-looking man into a fool. The creative jumps of an artist destroy previous conceptions and build new attitudes in his art, always out of the unexpected.

In considering the various encoding possibilities of art it is useful to think of them as being divided into two main classes: those existing at the primary level of physical sensation, and those once removed to a secondary level where a physical sensation is suggested and rebuilt in our minds. This is not always a simple division to apply to the arts since the one can sometimes be reduced to the other. If the sensual arts like music and painting are thought of as being primary-level arts, and those arts which use words secondary-level arts, some valuable theoretical distinctions can be made when discussing the encoding of art forms. The overlap between them in some art forms, as when opera uses words and music, or even when the movies and the theater have their visual element, gives us another level of encoding, but one which can be more clearly outlined when its components are clearly recognized. This will become clear in the following chapters that discuss the various encoding problems of all the practical arts.

To distinguish painting and music as primary physical phenomenal arts is not to revert to the "innocent eye" (or ear) theory of Ruskin, based on Bishop Berkeley. Conceptually all art forms must be sensual-mental organizations; they must be all but innocent, however they are presented to the brain, as Gombrich and Arnheim both emphasize for painting, but which is certainly also true for the other arts as well.[18] Nevertheless most encoding in painting and music is achieved directly at the level of the physical sensation, whereas in the language arts the encoding is more conventionally achieved at the sensation level, and only sensually suggested at the mental level. The sensations of the word level of language can be replaced by other forms of words (with the exception of poetry, which uses its sounds in a kind of music). A novel can be put into braille, or into Morse code; written in green ink or on an electric typewriter; translated into any foreign language, within limits. If the sense is preserved and the form is accurate, the art still remains valid, whatever the physical medium of the literal, verbal arts. No such translation is possible in the arts that depend directly on physical qualities for their meaning; to translate or even to reproduce is to destroy the arts of music and painting, or any other art *qua* physical in this sense.

Although painting suggests a volume, it does so by means of an illusion, residing point-by-point across the two-dimensional canvas. A painting may be realistic or literal, or it may be suggestive of other worlds, dreamlike or mythical, but it is always primarily physical. The eye-brain rationalizes painting, and it functions as the data-processing system. On the other hand when we read a story we forget the visual scratches on the paper, the dots of braille if we are blind. Higher mental processes, relieved of a dependence on physical sensations, are brought into play. The difficulties of these arts lie in trying to discover just how their perceptual communications are meaningful to us in a direct way like the other arts, and to discover how it is that they can be autonomous (whereas mathematics cannot be). What is the difference if we have to learn how to read the symbols of writing, just as we have to learn the rules of mathematics, between literature as an art and mathematics as a science or logic? The answer is that the illusion of writing causes a secondary sensation which is manipulated by the brain in the same way that the physical arts are manipulated in a physical form, and they can attach themselves to other literal encodings in a more direct way within the brain than can the other arts whose suggestive qualities are more clearly established by their actual physicality. This is not the case with mathematics, as will be clarified in the subsequent chapters.

9

The boundaries of art—in the sense of beginning and ending, manifest as frames, introductions, codas, pro- and epilogues—are the means of art which allows it to be built into closed systems. In information theory all messages simply commence, whereas in art there is a big to-do about the boundary conditions. Such boundaries act like an insulation, much as the vacuum is required in a thermos bottle to prevent seepage of heat. The establishment of a strict frame of reference reinforces the formality of art, and sometimes also establishes some of the actual encoding qualities. For instance, the rectangularity of the picture's edge and its frame give greater meaning to rectangles and also all vertical or horizontal lines, by virtue of their being emphasized as echoes or repetitions of this edge line. Without a boundary the art becomes literally a magician's illusion and begins to suggest hallucinations. Art is never so false, and to destroy the boundary is to turn it into an open system which tries to pull us within it and also to let its internal ideas seep out, much like the heat in a thermos bottle. The motion picture tries again and again to pull us away from our practical world into its never-never land of false but thrilling realities, due to many subtle attempts to transcend its boundaries and separateness.

A clear and decisive boundary is as necessary to art as it is to life, without which a sense of urgency would be missing. A life without death would radically transform the role of man and give meanings which we cannot begin to imagine to everything. It would be absolutely meaningless to do many things which we consider vital if there were an eternity to do absolutely everything. The Methuselah urge in man is natural and every age is compelled to search for its fountain of youth, yet immortality might lead mankind to a new death. This situation in life would be analogous to the artistic one in which the entropic minimum is immediately realized: a perfect infinity of information becomes equated with an infinite life, having no more meaning to us than a zero communication or an unborn life. If we were ever to get Methuselah pills from our medical researchers, I think that life as we know it would be destroyed. When life is infinite, learning and growing are totally unnecessary.

All attempts to destroy the boundary of art, to break down the "apartness illusion" of art, leave us with a sense of failure. Reality never had it so strange and wonderful as in the Cinerama replete with stereophonic sound, and we are loath to return to the real world after these experiences. The drug experience is similar, and given an infinitely enhanced unreality that seems interminable we may, in our drugged unwisdom, try to keep it indefinitely. There is a danger of psychological addiction to drugs probably because of the fact that our very humanness is built on such perceptual expansions, and people may be willing to pay any price to be "human," even the ultimate one which loses all contact and actually resigns from the human race.

Art instead must heighten the real experiences of our conscious, normal selves; normal because experience is always with us, disappearing only in sleep (and its echoes are still at work in our dreams). An art which consistently draws us out of ourselves serves not to build our perceptual apparatus so that we can better cope with experience, but rather to satisfy the most immediate need for sensation—a strong need, it is true, but one which cannot dominate life to the exclusion of all else.

Expressing the infinite in art is another matter. The artist strives to encode more and more in smaller and smaller packages, and the infinite is sometimes his goal. But when a work of art leads you right off into infinity and leaves you there, it has lost all communicative value for us. If, like modern Pop music that simply fades away, or like an art whose pattern seems to start at infinity left and extends to infinity right, the art form strives to lull you into the pure redundancy of the constant and the never-ending, it does so at the sacrifice of information content. The infinite or repetitive, like the zero, is boringly lacking all information content. There may be an unusual initial impression on seeing these arts, an initial pulse of meaning due to the unexpectedness of their occurence, but it quickly fades once the pattern has established itself. The repetitive quality of Op art causes an initial wave of curiosity, then a sudden zoom to zero curiosity, as does a fun-house novelty or a very poor pun.

The secret of meaningful art communication is unlocked when one knows the cipher, which is hidden in the art like figures in a children's game, but easily available. It is necessary to build these ciphers and learn to recognize them in art in order to establish a human continuity and an extended awareness of the possibilities for the human psyche's enlargement. The revolt against man's fate, which Malraux says is art's purpose, is more naturally a consequence of our desire for order than it is a desire to overturn death.[19]

5

Music as a Message

Imagination in Sound

1

MUSIC, Congreve said, "has charms to soothe the savage breast"; but how are music's charms communicated? The first of all the arts to be investigated by science, music has survived the measurings and analysis of age after age. Pythagoras studied music in Babylonia and in Egyptian temples, and he borrowed the Chaldean (sixth century B.C.) idea that man made music to come in tune with the harmony of the universe, conceiving the musical scale as a structural element in the cosmos. The Chaldeans closely connected music with mathematics and astrology.[1] Like a good cyberneticist, Pythagoras conceived his "music of the spheres"—the cosmic harmony—which man could not hear because it was always sounding. Music was not so much communication as a manifestation of nature itself; the *ethos* of music, derived from the different scales or modalities, established a mental culture for the ethical improvement of man.

Since early time man had an intuitive feeling of the moral importance of music. We seem to have lost this attitude in modern times, relegating this exacting mental discipline and soul-building art to a hedonistic cultural embellishment. Plato believed that music imitated nature and that each mode of music was characteristic of an ethical sentiment (Dorian was ennobling, Phrygian headstrong, and Lydian effeminate). But the term *mousike*, meaning *mental culture*, was soon replaced by *musica*, meaning *harmonic science*, or the study of theories of intervals and the tuning of musical instruments.[2] This scientific approach to music continued almost until St. Augustine attempted to coordinate music with Christianity in the fifth century, thus reinstating the earlier moral views which elevated music from a simple science or diversion to a higher human level. The burden this placed on musicians and listeners seemed to preclude the possibility that music would ever again become sheer entertainment. It was Boethius who, a hundred years later, reevaluated the Augustinian attitude that our minds work on music to convert it into moral power, concluding the converse, that music has a power itself either to improve or to debase our character. He felt that the highest level musician was one whose intellectual and scientific abilities were supreme, and that inspiration was debasing unless subjugated.[3]

But the intellectual and scientific aspects of music gave way to the practical discipline derived from an instinctual and musical sensitivity about tone-combining and the craft of using the human voice and instruments. Johann Fux, a contemporary of Bach, wrote *Steps to Parnassus*[4] in 1725; this book, a compilation of the practical logic of contrapuntal composition acquired by musicians, has exerted its influence down to this day. A work like Helmholtz's *On the Sensations of Tone*,[5] which brought to bear a modern scientific approach to the investigation of musical phenomena, suggesting physiological and psychological reasons why the human being reacts to certain tone combinations, was read, nodded at, but put aside by musicians who were less concerned with reasons than with practical results. Some musicians, however, notably Hindemith, were impressed with the problems of the science of music, feeling that something could indeed be learned of practical musical value. His work *The Craft of Musical Composition*[6] returned to a natural basis of musical order, and he insisted that this acoustical-aural-physiological-psychological necessity determined music's path and established the criteria by which to measure the success of any new piece of music. Further, he backs up this early idea with a later thesis: that all good music is accounted for by the pleasure derived from a perfect coincidence of perceived music with expected music. Hindemith suggests that a person builds a musical "co-construction" in his brain as he listens to a certain piece of music, and the possibility of forseeing and anticipating a new musical structure as it is played gives him his aesthetic satisfaction,[7] which is similar to Leonard B. Meyer's theory discussed below. Music must not only be natural, it must also be known prior to its experience, and thus be predictable. The primordial musical experience in music which gives Hindemith's theory its starting point is the experience of motion from which all subsequent musical complexities are derived.

This theory is of course reasonable as an explanation for our pleasures on hearing harmonious and traditional music, and it also satisfies the naive need to explain why strange modalities or unexpected innovations in music are unpleasant: they are simply not music at all! If we are more optimistic, if we have had the good fortune to discover a rational music even in the non-natural and artificial system of atonality or serial constructions, if we consider music from the standpoint of cybernetics and communication theory, we can then expect an alternate theory to be more useful.

Leonard B. Meyer in his book *Emotion and Meaning in Music*[8] continues Hindemith's line of reasoning to solve this problem, asking very precise questions to which he gives cogent psychological answers, based also on a very scholarly set of musical proofs. He suggests in brief that we react emotionally to the inhibition of expectation, and that the pattern of music sets up an expectation (in rhythm, form pattern, decay or movement, and so on) which it sometimes fulfills, sometimes suspends, leading us through an elaborate series of emotive states. This offers a very good explanation of how music could possibly communicate complex emotional states.

In addition, Susanne Langer has indicated in *Feeling and Form*[9] and other books that all art articulates the form of feeling, not demonstrating as clearly as Meyer does just how that articulation is practically realized in any of the arts. For her, music is an analogous morphological symbolization of our sentient world, suggesting its growths and decays, speeds and retards, building in tone the complicated body of our vital emotional sentiments. We listen to music and recognize the similarity of its patterns to our feelings, and react as if experiencing the feelings ourselves—at least we can intellectually perceive a symbol of feeling. And insofar as the other arts are musical and imitative of emotive worlds they become humanly valuable.

These theories are not in accord with the cybernetics of art that suggests that we are bored by all information which we already possess—even by emotions which we have once experienced. Yet we all agree with Hindemith that there is a certain pleasure in listening to good music again and again. Perhaps this pleasure is like having our backs rubbed, being instead a sensual tickling or tracing over of previously established or memorized neural patterns in our brains. We enjoy listening to or repeating an art experience in order to sustain the memory, to entrench the pattern, to maintain what part of our brain is involved in a high state of order—and thus to keep ourselves in a high state of boredom, as suggested earlier. It is boring when we consider that the unusual, the novel, and the creative bring us something that is very informed, highly charged with information content. When a new and creative music impinges on our brains it begins the formation of a new neural system, thus enlarging the volume of our brain which is tending toward a high state of order with a low entropy condition. Reevaluations of old art also serve to enlarge their volumetric encoding implications through a new cross structuring with other ideas, either old or newly introduced ones, and it results in a further entropy reduction within a given volume.

And what about creativity in music? Is creativity but the imitation of emotions, the repetition of remembered and anticipated forms, the structuring of forms similar to our sentient life? Is the manufacturing of something with an illusionary quality that we seem to think is analogous to our own internal world of feeling sufficient to be called a creative act? The making the virtual time in music may be difficult, and it may be hard to make such an illusion cogent in its own right, but is this all that is required to fascinate us to the point that we can value it as we obviously do music?

I do not believe that the difficulty of production justifies the value we attach to art, any more than reproduction or literalness in painting, or sociology or psychology in literature, establishes its value. If we mirror an emotion or generate a replica of an emotion it may explain communication, but does it explain value?

The further suggestion that art must be a means to a creative insight, which reaches to the core of our human perceptual world, seems to me to be necessary before we can accept music and value it as we do. In this case music must be an intense synthesis of an experience which combines two or more unusual perceptions in such a way that we sense their relations on hearing them and are also impressed by the originality of their combination. By bringing together tone clusters or forms of tone which we would never dream were brothers, music builds new experiences out of past tonal experience. It is not mere contiguity, however, because it is their structural relation which is sensed to be creatively related, not just their juxtaposition serving as a novelty. There is a new acoustical space built in music into which our perceptual mechanisms can expand. Once inside this elaborated and creative acoustical space, man's experiential world is enlarged. This not only gives man pleasure or allows him to have new emotions, but enlarges his concept of humanness a little more, and perhaps also supplements his intellectuality.

2

Because it is the least literal of the arts, what music encodes is not immediately apparent. Further, as we have seen, the creativity of so abstract a form is hard to understand. Musicologists tell us that music had a religious or ritualistic origin; early people felt that the gods were taking to their voices in music. In fact the ethereal world still seems to hold sway in the realm of music. Meyer admits that the emotional response we have from music is not specific, and he says that our general reaction to music is "aroused when a tendency to respond (either consciously or unconsciously) is arrested or inhibited."[10] When one musical stimulus, based on past experience, leads us to expect another musical consequence, and it is either provided or denied, depending on the desire of the composer, then, Meyer argues, an emotion is induced in us by music. He lists and explores the principles which operate when we listen to music: the conciseness, or Prägnanz principle, that forces us to search for the simplest order; the law of good continuation, by which our minds can become saturated with an idea; the idea of return, where we expect any deviation to return back again to normal; and the principle of completion and closure, which makes us fill in missing gaps to make them seem continuous or complete.

Meyer says that music which does not work this way is bad music—actually not music at all. This sounds like the Hindemithian dicta, and it obviously would make many composers get their fur up. The trouble is that a mode of music is likely to come along which throws all of these ideas to the wind and which we must learn to accept—for the reason that it may be creative and communicate in a new and unsuspecting way. That is the trouble with methods—which includes the present work, if it be interpreted as a method. We know from linguistics that sounds have a form which can impress our ears, and that these sounds can carry meanings which can relate, not by virtue of the sounds themselves, but by virtue of the associations we have established between certain sounds and certain ideas. Can music work this way also? If it does, are the associations necessarily the same literal things to which language applies? The answer to these questions is that music can, and does, I think, have such associations, and they are not only associations of a literal nature, such as the chirping of a bird or the toot of a horn, but they are associations which derive from the very history of form in music which Meyer has decided to deny—namely the total backlog of previous musical ideas by which a composer is recognized for his style and meaning. At the same time music can also have a correspondence, as Langer insists, with our emotional sentient world—but this is only one and probably not the most fundamental correspondence which we value in music.

Countless human experiences can take on unexpected art meaning, not just a few like physiognomic features of the human face, the sounds of the human voice, the feelings within our chest perhaps gushing like a stream or still like a lake. Music, the most abstract and amorphous of the arts, can reach into our minds and souls and set these cognitive processes into operation, and it can at the same time establish itself at another level within that process and because of this take on a particular human importance. The elements for an abstract communication of this nature can be minimal, or they can be transmitted in great bursts; the only criteria is that they include a possible means of detecting relationships along with the elements. When the relation is sensed, it must be an unusual one, a creative one. Acoustical physics and our human perceptual mechanism provide the basis for saying that music can establish sufficient relations so that we can use it in the way of all creative communications. And beyond the given musical reactions, we have to admit the efficacy of a more arbitrary system like that proposed by Schoenberg, especially in the light of some of the productions of the practitioners of this new modern form of music.

Our modern communicative world, the electric culture of

which McLuhan speaks, has begun to make us aware of a larger, perhaps foreboding but nevertheless extensive and almost monumental realm of experience, which inevitably will begin to operate on the given arts which history provides. It will allow new interactions and new relationships will evolve, sometimes freeing old media that are locked in a perceptual vault, or again stagnating others which are now flowing freely. The technology of communication brings the entire world into the study or studio of the creator, and no art will survive its influence unscathed. The curious contradictions which this new electric culture causes in music are nowhere better illustrated than in chamber music, originally conceived for four delicate instruments, blown up to gigantic proportions in a contemporary orchestral arrangement, then heard on a car radio or a small portable transistor radio whose fidelity is so poor that it cuts the music right back to chamber-music dimensions! Or when a good amateur group, recorded on a two-dollar transistor tape recorder, can match the New York Philharmonic—on the same gadget, of course.

Electronics allows us to magnify a mandolin to match a mammoth orchestra. The implications of these possibilities will bring about changes in our perception of music which are more fundamental than we or musicians care to admit, complicating our reaction to music, elaborating the communicative situation of music. The music we knew is supplemented by all of the new electric manipulators, which will confuse aesthetic values and change situations we thought were granite. Music can become confused with visual associations or displaced into a sphere of sound which surrounds but nondirectionally does not impress us. Raised on music, we eat, sleep, drive to and study to music; and we forget that we can turn it off, because, like Pythagoras' music of the spheres, it is there all the time, and we have forgotten it. Today music satiates our perceptual senses in a sensual overkill which deprives it of all meaning until we can learn to make a special effort to understand it, or until the creation of a form so radical that we are forced to listen to it. This is probably part of the motivation of the trend of Modern musicians toward the Schoenbergian idiom. Music since Palestrina has tended toward increasing order and it may have reached its human saturation point, a point so high in complex entropy content that the mind was forced to invent a new purity at a very low order of entropy and very high information content to begin anew in the trend toward a large entropy.

Music is a natural part of our internal world; we hum it, dream it, cannot get themes out of our minds, so much so that we accept it even in our movies as a constant background effect, and get tripped up on some phrases that nearly drive us crazy with repetition. There is a constant intermingling in our minds of music and old associations, including ideas—as Theodore Reik so beautifully traced within himself in *The Haunting Melody*.[11] Perhaps we have not learned to single out this internal melody as explicitly as Reik, but it is there just the same, intermingling with our thoughts and feelings.*

But music does not successfully draw on directly associative melodies within each of us, because they differ so much from person to person. Insofar as associative meanings are explicit, as they are when a culture has a common folk experience in its music (which television may turn into a world experience, although also associated perhaps with certain commercials so that we will not only think of such and such a musical phrase, but also of the soap or hair cream or automobile associated with it); insofar as a culture develops meaningful musical themes, each theme has the potential for becoming a meaningful musical encoding for a work of art which everyone will grasp. That is all that is required to turn an expression into a useful artistic encoding device: common or immediate sense-knowledge of its significance.

Music then is but a stage in the never ending pattern of

---

* Given time and sufficient exposure, perhaps we can assume that abstract colors derived from a wide exposure to abstract paintings would comfortably fit into the background of movies and have a similar suggestive and associative force on our perceptual apparatus.

man's seeking and finding structures in sensual form which can enable him to build up a novel perceptual complex. This fabric is not confined to the inner mind, but is a combined fabric built both out of experience and out of remembered experience. Taken as an audio event, music is paltry, but taken as an audio event which is at the peak of a mountain of sound, it is the spearhead of an overwhelming force. It works like a didactic push which propels us into another, partially understood but now completely realized world of experience. I say didactic because the creator is after all edifying us, training our ears and our minds, giving us musical insights that go deep into our souls and articulate our being.

If you realize that chess, with but six basic pieces, thirty-two in all, moving over sixty-four squares, has fascinated man and given him many worlds of perceptual and intellectual experience since before and Middle Ages; that such a limited and finite count of mental acts or choices, however much they can be multiplied, is so complex that it exceeds the capabilities of modern, mass-memory computers; you can readily understand the greater appreciation and effect of even the most elementary of art forms, whose choice patterns are infinitely greater and eminently sensual. An unaccompanied flute for instance has so many permutational combinations of choice possibilities that they can barely be figured; imagine how much more complex a symphony orchestra can become with all of its sounds.

People who wonder how such vague things as sounds can be humanly meaningful, in a deeper sense than just the sheer pleasure of the tones titillating the inner ear, have not allowed themselves to recognize other than practical, pragmatic truths. It is not necessary to become religious, however, to allow for intangibles, although it probably helps; it is only necessary to become aware of man's own spiritual being. The unfathomable core of our personal existence is sufficient justification for the abstractions which even our unconscious barely understands. As Albert Hofstadter writes in *Truth and Art*: "In every age the greatest artists have worked to uncover in a symbol the inner meanings of the real truth of human existence, by articulating its character as a fundamental concern for truth of being—in love of beauty, admiration of greatness, grief and gladness at the tragic, pathetic, and happy, carefree unconcern regarding the trivial, or piercing despair over absolute nothingness. The image of the nothing and the image of true being are two sides of the same coin."[12]

Music also has the unusual attribute of being timeless in a way few of the other arts can match. Its perceptual independence gives it a lasting quality, and also perhaps the fact that it articulates one of the basic phenomena of human experience so vividly: time. I can listen to my wife, Diana, playing William Byrd's "My Lady Neville's Book" on our harpsichord, and marvel at the freshness and contemporary quality of this work, which was created in 1519. It is easy to perceive his point by simple listening, sensing the clash of the horizontal line against the vertical harmony, the ambiguity of the false relationships that sound like discords, resolving themselves again and again in a progression. The Bach flute sonatas we play are still fresh to me even though I have played them for fifteen years and will probably continue to play them and profit from them for the rest of my life—and these were composed by Bach in 1720. The point is that the creative insights of music do not wear out very easily, much less easily than those of the literal arts which are subject more to whim of fashion and use of words. To truly appreciate Shakespeare today you have to understand the meaning of many words used in his day, whereas Bach's particular ornamentation which may have been lost is not essential to a true appreciation of his music.

As every new generation of chess players studies the important games of previous masters, marveling and profiting by their creative ingenuity, so every generation of art lovers has to experience the cumulative residue of past art in order to build up their perceptual worlds to the point that they can grasp the most modern art. The reason a young student can catch up so quickly is that he has the experience and analysis of his teacher to help him through the labyrinth of history, plus his own unconscious history of almost extrasensory listening which occurred without pain over the years since his birth. Anyone who has taken the time to sit down with an analysis of some piece of music, or perhaps followed a good David Randolph or Leonard Bernstein analysis on a record, knows how the awareness of the inner workings of music improves his appreciation. If we learn, for instance, the folk melody behind an esoteric-sounding work by Bartók, we immediately see what he has done with it, and get a glimpse of his creativity in operation. We are learning the codes of the cryptograms of art, codes which we might have discovered without help, but which when learned directly facilitate our listening.

The lyrical façade of music, to which we might respond without analysis if we are untrained in its structure, is but a thin veneer of beauty in comparison to the core of gold beneath its surface, waiting there for us to reveal it by a little deeper digging. And even without analysis—or long exposure—we are able to sense more and more complex music due to the almost subliminal learning that circulates in the world of sound to which we are constantly exposed. If that world—the commercial world of radio, television, or even concert-hall music—were but a bit richer, if it were but a little more radical and up-to-date in terms of contemporary sounds, then we would be able to broaden the spectrum of our humanness in the volume of musical space to an unimaginable richness.

3

The deeper layers of musical meaning are fabricated from the structural possibilities of complex tones working together, the tones of musical instruments and the human voice. At the most elemental level of musical language is the simple, sinusoid tone, seldom met in music, built up by a practical musical instrument into different pitches and timbres and textures. Sounds in combination with one another cause two things to happen in the ear and the brain: they combine and impress

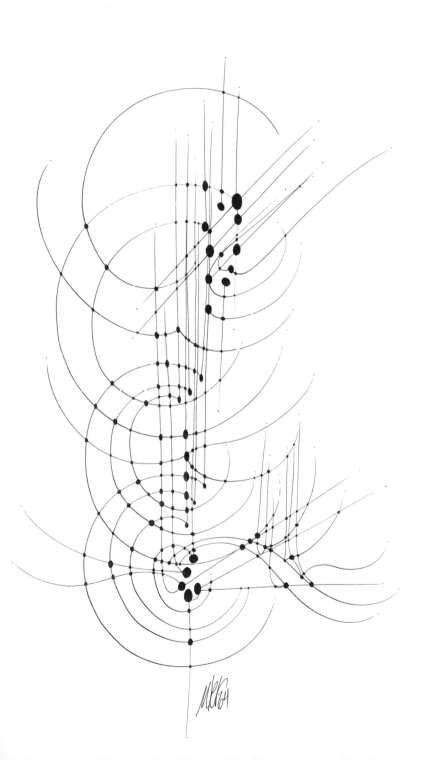

us sometimes more, sometimes less, and they have different textural qualities. The elementary musical material comes in two hierarchies: combinatorial tones and overtones due to mixing. These hierarchies are either embraced or they are denied, but they are always present—although use and conditioning can minimize and discharge the artistic importance of their effects.

Combinatorial tones were first investigated scientifically by Helmholtz and later by Hindemith, but intuitively long recognized by Fux and most composers. Musical theory, by which is meant solfége, harmony, counterpoint, fugue, and composition, rests not on the granite of scientific fact, but on the sand of shifting acoustical values, as Abraham Moles' notes.[13] For every exotic scale which we can discover in a primitive or ancient culture that rests on the hierarchy of combinatorial tones, another can be found which does not. Ignoring his own wisdom, Moles proceeds to look for Hindemith's "natural laws in music . . . as concrete as the laws of electron flow or of hydrodynamics,"[14] particularly in the statistical structural organization of music. He distinguishes semantic and the aesthetic information in art, but this is the old form-content dichotomy which Langer has exposed as an irrelevant paradox,[15] and need not concern us here. Nevertheless there is a value in Moles' work, and it is in his distinguishing how meaning in art can be materialized in a communicative form, and how the human artistic communication channels are subject to definite scientific analysis.[16] It is not the new media, however, which enables man to perceive that the materiality of communication is important, so much as the new modes of creative encoding which man generates in art—and this need not specifically be derived from a new media.

Moles' ideas combined with those of Meyer put the music-oriented scientist in a position to exploit the meaning of communicative exchanges in sonic form, but he must recognize that the structure is autonomous in a different way than Moles suggests. Moles wisely states: "The etymological meaning of the word intelligence, *interligere*, justifies the assertion that what is most intelligible is what has the most bonds (liaisons), and is thus what is most often encountered in the networks of thought," but still overlooks the importance of this structural tightening, which is also a creative manifestation since it reveals new relationships and liaisons.[17] There is an explicit order of combinatorial tones due to the two separate tones striking the eardrum simultaneously, and causing a beatnote heard as a dissonance or a harmony. This is due to the fact that the ear is a non-linear sound-recording device (a phenomenon which does not occur when the separate tones are supplied individually to each ear, a fact which C. Hirsch noted and suggested might lead to new musical possibilities).[18] This provides one aspect of musical deviation which is the basis of one structural system in music. The natural hierarchy of tone which results from a ranking of sounds according to the overtone content is another important aspect which is communicated and which serves as the stuff of creative relationships in music. Beginning with the simple sinusoid as number one we can add overtones until we build up the characteristic quality or timbre of all the instruments. The tuning fork or the flute in a high register generates this simple sinusoid; the clarinet and the oboe are instruments with many overtones. The extent to which a musical note differs from the sinusoidal pure note would be a measure of the complexity of its overtones. A wave analyzer can be used to determine the overtone series of a given musical instrument.[19] The effect of the overtones of given instruments is also a matter of conditioning, since we grow accustomed to the sound of particular instruments, and are shocked when a new instrument is used. This makes all scientific attempts to justify one or the other sound package difficult if not incorrect. Nevertheless, when we become accustomed to all the instruments in the world including the father of all musical instruments—the human voice, we have the feeling that there is a certain common denominator. Perhaps this is about as far as we can be expected to go in such an analysis.

Dayton C. Miller once tried to determine the ideal musical tone, realizing that a pure tone is a poor tone; and he concluded experimentally that the ideal note must have a strong fundamental plus a complete series of at least twenty successive overtones, in which at least fifty percent of the overtone intensity must reside.[20] Most musical instruments fall short of this ideal (if indeed it is an ideal at all). I once tried to establish a periodic table of all musical instruments according to their overtone series, hopefully, like Mendeleev, to be able to predict those gaps with significant musical sound possibilities. It would have been possible then to build new instruments, or to simulate the sounds electronically, in an attempt to fill in the gap of all possible musical sounds. But I had to give up my attempt because the complexity of overtones is so great for each instrument, and they vary erratically from note to note. This is something the computer, suited for such herculean sorting difficulties, could better try to solve.

A composer can also deny the hierarchy of the physical combination tones, as did Schoenberg, by establishing an order which is arbitrary although consistent; or he can deny the hierarchy of timbre orders, either by contradicting them in his orchestration, or by turning to some artificial means to generate tones that are unencumbered with these qualities. The departures in both cases owe part of their originality to the unexpectedness they generate. We value these departures, however, not because of this unexpectedness, but rather because of something which all art must have: an originality of its own.

As mentioned earlier, conditioning can oppose the ear, and counteract the natural effects of the nonlinearity of the inner ear. This has been the case, Helmholtz showed, as illustrated by the example of our becoming conditioned to equal temperament. Despite Hindemith, who maintains that he and any good string player can immediately sense when they are tuned harmonically instead of equal tempered, it is extremely hard for most people to detect the difference; we are so accustomed to equal tempering that the true harmonic music no longer has meaning to our ear, and it may even be annoying. This could be the source of a new encoding idea with creative possibilities since it is essentially lost to our modern ear.

These structural fundamentals underlie all music; the music of those composers who follow them has a classical flavor, and the music of those who do not has the quality we wrongly call "modern." It has been shown many times in the history of music that conditioning can accustom man to the most unusual harmonies and discords, transcending the acoustics and psychophysical effects of the ear. Any meaning in music must develop through structures which have their own autonomous merit, whether or not they are supported by a natural system or not. Even a brief review of the elaborate structures of music in the Middle Ages shows that the serialist devices are even less "modern" than Op art is in painting, (the latter having precedents in Greek mosaics, in many Oriental designs, as well as in the Dada extremes). The modern composer who practices a current fad, for other than serious creative reasons, does so at peril of losing not only his audience and perhaps a bit of his integrity, but also his grasp of the meaning and practice of creative music.

4

Pop music, like that of the Beatles or Frank Sinatra, has a lyrical or romantic rhythmic quality, only as imaginative as is required to support the order of a limited mood. And folk music has two components of importance: a primary musical quality which, due to its humble origin, sometimes reaches toward or touches the primordial well of originality, and also an ethnic tradition that preserves in sound the essence of a particular cultural heritage. I think that both Pop and folk music can rise to the condition of creativity, which is why classical musicians sometimes borrow their ideas. The deeply felt and simply motivated human quality of say a ballad singer like Pete Seeger or Joan Baez can make music which will not only bind an audience to his or her every word in an almost magical way, but can also capture a significant mood and musical form to which the greatest composer or singer might remark that it is well done. The creativity of any medium does not depend on any particular learned or intellectual background, dictating that only those who graduate from such-and-such an academy have the sole license to originality. In fact some of the more original composers have had to fight their way to even a rudimentary knowledge of the more formal or intellectual problems of music. Not only does George Gershwin come to mind, but also the early stumblings of Schubert, even Beethoven's struggle to give his ideas form. Naturally these artists had to acquire a more technical knowledge—Gershwin recognized that he was sadly lacking in technical knowledge of composition, and it is a pity that he did not live long enough to put his European studies to better advantage, having the power of a popular musical training behind him.

The folk idiom can be a gold mine of archetypal musical ideas, reaching back into our distant cultural past. As Theodore Reik suggests for myths in general[21] they contain many fundamental meanings and deep-seated human attitudes, which in music could be appreciated if not analyzed as they can be in the myth. The composer who learns to exploit folk music in a creative way has an ensemble of root musical ideas at his command which reach deeply into the human past. They contain a subtle transmission from ages gone by, through snatches of melody here, suggestive forms there, sometimes dancelike in quality, other times soul-searching or filled with human pathos.

The revolutionary spirit in Europe of the last century gave rise to a nationalistic school of music which used folk or nationalistic ideas: the mazurkas of Chopin, the Hungarian rhapsodies of Liszt, the Slavonic dances of Dvôrák, and the Norwegian dances of Grieg (not to mention Weber, Smetana and Tchaikovsky). Native poetry, set in songs by Schubert and Schumann, was a powerful literal enrichment of this romantic encoding of folk ideas, and it led to the exotic suggestions of Rimski-Korsakov, Borodin, and others. The creative aspects of these encodings are achieved in the setting by the integration of the ancient almost mythical music with a tone vision that is sympathetic to it.

The purer music begun around Bach's time built a structure devoid of any literal or archetypal suggestion—which is a rather unusual condition for music, traditionally an intimate part of folk and social life. Bach did of course use folk themes, but they were obscured and finally left behind in his prolific search for musical ideas. Although it may seem unnatural when considered in this way, pure music now seems so natural to us that it is as accepted as the sunrise. Mozart's music seems to have a logic so close to the basic structure of music that it is difficult to conceive of an alternative that could possibly be so pure. Yet musical idioms continually come on the scene to surprise us, and as we become familiar with them we accept them as truly as we do Mozart. Bartók used to sound strange to my ear, but I confess that there is hardly a note today which does not seem as natural as a scale to me; this is not boasting, but indicative of the attitude of any serious music lover today who takes the time to listen and study, and occasionally perform if he can.

When you listen for the first time to the complex semitones of, say, an Indian sitar it is quite overwhelming and confusing—try your children on an Indian sitar and watch their grimaces! But in time the music irons itself out in the mind— the faces of the children become less and less distorted if you continue to put sitar records on your hi-fi. You no longer hear buzzings and slidings delicately balancing within a chaos of sound, like so many radio stations broadcasting unintelligible messages to confuse you.

When I was a boy I spent hours with earphones, concentrating multitones from amateur radio stations into my head, radio signals from all over the world. The Morse telegraphic signals of an amateur radio band vary in pitch from the pure and ethereal to the rough and earthy, suggesting many different personalities. You can sense an intelligence within this tone system, single it out, over and above the intelligence that the code actually carries, if you have been at it long enough. Yet it seems as if this intelligence is other-worldly, not another person like yourself, up at dawn and across the globe from you. Music also presents countless intelligences to the mind, and an orchestra of tones allows for their simultaneous reception and creative comparison.

Most modern composers (with some notable exceptions) have bowed down to the creativity of the serial tone-row idea (including Stravinsky), and if you have had any experience in listening to classical music, you do sense that the more vital modern musics are related if not derived from this school. Yet an audience of any significant size is lacking, mainly because only the generally accepted classical music dominates all concerts. The recent school of music which Gunther Schuller called "third stream," borrows its ideas both from the serial and from the jazz idiom. Our mass audience, soaked in jazz, may find this an acceptable way to creep into the meanings of serial music. Schuller's compositions are unusually imaginative (although sometimes too obviously derivative from jazz), trying to eclectically blend the serial and the jazz—and since I have suggested that all eclecticism is potentially creative by virtue of the creative welding of two disparate ideas, I feel that the aspiration is essentially good. Schuller's "Seven Studies After Paul Klee"[22] is unusually imaginative, and it is in the tradition of Moussorgsky-Ravel's "Pictures at an Exhibition," another great attempt to bind together the moods of different media.

The modern extreme is of course the new anything-goes music pioneered by John Cage. Here radios are turned on at random (Cage) or iron plates are hammered (Lukas Foss). Foss has conceived of a type of classical jam session which is analogous to the "happenings" of the theater, in which he outlines but the barest phrase limits for his instrumentalists, allowing them to improvise within this frame at will. Like a "happening" this is on the brink of theater. I think that both of these phenomena—happenings and aleatoric music—are due to the need for the composer or artist to reassert the human in the act of making art. All artists desire to be involved in our difficult social-political world, and recently they have been coming down from their ivory towers in unusual ways. Aleatoric music is not so much random as it is human—humanly unpredictable, and produced during the act of performance by an actual human agent within sight of all; it is a plea for the human being in the act of making art, and an argument against such things as the production of music by mechanical or electronic devices or the existence of abstract painting.

This is of course understandable, and the motives are to be admired; but only the end result will justify the means in all such cases. To be composing minuets for Martians on miniature computers is a thankless task, in the light of the pressing realities of the modern world. But attempts to turn political or social realism into art are always beset by extreme technical difficulties; the message must be creatively assimilated by the medium in all such cases. If an artist feels strongly about social conditions in the world it is natural that he may want to turn his emotions to artistic account. The problem is that sometimes his art is unable to accept literal ideas and that it is foolish to attempt to do so.

But obviously the encoding techniques of art are many, and they can include both the literal and the abstract as well. Insights flow from literal ideas perhaps more readily than they do from the abstract ones, although to compare their depth is mistaken. Though this dual acceptance may not satisfy the desire for a pristine theory that is uncluttered with opposites, it satisfies a human need for diversity and abundance. To try to appropriate the inappropriate code of one art form in another can be as disastrous artistically as it appears to be socially desirable. The mature artist must, I think, keep his vision personal and pure, as he originally evolved it, even in the face of trying personal or upsetting world problems. The only way to satisfy the other needs is to see a social worker or a psychiatrist, or to write essays, letters to congressmen, or even to take part in demonstrations. The art which is most creative, even if it is abstract to the point of no return, will have its social or even political effect in less easily perceived, but nonetheless socially important fashions, when it is most powerful creatively. I think that the best social message an artist can put into his art is the message of his own personal creative communication.

5

Science has provided the modern musician with unique new electronic musical instruments, thanks mainly to the efforts of two sound engineers of the RCA Research Laboratories. Harry F. Olsen and Herbert Belar were investigating the problems of reproduction of music with phonograph systems, and they analyzed the various natural instruments to determine if they could synthesize them (I call them natural but of course they are man-made, being so familiar that they are "natural" to most musicians as one's car is natural to him). After Olsen and Belar had completed their analysis they realized that the actual synthesis of tones might have musical interest. They built the circuits and the results were so accurate that the lay ear could barely detect the difference.[23] This led to the development of

the Electronic Music Synthesizer, now located in the Princeton-Columbia Electronic Music Center in New York City. This remarkable new musical instrument is providing much interesting music today, allowing the composer to synthesize practically any sound or group of sounds, at any speed, with any desired attack pattern.[24] A composer need only learn to punch his composition onto a roll of paper fed into the control device of the unit to set any desired tones into operation—a not too difficult task, certainly one less difficult than learning to score a musical compositon.

The tape recorder also gives the musician many new technical possibilities for the generation of music. He can, for instance, take natural sounds and manipulate them, as when he records a cricket and speeds it up to the warbling of a canary, or records a birdcall and slows it down to the moan of a sick hippopotamus. He can invert sounds, recombine them, modulate them together, and so on ad infinitum. The possibilities are unlimited—which is one of the difficulties of all electronic music. The composer using electronic sounds probably has to throw all previous conceptions of music aside—he has absolute freedom, and he is swimming around in a sea of utterly novel sounds—unless of course he chooses to imitate natural instruments playing traditional music, which is obviously trivial. It is as difficult to find islands in this sea of sounds that are in a meaningful order, as it is for the Abstract Expressionist to find forms in his splashy world of colors and shapes. Complete freedom for artistic production is like the political freedom of which Erich Fromm writes: it must be escaped from to relieve man of the anxiety of choice.[25] The dictatorial rule of tradition is less anxiety-ridden than the novelty of invention; it is less frightening because you know what cave you are wandering in, and can almost predict every turn and twist. Still, if it is possible for composers to find something significant in this new world of sound—and I believe that it is—we can hope that in his new democracy he will arrive at a level of creativity beyond the capability of current musical form and media.

Analogously in the visual arts when video tape is available for general use—as it will be within the immediate future thanks to the new Sony home television tape-recording system, the painter can give us something electronically interesting for our eyes. Electronic pictures would differ radically from any other possible manipulation of vision, for instance the motion picture, because television's scansion basis allows for a 525- or 1000-line shredding of image. And further as science develops and makes available other new ways to manipulate perceptual media, the artist will rise to their exploitation. If brain waves are ever made accessible so that they can be manipulated, recorded, and reinserted into the brain, we will have a brain-art for our edification and amusement. Probably all that is required of a new perceptual discovery is that it be easily available, otherwise its technical limitations will prevent other than the specialist from manipulating it. It will not be the new invention which inspires the artist so much as his dissatisfaction with previous methods and ideas in art.

These devices—the tape recorder and the music synthesizer—have come onto the musical scene at the point in the history of music when composers have just about reached their limit of demands on the instrumentalist. There is a myth in the music world that a new composition which today makes impossible demands on an instrumentalist, will tomorrow be commonplace and simple. The fact is, however, that the development of musical instruments has kept pace with the demands of musical technique by composers. Without Theobald Boehm's invention of the key system and the conical-bore head piece of the modern flute,[26] certain technical passages would be impossible. Richard Strauss, for instance, makes demands of the flute which are impossible on the old eight-keyed system. And the modern improvements of the violin are absolutely necessary to help the instrumentalist obtain the dynamics demanded by modern composers. The synthesizer will allow the composer to make any demand he desires of his electronic instrumentalist. Of course we no longer have the performer with his imperfections and possibilities for perfection, and we also lose his passionate grimaces (unless some bright engineer and a puppeteer collaborate and program a physiognomy accordingly). We can seldom expect a breakdown of technique with an electronic device, and if one happens, we will have little sympathy with a transistor. The uncertainty of production in the concert hall is a definite pleasure for us, as mentioned earlier. But without it there may be a relaxation in our appreciation which may shift us to a new level of musical meaning. The hi-fi record has already taken all uncertainty away from its output since we expect no mistakes from RCA Victor.

But, as Mel Powell suggests, "the history of music is not a history of musical instruments, but rather the much richer history that outlines a sequence of composer's boredoms."[27] Synthesized musical sounds will obviously have far-reaching effects on music, however, and also on all of the other arts since the total human sensorium is related.[28] This can be illustrated most strikingly by considering how radioed musical concerts have affected our conception and use of abstraction. It was the radio that first took the human instrumentalist away, and we could no longer see him, having to imagine him playing his instrument from the sounds we heard. This had a tremendous impact on all of the arts. Invention was hampered by early man's inability to disassociate mechanical structure from animal form, and when the wheel was discovered to be a good substitute for legs, the imagination of man was released and invention proliferated.[29] When the human productive mechanism is taken away, as in radioed music, then the imagination has a new impetus to create abstraction in all of the arts. This may have been the needed suggestion to abstract images from recognizable forms in painting, and also in sculpture, dance, and perhaps even the theater of the future.

The notation scheme of classic music has been visual, but there is no notation possible for electronic music which is built immediately at the console of a synthesizer or with several tape recorders. Like a painter the composer now directly forms his materials (sounds) which he composes in a permanent form once and for all (on tape). Performance is eliminated and silent reading of the score is no longer possible. This encourages a deeper dedication to abstraction, and it will obviously condition us, when we have an opportunity to hear more electronic music, to an even further abstraction, which will no doubt in turn influence the other arts. The art of music began as a remembered song in the mind of a troubadour. The scored musical notation, which divorces word (poetry) from music (song), probably made its contribution to the original musical depersonalization and abstraction, and led to the development of musical instruments. Similarly, it seems certain that the electronic synthesis of music will continue this rush toward increasingly abstract, but still humanly meaningful arts.

Memory considerations also contributed to the increasing value which humans place on abstract art. The troubadour remembered everything, and printed musical notation made this unnecessary. When the sound of music itself is carried onto a mechanical memory, as with recorded music, even the score is unnecessary and its function is altered. Ivins and McLuhan have traced a similar evolution for the word, beginning with memorized stories, advancing to handwritten manuscripts which are unique in number, and then to mass-printed books and the recorded word.[30] It is obvious that the human memory system very profoundly alters man's idea of abstraction, removing it further and further from common-sense ideas as it becomes symbolized and mechanized, while still preserving its actual human meaning. When our engineers build us a simple miniaturized rapid-retrieval memory system for our belts, which accurately supplement and speed up our own memories and personal file systems, we can expect it to drastically alter our present methods of learning and thinking and help us achieve a fantastic intelligence amplification. This is what the computer is already doing on a large scale.

That highly abstract instrumentalities can be humanly interpreted is nowhere better illustrated than in the example of telegraph operators. The exposure of a ham radio operator to Morse code radio telegraphic communication with another person gives a very special interpersonal link which neither the voice nor the picture can duplicate. As a boy I quite definitely preferred the dits and dahs of code to voice communication because I felt that it was a more intimate form of communication—as if I were tuned almost directly into the brain of the other person I was talking to, and could hear and comprehend his neurons firing one by one as he thought. I built great friendships across oceans and continents this way. There was nothing even remotely abstract to me about those highly personal tones that buzzed into my ears from beneath countless other tones, also charged with their own indistinguishable humanity.

When music became sufficiently depersonalized by radio and the phonograph, we were able to forget that humans were ever involved; only when we became used to this separation of music and musicians could we realize that after all music *is* abstract. It is true that in some cases past evolving visual art forms have tended toward a corruption of images which superficially look like abstraction in this sense. Malraux and others have shown how the images used on coins or on pottery have become increasingly distorted, each successive generation stylizing the form a little more, like the childhood game of telephone.[31] But the end result of this kind of corruption is not given a direct human significance since it has become purely decorative with no vestige of the original idea, much less any correspondence to anything human. But when the humanity is preserved, as this radio theory of abstraction indicates, a new media that carries abstraction even further can have surprising and far-reaching effects on all the arts.

The music synthesizer would allow the realization of the dream of filling in the complete periodic table of all possible significant sound spectrums, equivalent to the natural musical instruments. Yet there are obvious limitations which all electronic musicians must face. An example of the problem, for instance, is that of determining how to best use vibrato in an electronically synthesized medium. To duplicate the tenuous pulsations which human instrumentalists introduce into their every tone requires a very complete understanding of what occurs. The synthesized tone cannot have a completely regular vibrato like a vibraphone's insistent wha-wha-wha, nor can it be a random one because even randomness is too consistent, leading to intolerable musical situations. If you play the flute, as as I do, you know that a strong vibrato is appropriate in many orchestral passages and often little or none at all is demanded for woodwind quintet ensembles. Sometimes an instrumentalist must match his vibrato with masses of strings, and at other times with a few solo woodwinds. As pure color is generally banal to the eye, so pure sinusoid tone is banal to the musical listener. Too large a vibrato at any given instant is usually disturbing because it too obviously causes a timbre change, whereas too fast a vibrato fades into the frequency of the note itself and tries to establish itself as a new pitch. The highly complex decisions of instrumentalists at every moment of playing make all the difference between a good orchestral performance and a poor one. The density of human intelligence at work in an orchestra is so enormous that to reproduce even a fraction of that quality by electronic means is almost inconceivable.

The direction that electronic music has taken differs from country to country, due in part to different technical approaches and in part to theoretical attitudes. The French use tape recorders to build their *Musique Concrète*, beginning with natural sounds that they manipulate until music evolves. Composers of the stature of Darius Milhaud and Edgar Varèse have used the facilities of the *Radio-diffusion Française*, directed by Pierre Schaeffer, for compositional experimentation.[32] The German group at the N.W.D.R. studios in Cologne employ purely electronically generated tones, and they call their music *Elektronische Musik*. Karlheinz Stockhausen creates an interesting, rough-hewn tone of electronic music which is essentially serial.[33] The French school sounds more sophisticated in comparison with the German's roughness of tone, but the American school, using the synthesizer, or other highly complex equipment, contains the most unusual sounds.

The music of Milton Babbit, Otto Leuning, Vladimir Ussachevsky, and the Argentinian Mario Davidovsky living in New York City, is representative of the American school of electronic music. It tends to be more dramatic, sometimes combining with voices or orchestras using natural instruments, and more mathematical than its European counterparts.[34] It is actually difficult if not impossible to evaluate the electronic music being composed today because we have so little opportunity to hear it.[35] And the composer himself has had little enough opportunity to feel his way around in this new idiom, because of equipment limitations. Students graduate and they cannot take their large and expensive instruments along with them to their teaching posts in small colleges. We have not yet come to value synthesizers as we do Stradivarius violins. Olsen and Belar are presently trying to develop small phonographs that use records that contain not physical analogs to sounds but the codes of sounds. This would hopefully lead to miniaturized synthesizers employing integrated circuits which all composers could afford.[36] Our affluence and general level of gadgetry allows almost anyone to take a few oscillators and tape recorders and set himself up in the electronic music business.

The computer is also a device which some composers, who have access to them, are trying to put to compositional or tone-generation use. Chapter 8 considers the contributions of a computer to composition in music. It seems that whether we like it or not, the music of the future will become increasingly electronic, although the complete elimination of all natural instruments is unthinkable. The natural orchestral instrument has a peculiar quality of its own, plus the fact of the performance and the greater density of human control in large, live orchestral and choral performances. The idea of transposing or transforming conventional instruments into electronic modes also suggests itself, and the composer Mario Davidovsky has done some experimentation with this possibility.[37] Intermodulation between the human voice and instruments has as yet barely begun to be explored, however. I recall the strange and wonderful sounds which countless intermixed signals and voices produce when crowded together on the twenty-meter amateur radio band. It is clear to me that an entire new gamut of sound can well proceed from such an admixture of the human and the electric.

I feel that even if music remains impersonal in the electronic idiom as it is today, without this human cross-fertilization that I have suggested, it will be significant perceptually and potentially a source of creative communications. We have to give it a chance, however, by buying records, requesting it from our radio stations, encouraging the local symphony orchestra to include it in a concert (even if it peers at us from the stage with its red electric eyes a-blinking). We have everything to gain, especially a new awareness of an important future of human articulation. As Howard Klein, the record critic of *The New York Times*, recently indicated,[38] the increased specialization of our age is also reflected in the composer's pulverization of sound by electronic quantizing. Yet we cannot say with certainty whether it is the specialization of electronic music or our own inability to bridge large gaps of subtle sounds which is the problem. To demand of electronic music the single-unit constructions of Beethoven or Mozart—or even Webern—is to fall into the trap of projecting past logics on current and future artistic visions by which they can never be measured.

6

What composers have had to fight for (being free of the logic of nature), the visual artist is given naturally (since color has no explicit physical logic that enables the construction of a meaningful hierarchy of combination, as I indicate in the next chapter). The one of course wants more freedom (the musician), as the other strives for more order (the painter). The scale of color tones is considerably greater for the painter than the scale of musical tones is for the composer. This is why many composers have dreamed of or even experimented with quarter-toned, or decimal-toned music. Although much folk music uses the same spectral slide from note to note which we naturally expect from color, as Rudolph Arnheim notes,[39] seldom does the glissando of gypsy music creep into the classical work. When it does, when a violinist is guilty of too much blending of notes, we accuse him of being a romantic.

All music is an intermix of tones, either in the glissando where notes glide together or in an overlap or other admixture of sound. The chord fights against the ongoing time element in music, tying together the vertical quality of harmony with the rhythm. The mind's memory also helps to tie together the two ends of a symphony. We repeatedly listen to a work of music in order, Mozart-like, to perceive it as a single, unified work, completely out of time. Yet music is very much in time, and to think of it as a remembered work instantaneously sounding in an infinite inner audio space is to turn your back on the essential and vital illusion it creates (as Langer suggests).[40] To be meaningful, music must be experienced in time, and it must be experienced within a specific time span. To rush the very slow lento movement of a Beethoven quartet is to lose the suspense of the lingering and belabored chords. The rate of transmission of a musical work, be it an andante, allegro, presto, or prestissimo, not only determines how long it will take to communicate itself, but also how its creativity is manifest, since time is such an important element in its encoding.

From the standpoint of communication theory many different kinds of music would have the same entropy measure, because complex music played slowly would be comparable to simple music played rapidly. Tempo is an element of creative communication as well as a means of voicing information. Amateurs accustomed to playing all prestos at andante rates are usually very surprised to hear a professional rendering of a work because it is so different as to be almost unrecognizable. The faster a movement, the more excitedly we react to it, and the slower, the calmer. The extremes of prestissimo and larghissimo (very fast and very slow) are almost intolerable for us to stand for any length of time, because the brain finds very fast things or very slow things difficult to assimilate, unless it is used to them.

The physical limitations which conventional instruments impose on a performer are perhaps more than a fortuitous accident, because they match the limitations of the mind with certain limitations of physical production—a fact that computer composers must consider. However it must be emphasized that limitations change, that our minds expand and we can encompass more than we dream. Human performers being human are not able to transcend a certain perceptual limitation, and therefore they may be unable to perform a more complex musical idea than they can conceive, since obviously they are governed by what they can perceive when they play.

The forms of old and new compositions are the larger units for musical encoding of which music is creatively constructed. They exist in traditional, neoclassic, or modern free-forms, giving the composer means to articulate greater masses of sound in time. These larger masses sometimes contain references to literal ideas, as in the tone poem invented by Franz Liszt. You can learn to read into the tone poem the particular ideas a composer desired to associate with it, just as you can feel that many of Beethoven's sonatas had a literal idea behind them. But Richard Wagner was perhaps more sensible when he tried to build this associative meaning more closely into the structure of the music, by developing what he called the leitmotiv, which was his powerful creative contribution to music.

The welding together of two artistic communicative phenomena is most easily understood by considering musical examples. The union must obviously be significantly structural, powerfully dependent on a technical factor, rather than on a purely associative one, otherwise we either fail to recognize its creative revelation, or the fact that the seams show disturbs us to the point that the creativity seems false. All palpable unions disturb us in art, whether they be poor music trying to support good theater, poor musicianship trying to rise to great music, poor plastic qualities trying to support great themes in painting, or poor structure in the novel or theater trying to sustain noble people.

It is sometimes advantageous that the literal idea to which music is welded be lame or superficial. The synthesis necessarily makes stringent demands on idea and form. Goethe, for instance, preferred that someone of a lesser musical stature than Schubert set his poems to music, feeling that once his poems were caught up in the jaws of this powerful young composer's creativity they would never be the same. Composers have often remarked how difficult it is to set Shakespeare or Milton to music. Lieder do not require the most profound of poems to make them grand, and opera in the hands of Mozart obviously did not require a very good play to turn out extremely well.

Opera often disturbs the purist because he expects both the music and the play to be at the same artistic level of excellence; but I have found my temperament suited to the almost ridiculous superimposition of song on story. The difficulty is probably in desiring that the drama be more realistic; wishing that the stories of opera better reflect reality—which is impossible unless you live in a home of opera singers. Tolstoy complained that Wagner was being ridiculous when he tried to suggest that stuffed divas could be romantic characters in a real-life drama.[41] Drama is after all artificial too, and to embellish it with music is acceptable in good theater as well as the movies. When the music raises a story to the realm of fantasy, in which words flow magically in song, with emotions expressing themselves as bursts of music, the strings raging for storms and the flutes tweeting with contentment, primitive instincts can be generated. A person responds to the super-heightened consciousness which these weldings impart with ease, and in the opera house we can partake of a vitalizing ritual, much as did ancient man in his cave or cathedral.

A turn toward contemporary realism in opera is represented by the three great modern operas: Alban Berg's *Wozzek* and *Lulu*, and Arnold Schoenberg's *Moses and Aaron*, all having exceedingly neurotic plots coupled with serial or atonal music, although strongly expressionistic and neoromantic. The atonal music is a natural, I think, for expressing the powerful emotions of these three operas. The recent opera *Don Rodrigo* by Alberto Ginestera suggests that it is wrong, however, to use atonality with the traditional Grand Opera. This work, recently mounted quite sumptuously for the premiere of the New York City Opera Company in its new location in Lincoln Center, suggests that atonality has certain definite limitations. Although atonal music can be close to the speech pattern, and easily made to match the human voice in extreme emotion, I think that it is insufficiently lyrical to raise the often inconsequential and illogical effects of Grand Opera to a sufficiently creative and tolerable level.

The types of musical encoding which are available to the composer are indicated in Table III.

TABLE III—TYPES OF MUSICAL ENCODING

1. FACT OF A PARTICULAR INSTRUMENT (or group of instruments) BEING PLAYED (or a recording, or an electronic instrument)
2. SEQUENTIAL PATTERNS OF SOUND
   a. Tendency to respond is inhibited (psychological)
   b. Repetition of phrase or idea
   c. Rhythm
      (1) Saturation (pedal point, repeated phrase)
      (2) Syncopation (off beats, unexpected changes, etc.)
      (3) Gaps, randomness (holes in the line, variations)
   d. Harmonic sequences (physical)
   e. Serial sequences (formal)

3. SIMULTANEOUS PATTERNS OF SOUND
   a. Single tone (overtones creating timbre of particular instrument or quality)
   b. Multiple tones (combination tones, new tone quality, suggestion of many musicians or instruments)
   c. Single harmony (physical laws of harmony, hierarchy, dissonances to be resolved, etc.)
   d. Arbitrary harmony (consistent pattern, row of tones, or other logic perceived formally)
   e. Minute modes (glissandos, quarter tones, or other unusual modes, either instrumental, vocal, or instrumental)
   f. Random (obvious variations, either vibrato that is controlled, or electronically generated changes, prepared pianos, radio noises, etc.)
4. SPECIFIC FORMS
   a. Old (symphony, sonata, concerto, dance forms, etc.)
   b. Neoclassic (revived but varied)
   c. New (completely newly created forms)
5. PROGRAMMED (tone poems, music with literal associations, etc.)
   a. Literal meaning, given idea for idea (as in Strauss)
   b. Literal meaning, suggested only by over-all feeling (as in expressionism of Debussy, etc.)
6. LITERAL (opera, lieder)
   a. Accompanying actually sung ideas
   b. Leitmotiv (ideas associated with phrases as in Wagner, Menotti)
   c. Combinations and Neoclassic suggestions (or extra suggested skeletal forms)

8

Art used to revel in the artificial, then it swung toward psychological realism, and today the reaction against mechanization and science is forcing it back again toward the artificial. Opera is coming back in vogue; it is "high camp" to appreciate opera, just as it is to appreciate *art nouveau* and the Mannerists. The essential artificiality of music makes it a test case which can help us measure the human importance of abstracted art forms. Here is a communication, originally inseparable from the human being, anchored first in the human throat, then in instruments that man directly manipulated in sight of everyone, ending up as indefinable tones that exist in some vague acoustical space that is artificial and electrically produced. That music was advanced from the human voice to the instrument well before our time reinforces the idea that the evolution of media of which McLuhan speaks is not unique with our age. And yet music is humanistic in all senses of the word. In this psychological age it is even more simple for us to attach humanistic ideas to this abstract form, because we know that man is a creature of many unaccountable moods, having mysterious rhythms and hidden motivations; and combined with an inventive evolution of form, we can easily attach a humanity to the most highly abstracted art forms. Music seems ideally suited to carry humanity in an abstract way, but this is true only because of a longer period in which man has been able to grow accustomed to its charms. Given an equally lengthy conditioning, it seems rather certain that any perceptual mode could likewise support an abstract humanism that we would accept as readily as we do music.

Polyphony is essentially a Western development, although its roots can be traced to the East. Yet the East never actually realized polyphony in an organized and notated form. Notation not only allowed the West to perpetuate past musical ideas unequivocally, but also allowed a structural enrichment to grow owing to the cumulative effect. It is always necessary that an art have a permanent communicative medium in order to build the necessary creativity out of past ideas and thus to raise it to higher and higher levels of complexity. We would forget all that has gone before otherwise. The Greeks had an "abstraction barrier" owing to their media development at a linear, largely tactile level, and it limited all their intellectual activities. They did not go beyond a certain exactly codified monophonic structure in their music, and their mathematics remained Euclidean. Salomon Bochner compares the Greek abstractness with the modern, and suggests that mathematics becomes an intellectual force commensurate to its "abstractness."[42] Instead, I think that the fact that a culture is bound closely to its artistic perceptual means sets an abstraction barrier. Mathematical development and musical complexity may be related phenomena, the former depending on and emanating from the awarenesses or consistent exposures to the latter. Musical awareness in particular seems to build an overt mental disposition to high levels of abstraction, especially spacial-temporal abstraction. All art, as I have suggested, essentially conditions man to respond to some new human perceptual knowledge, filling out man's humanness in new areas.

Mathematicians generally love music—I play chamber music with mathematicians who are musical amateurs of the most superb musicianship and seriousness. Perhaps music is the lifeline of the mathematician and he does not know it. The articulation of sound in flowing, playful ways does not seem to be particularly logical, yet we can begin to appreciate how it is possible for its structures to excavate volumes within our brain and form a scaffolding on which we can hang new orders of understanding. It fabricates structures and neural passages or nets that set foundations for deeper logic of an intellectual nature. It is of course necessary to reevaluate Kant's transcendental aesthetics and logic, to reconsider the gestalt approach to epistemology, and to study all methods by which the human mind builds concepts and forms logic, in order to support this very speculative thesis; I advance it nevertheless because it seems to me to have more meaning than previous theories which confuse our emotions with our artistic experiences, restricting art to the purely delirious. Our emotions are involved, of course, as they are in all human actions, intellectual or otherwise. But I feel that we have too long limited what we mean by emotion by saying that art is its strict province; we should allow it to creep meaningfully into *all* our human disciplines, including the scientific.

The cosmic correspondence of music proposed by the Chaldeans, and taken over by the Pythagoreans in their derivation of number which is related to the harmony of the spheres, exerted a direct influence on many early scientists. The second century astronomer Ptolemy, who conceived the first planetary system, also wrote extensively on Greek musical theory. As Hindemith pointed out, the geometrician Euclid, the physicist Huygens, and the mathematician Euler all studied music quite extensively and were directly influenced by it in their theoretical systems. Kepler's famous laws of planetary motions were themselves the product of a mind steeped in the seventeenth-century musical sciences, and he formulated them as the harmonies of bodies in motion. Hindemith wisely observed, "It may well be that the last word concerning the interdependence of music and the exact sciences has not been spoken."[43]

I have learned in conversations with Margot Einstein and Einstein's long-time secretary Helen Dukas that he was brought up in an atmosphere charged with music, playing the violin first with his mother and sister as a boy and young man, and throughout his life with friends. Almost all of his assistants and associates could join him in a chamber-music session. It is not generally known that Einstein also loved to improvise for long hours on the piano. He was very fond of the more formal and architectonic musics, and it is particularly interesting that the personal or dramatic did not interest him as much as the more abstract arts. His most beloved composers were Bach, Mozart, Schubert, and old Italian or English masters, but he also liked Haydn, and Beethoven, although he considered Beethoven less impressive. Wagner was decadent and Debussy and the moderns so refined as to be almost nonexistent. He could not perceive the architecture of the more modern musics, and he was unable to grasp them emotionally. He also did not like fiction or creative literature particularly because he got too involved in the characters and was unable to grasp any "aesthetic" quality as a result. Einstein was preeminently disposed to musical abstraction. Recorded music pleased him, and although he did not have an extensive record collection, he played what he had consistently or listened to classical music on the radio. An early biographer, Alexander Moszkowski, says that Einstein recognized an unexplainable connection between music and his science, and notes that his mentor Ernst Mach had indicated that music and the aural experience were the organ for describing space.[44]

The peculiarly unique and historically unprecedented intellectual jump in the history of ideas which Einstein made of course resulted primarily from his towering genius. Yet it is clear that this genius was supported not only by the giants of science on whose shoulders he stood, but also by an extremely refined mental apparatus. He was highly disposed to architectonic abstractions, and you can say that this was reflected in his taste in music. It is also conceivable to me, however, that this disposition to the architectonic logics of abstraction was formulated by Einstein's early musical experiences, and even *enlarged* by a constant struggle for musical experiences which helped him build a rich mental perceptual fabric of space and time in which to perform his scientific theorizing.

6

Visual Communication

Insights of the Visual Arts

1

Vision dominates our concept of reality, and to visualize is to understand. The eye has more neurons sending information to our brain than all the other senses combined—it has, as the communication engineer would say, the largest bandwidth of all the human sensors. This does not actually give the eye a communicative superiority over the other sensors and also the art associated with it, but it does suggest that the visual message can be exchanged more rapidly. We take in a picture immediately on looking at it; the various elements are simultaneously sent over the separate groups of neurons spread across our retina, whereas the parts of all other communications in art are sent to our brain sequentially in time. The product of information density times time may, of course, be identical, in given cases of the various arts.

The fact that painting *imitates* reality has led some painters like Delacroix to write that it is superior to literature, because, due to the illusion of seeing, painting presents realities indistinguishable from the real thing, and not just symbols from which we imagine a reality.[1] But one could look at it the other way around just as easily, and say that a picture weakens our imagination. Gainsborough felt this way and purposely made his portraits vague and suggestive of his subject, so that everyone who knew the person could supply his own, more accurate details.[2]

Although the grandeur of the world comes across to us through our eyes, and the art which also does so might be considered most important, creative visual communication and the pictorial arts suffer from the fact that looking has been emphasized in every human being since his birth. We are conditioned to looking in a certain general way, and this way of looking at reality is not the same as when we look at a picture. Looking must shift to a special mode before we can actually see what is to be seen in a good painting. The clues of sight are usually directed toward a particular object in everyday life: as I sit here writing, I concentrate my eyes on the moving pencil, and only with great effort can I "see" my surrounding study, or catch a peripheral glimpse of a bird perched outside my window in the blazing sun. I can hear the bird chirping all the time, however—although naturally my attention shifts off it while thinking about writing. Sounds are ubiquitous; they are sensed directionally and can be put out of mind, but they are uninterruptible physically, and their sources are unimportant as long as we can hear them. The source of every detail in a pictorial image is, on the other hand, of supreme importance—we must be focused on the source of light to see it, we must actually look at the variation of color tone or the movement of line in order to perceive it.

To look at a Renoir nude and see a voluptuous, widemouthed, pink-skinned lady is to forget the flowers around her, to ignore the texture of her hair, the flow of the drapery, the arrangement of the forms: in sum, the total interplay of the lines and colors and forms. This is one argument abstract painters advance to justify their equilibrating the visual experience of a picture by removing prejudicial recognizable objects: everything in an abstract picture receives the same visual attention when you cannot place any of the individual objects. But a trained eye can transcend the restrictions of recognizability and comprehend both the negative and the positive shapes— the figure and its background. Recognizability is definitely a coding element in painting to be reckoned with as an element of creative communication, and to eliminate it because it gets in our mental way is absurd.

Recognizability is of course a *literal* encoding element, and as such it is able to communicate beauty or deep feelings which we comprehend almost as precisely as the meaning of a word. We can see a picture of a beautiful woman whose form is agreeable and near to our current ideal of femininity, and we respond with a definite feeling of pleasure; and contrariwise, we can see a human figure dismembered by war, and react with horror. The human condition, in all its beautiful or troubled aspects, certainly has its visual qualities which are important elements in the communication situation. Man's humanness must proceed from natural reality and experience as readily as it does from the other more abstract qualities of sound or color combinations or words or mythical poetical ideas. The literal is a powerful visual idea, but in itself it is relatively easy to make and not particularly enlightening artistically. Literalness has to be justified in a realistic picture as an element in a creative relationship, just as do the other means of encoding visual ideas such as line, space, or color. The depth or extent of human psychological experiences in the social condition can only receive fleeting impressions by visual means, but it is also true that the force of the eye as a communication channel can make these fleeting forms poignant and creative beyond words. The justification for using literal, deeply moving views in pictures is their ability to contribute some insight into the perceptual possibilities of our vision of life. They border on sociological insights, but they are more artistically than scientifically meaningful when they express human truths whose being is formulated in communication situations, due to their very birth in a visual form.

Our literal visual remembrances have two components: first,

views of specific things which have an emotional or intellectual significance to us; and second, impersonal bits and fragments that we have accumulated during a lifetime of looking, which we can piece together into recognizable or even abstract things. We perceive forms and accept them in our brains, comparing them with the storehouse in our memory, seeking similiarities and noting differences. It is commonplace that when we see a new face, for instance, we are a little pleased that a stranger looks like somebody we already know. We all play a constant game of matching relatives and famous people, of noting that a new acquaintance looks like some television personality or an old friend. We are most content when the visually new is somehow already part of our personal remembered visual experience—but is this sufficient to make it a valuable art experience?

Since experience varies considerably from person to person, it is clear that our literal views do also—within the limits of common experience shared by the members of a particular society. The story quality of a picture begins to operate when intuited shapes, forming recognizable people and objects, begin to suggest propositions or events. This literal meaning is derived not from formal conventions or learned perceptions, but rather from an experience of events in our own life. We have seen many poses, many situations in life, and one glance at a new posed picture will tell us the entire story. If we see a Norman Rockwell picture we can quickly extend the moment of frozen history into its past, and also predict its future. Picasso's "Guernica" shows us distorted scenes which depict in a literal way the horrors of bombing, a slice out of experience, full-blown into a terrifying vision, obviously having the most meaning for someone who himself has gone through a frightening bombing raid.

But there are other types of literalnesses, depending on your experiences. If you are a painter you can look at the drippings of Jackson Pollock and see labyrinthine rhythms and also sense a nonbrushed mode of making pictures. As faces are compared, so any new scene is compared with similar ones out of your past, even if they are esoteric ones that reside on canvases seen in a museum. We are apt to project an emotion on any given picture due to the associations it may evoke. This makes an explicit artistic communication difficult because it is difficult to surmount those images which we bring, as well as their emotions—emotions which may not be what the artist desired to evoke.

The historical fact is, however, that the majority of pictures have used recognizable images. Seldom are the recognizable images of painting as photographically equivalent to our eye's optical rendition of reality as the lay observer might suppose; only since the Renaissance in fact has the standard of the eye's window been applied to art. Étienne Gilson's brilliant discussion of imitation and creation in his *Painting and Reality*[3] traces the ever-evolving meaning of visual reality for a painter. Prior to the Renaissance the reality of optical vision was less important because the pictorial idea could be derived from whatever familiar object was at hand, and sufficiently interesting or important to inspire an artist. Modern abstract painting has turned back to the use of the ordinary as material for successful painting, going further toward the ordinary to give up the realistic image completely. When literalness is abandoned, humanity is not being left behind, but instead the artist is concerning himself with humanity in a different mode of being than can be expressed by the eye as an optical camera.

2

The reality of the visual arts is almost as tangible as our own experiential reality: the picture traps a certain vitality within its physical confines which we are apt to confuse with physical reality in a visual form. The visual, living, and animated form in art, carried to its logical extreme in the motion picture, can be more real than life, especially when magnified in size, intensified in color, or made active in movement or depth. The realism of a good portrait or a suggestive landscape can be somehow more impressive than the person or the actual view in reality. The illusion of art can amaze and confound us when it is extremely vivid, and it is humanly understandable how realism can be valued for itself, as most virtuosity deserves our admiration.

It is important, however, to distinguish our emotional reaction to virtuosity from that due to a creative communication of visual insights. The *ne plus ultra* of realism is to create a vision greater than life itself, and a vitality transcending reality which has an organic vitality of its own. Susanne Langer likens the organic quality or living form of art to life itself, suggesting that we value its interrelationship of elements, the rhythmic processes and order, because it is symbolic of life and analogically meaningful.[4] Organisms, however, have a vitality which interacts with their environment, and unless you carry art to the point of using an electric eye to build a feedback loop so that it will react more meaningfully—say in a work of kinetic sculpture—it can never be truly organic like life. You can go to the creation of sculpturesque robots too, and make them lifelike in all ways, limited only by your technology—but is this symbolic of organic vitality and therefore containing artistic import? The living quality of art which Langer recognized, the organic interrelationships she perceived, lies in an interaction of encoding elements, whose value is not in its analogy to life, I think, but in its ability to function as a perceptual articulation for our communicative edification. This is considerably different and more than saying that the symbolic quality of organic forms in art appears like or corresponds to human living form, to our human, sentient world of feeling. Instead of being a *reflection* of human life, art is a *building* of human life, whose communicative exchange establishes a perceptual awareness to build and expand our humanness.

The Spanish philosopher Ortega y Gasset wrote that the modern artist has dehumanized art by taking out images of living forms, or by distorting them beyond recognition.[5] He tells the story of the romantic Englishman who falls in love with Leonardo's "Gioconda," and finds it hard to imagine anyone falling in love with one of Picasso's twisted-faced women. He thinks that the lack of human intercourse in the world of art has thrown art into an unintelligible realm beyond the capabilities of the human being to understand and appreciate. This denial of representation in some modern painting is, instead of being a change of heart on the part of the artist, a new emphasis which makes our vision see a new world. Naturally if you are not familiar with the codes of modern art you do not comprehend the communications they effect. Of course it is not possible to fall in love with a Picasso painting, because it is not a woman—any more than Leonardo's painting is. A different kind of love is possible, however, if you can sense the creativity of the communication and react to it with an emotion of joy. It will make you richer for the experience, whereas love of a picture of a woman can only make you nostalgic, or perhaps release a certain old anxiety in your heart.

Naturally art can suggest some romantic period in your own life—for instance, I cannot hear Tchaikovsky's Pathétique symphony without recalling quite agreeably a certain vivacious redhead I knew in college; nor can I see Giotto without being reminded with intense pleasure of the trip my wife and I made to the Scrovegni Chapel in Padua. But obviously art should be more than just an elaborate mnemonic. And it should no more remind you of certain experiences than it should remind you of a particular experience called Life: it should only remind you of itself, and in doing so, it should give you an awareness of something which is vital and meaningful *to* life in the very act of its perception.

3

The problem of how we visually intuit shape and form and color must be solved before it is possible to justify their being used as encoding elements in the visual arts. The meaning of visual form and how the human mind evolves its perceptual reality is essentially a physiological-psychological problem. Rudolph Arnheim in his great book *Art and Visual Percep-*

tion[6] has presented convincing and detailed arguments to substantiate the belief that we actually do *learn* how to perceive all visual shapes. Using gestalt concepts Arnheim shows how impressions which have built themselves in our mind's eye do so through a slowly evolving perceptual exposure. Arnheim then goes on to discuss in detail how these visual elements are used to achieve balance, shape, form, growth, space, light, color, movement, and tension. He does not, however, give an adequate explanation of the possible creative relationships which might exist between the important qualities of our visual world, nor does he suggest how they could be given greater human importance than that of a visual reality in which we function. About as close as he gets to establishing any criteria for art is summed up in this sentence: "The mature work of art succeeds in subjecting everything to a dominant law of structure."[7] I feel that it should be possible to go deeper into an understanding of the creativity of formal elements of art and into their explicit value for us as humans, especially because of Arnheim's work itself. What is this "law of structure" in the arts, and how does it have meaning to us when it commands a work of art?

Walter Pitts and W. S. McCulloch have investigated and theorized about the way in which the human brain knows the universals of auditory and visual forms[8]—those common qualities of shapes or of sounds by which we can distinguish the one from the other. A square, for instance, is recognized because of the fact that all squares we might see have one universal in common: the diagonals through the four corners. As Langer has pointed out, however, it is not enough to explain how we form universals, without also explaining how we *know* them.[9] A mathematical description of how some mechanism in the brain recognizes universals could be meaningful for a computer; but for the human, the omissions are the other human responses which may accompany universals. Langer says that it is the *feeling* which is missing from this analysis, but I would suggest that it lacks a clarification of how we use universals for perceptual building, in the frame of our entire intellectual-emotional history.

New shapes are perceived by virtue of our mentally established universals, rationalized in terms of the various elements which the brain as a data processor can single out. But these *new* shapes also establish themselves in our brain and set a new structural standard for the formation of future universals. Given a piece of sculpture by Noguchi, or a handsome Japanese ceramic vase—or a poetic couplet, sonata, or an opera—we react immediately, and if it is sufficiently original in its form, and we are correctly prepared, we grasp it in its entirety as a new universal by which we can measure future unusual forms.

Arnheim suggests that the act of perception by a person is a creative act; that everyman's eye-mind sight anticipates the creativity of the artist; and that the creativity is in the ability to accept and grasp this new vision.[10] John Dewey has also generalized this creativity and written that it is one of the highest integrative acts that the human can perform.[11] I think that this view is carrying creativity too far. To the extent that a person can grasp an artistic meaning that is creative he is exhibiting unusual powers, but this is quite a bit different from originating the insights that we call creative.

The effect of our evolving mental equipment by which we establish universals is more complex than we imagine, providing us with universals of many different types: myths, heroes, folk melodies, special relationships, shapes, dances—archetypes of many descriptions which embrace our entire social and artistic experience. While we have to begin somewhere, especially if we want to discover a model for its description, we must realize that all such models would be vastly oversimplified. The question occurs if there is a limit to our brain's ability to establish more and more universals. Norbert Wiener fears that we may already have exceeded the serviceable degree of complication in the cortex of the human brain,[12] and that we are leading ourselves to human extinction. I feel, however, that the brain's infinite abilities to abstract, to pile abstraction on abstraction, and its ability to encode, are its saving graces, built-in mechanisms which prevent a saturation of the cortex. This will save us as perpetual observers of the universal scene— if we continue to allow ourselves the option.

4

In addition to associative form which suggests previous shapes or events, the visual arts can communicate form which is immediately fascinating to the beholder. Like music the visual space can articulate similar categories of experience such as succession, anticipation, fulfillment, suspense, or consummated expectation—but the message is displayed in space, and the imports are received not in time but simultaneously (although perhaps accurately sorted out only in time with repeated viewings). Color also contains many elements for the communication of relationships and sensations. How can these abstract shapes and tones of color and suggestion of direction and space affect a creative communication?

Chess masters or mathematicians have often expressed the idea that their disciplines were akin to the aesthetic operations of art. When they contemplate a good move, or follow a mathematical proof, they discover that it is easily likened to the perception of art—usually they would say that it is like listening to a Mozart symphony or looking at an artistic painting. When they follow a chess game, or do a mathematical proof, they are reenacting a situation which is a creative insight into chess or mathematics—it is usually the imaginative chess moves or mathematical discoveries which give this feeling. The logic of the game of chess has many imaginative contingencies, and mathematics too is unbounded in its terms and creative relationships. The "eureka" feeling accompanies chess masters, mathematicians, creative scientists—and artists. The extra feeling of the arts is that their explication is immediately obvious in sensual, perceptual terms, which can be intuited without the need of formal knowledge—other than naturally developed conditioning to the normal gamut of human universals. This gamut is a growing thing, instead of the static spectacle which Kant assumed to color all experience. Unlike chess, the insights of art are frozen in the medium; unlike mathematics, these insights are directly sensed (or brought into being as shadows of sensations via the printed or spoken word). Mathematics suggests no equivalent sensation, unless it is applied mathematics (or constructed—made sensual.) Art has the feature that it is so fundamental to our perceptual fabric that it can supplement, extend, proliferate it, and grow a more extensive human reality for man to experience. Mathematics can proliferate our symbolic world, but it does not build a humanness in the sense of creating a world in which our emotions can range if they so desire. This is the difference, I think, between a symbol and a work of art—the symbol is a carrier, the work of art a builder. The warp and weft of the materials of art allow us to play the bead game of perceptual experience on which the design of our human experience can be hung, much as Herman Hess conceived in his great philosophical novel, *The Bead Game*.[13] Art is creative when the design builds a sensual experience which reveals something to us of its formal, logical, or conventional use.

The creativity of the pictorial art space is intuited, but it is unambiguous and revealing, just as a mathematical insight is revealing although of less importance to us in our moral lives. Ambiguity resolved, uncertainty resolved, as Leonard B. Meyer suggests,[14] is insufficient explanation, I think, for human creativity. There is no ambiguity in a mathematical discovery and there is also none in a great work of art. Ambiguous elements may be a part of art, as when contrary elements are used; but if the art succeeds, it resolves itself in a new creative relationship which is far from being ambiguous—ambiguity is exchanged for creativity. We actually experience cortical forces when we look at a black dot that is not exactly in the center of a rectangle of white; forces which, as Arnheim noted, desire us to restore the dot back to the center.[15] With a simple dot the forces are elementary, but they become very complex for a more highly varied picture. The discoveries of Edwin Land in color perception also suggest that colors cause a distribution of cortical forces which influence one another, to establish the mechanisms whereby we perceive different colors in a given scene.[16] This does not mean to suggest that we prefer either a simple dot or a complex cortical distribution—they are merely different phenomena of our visual system, to which we react in different ways. Superiority in art does not derive from complexity, as we have shown, rather from a revelation of new relationships, which may or may not be simple or complex.

The dot, in arrays or patterns, begins the repertory of elementary visual encoding devices for the visual artist. A small dot is a halt of time because it is done instantaneously, welding itself to space at the same instant because it is localized. Read symbolically a dot is life itself, a unit of existence, caught in the web of infinite space. As with all visual elements, the dot represents itself, however, unless we read the general into it; and it encodes but a discrete halt for the eye, an arresting of vision's force in a momentary pool of calm. It is usually a diminutive circle, but it can grow into a form with a definite shape. The mind has a tendency to turn the trails of force which successive dots establish into lines, generated in our mind due to its closure principle. The line, an ongoing dot, the locus, as geometricians would say, of a dot in motion, is an indication of motion, pure decision rampant in time. The onward moving line can also be directional and varying, thick or thin, broken or solid, stippled or striking, etchy or smooth. A line is a pure directionality and a one-dimensional continuum which can delve into deep space to fabricate novel form.

That line alone can support a creative communication justifies all art and attests to the power of the human mind to apotheosize even the most elemental of sensual means. The etchings of Rembrandt, the lithographs of Goya, the fantasies of Klee, the abstractions of Kandinsky, these indicate the power and value of line. Like an unaccompanied violin tone, the line carves out a form which we can value, whether it uses encodings that we accept literally, or builds forms whose abstraction contains vestiges of human meaning which we sense but cannot justify in words. Poetry, drama, or music seems most able to engender a "cutaneous shiver" of appreciation, as William James calls it,[17] but the visual arts can also affect violent emotions of insight and value when we view them at their best.

My illustrations in this book try to create such a humanly meaningful abstraction, in a limited and simple form. I use suspenses of movement, directional varieties, contrasts and balances, sometimes proliferating into activity or dying in pools of dots. They are at best virtuoso products of my humanity caught in visual form. The juncture dot, a variable and necessary thing, relates these movements by a periodic contingency which is striving for a new aspect that evolves, hopefully, into novelty before your eyes. One would not think that Picasso's original idea in his visual introduction to Balzac's *Unknown Masterpiece* could be developed to this extent. After some ten notebooks, hundreds of such schemas, I am still amazed to discover fresh surprises flowing from my pen when I sit down at my drawing board to create more of them.

The novelty or the revelation of unexpected new relationships between the forms of movement and the plasticity of space, which is achievable with line, includes an articulation of volume or space. Chaotic lines no longer reside on a surface, but they delve into a deep space and call out a new order when we can recognize it—and we can only recognize it by looking and letting the order slowly creep into our consciousness. The line can weave a synthesis of static form and motion which expresses an interrupted agitation much as poetic metaphors can contradict themselves to bring forth a new sense of reality. I am not only stating my belief when I attest to the power of pure line, I am echoing what artists and viewers have felt at least since prehistoric Magdalenian times. There is nothing mystical about the magic of line since it hides nothing and only a little training is required to reach an appreciation at a rather high level of understanding—its simplicity is its virtue. Many people prefer graphics to more complex art forms. Its creativity may escape analysis, but its fascination is undeniable.

Creativity can come from many sources. The ambiguity of contour which a line delineates on a page, for instance, makes it susceptible to different interpretations, as when it carves out one particular shape to the right, which, by virtue of a shared boundary, is related to the new shape to the left. This negative-positive relationship is complementary and yet ambiguous—from which a successful form could derive a creative visual statement. The rhythmic element in a line (or in a series of lines between which a periodic space is generated) could pull the eye along to a new understanding of space itself, realized in a more conscious and obvious element which is related but sufficiently novel that we do not expect it. Rhythm can be a periodicity of direction, a space movement, a multiplication of forms that are similar, or an actual weaving within the width itself. These are only a few of the creative potentials of line. Consulting a good book on drawing like Harold Speed's *The Practice and Science of Drawing*[18] can reveal many more which space does not permit me to enumerate. The illustrations should suffice to define some of the creative possibilities of lines and dots.

After the linear quality we can consider that the surface on which it is displayed can be smooth or rough—and texture is the next logical consideration. Texture can be obvious or subtle, and it can be emphasized, as when a collage supports a line drawing, or it can be ignored. The plastic qualities of the medium which is used to emphasize texture are now obvious, and going from a line to a more complex picture, this plastic quality can assume a new dominance. A brush stroke communicates the delicate movements of an artist in his studio, and a drip the more bold motions of a man astride a painting on the floor—the one is feminine and the other masculine by contrast, although they need not be so in themselves. The strokes of a brush can complement the shapes by working them out, or they can oppose the shapes like the texture of a canvas, going their own merry way.

The idea which fascinated Cézanne was that an obvious brush stroke emphasized the picture plane and made it clear that this was not a photograph, not an attempt to be realistic in the optical way of the eye. This was actually the beginning of intellectual pictorial abstraction, not his famous cube, cylinder, and pyramid. The simple delving into natural forms which, for instance, Turner has evolved, sometimes so moody and vague that we might call it abstract, is a different intellectual goal than that of the abstraction urge of Cézanne. The modern change of view from the single one of the Renaissance to the multiple, cubistic and finally completely nonobjective one, is a more profound change than Turner's simple experiments in capturing a mood of reality with his eye. It reflects our evolving complexity of communication, as initially stimulated by the the photograph, and it suggests difficulties which we have not yet resolved. The artist has long since passed through the early stages of multiple views, but the public is only today catching up with him in his modern technical conveniences, namely television and the newspaper which juxtapose the most unrelated ideas as if it were most natural.[19] Present-day art, if it is to be viable and of importance in the future, must be a more highly articulated multifaceted vision than any we know today, paving the way for our delayed educational reaction to our age and to the exegesis of past art.

When texture is carried too far, or when the plane of a picture is broken, as in the recent "primary structures" that give us irregular, but geometric shapes, there is introduced a new set of reactions from which encoding can be evolved. Unfortunately the primary structures are extremely sterile drawing-board designs blown up to an unmanageable size—the only impressive thing about them. Their originality is seriously lacking because the arbitrariness of their shape comes only from a simple color plane out of which it sometimes grows. In the hands

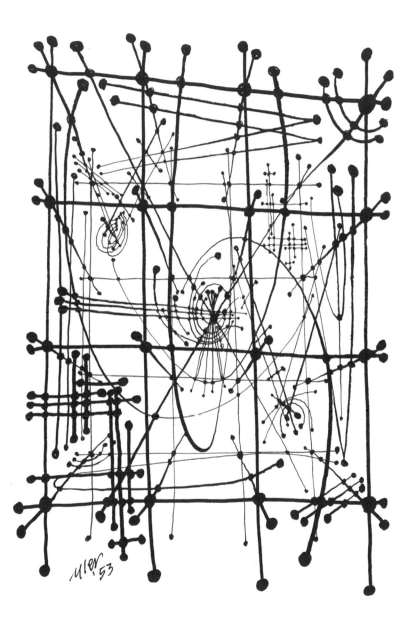

of a good sculptor (and they are essentially sculpturesque rather than paintings that have gone astray), the results can be stimulating, as for instance the work of Anthony Caro. This idea is not new since Gabo led the way early in this century. Depth, which was previously an illusion, now becomes a reality. We are on the threshold of sculpture, but maintained in a picture world by virtue of a wall, or by virtue of the suggestion of a boundary which cannot be transcended by our own movement (within limits). The encoding becomes slowly ambiguous due to the position of the observer, and he is let in on the communication in stages, the introduction of an element of time in a purely stable plastic medium. Of course the Futurists and Duchamp attempted this sequence-encoding by spreading the same image over a canvas in different, interlocking poses, similar to the way in which medieval artists depicted motion or change. The sequence of a relief is less determined, however, because you can change your place in front of it at will, giving the viewer some choice.

Jumping then from the flat we must first hit the cylinder, first a scroll painting which puts us inside the cylinder, and then a relief carving around a dias or other article that is curved. This many-sided possibility of flat form is in itself actually a creative insight into the use of form, albeit a technical one, and it represents a significant jump for the primitive artist. Sculpture at last arrives and it is a little closer to the reality to which we are conditioned with our two eyes, possessing as it does a depth and also a discrete form—which used to be heightened by brilliant-colored painting. The illusion of sculpture is less than that of painting, because it is actually formed for us and we no longer have to transform a flat surface into a space by noting perspective or other clues. Pictures seem so artificial because they need a wall; sculpture fits into our rooms much as we do; a picture tries to trick you into believing that it is a window, but a sculpture does not even hide its marbleness or metallic quality. Being so close to our reality then, a work of sculpture is most readily accepted when it is similar to forms which we see in our own reality. A distorted figure is less bothersome in a painting than a distorted figure in sculpture. It takes considerable visual understanding to learn to appreciate and love Henry Moore's sculptures of highly abstracted human forms.

This vitality of sculpture, derived from its closeness to the form which it is trying to suggest, sometimes limits the potential of sculpting—which is perhaps why sculptors have given up painting their productions (unless they are puppeteers and wish to exploit this literal quality in their forms). Marisol, on the other hand, paints most of her figures because she is playing on this very literalness which disturbs us—she is trying to disturb us about our attitudes in many respects, not only with regard to our own humanness, which she is questioning at its roots, but also with regard to our fractioned concept of humanness. Who has not looked at a great work of sculpture and questioned the validity of his own plastic vision? Giacometti gives us a deathlike reality he peoples with parodies of humans, only reluctantly colored, as is all humanity, combining to give us a surrealistic vision of man that emphasizes his other-worldly depravity.

An intuited shape is encoded by itself—it is a new universal for the brain. It is like the pleasant design of a good automobile, or the graceful handle of a knife. The pure aesthetic pleasure of good design is not accountable in terms of recognition or past sculpturesque reminiscences; it is rather the result of an intuitive sense of appropriateness which the artist has created out of all forms to contribute a new slim dimension to the world of our looking (and feeling, if we can grasp that form). Although a shape in a picture may not be a designer's dream, we intuit it and judge it with respect to all other shapes in the picture, and we try to size it up as a creative addition to all other shapes we have ever seen.

The globular shapes of a sculptor like Jean Arp are extremely pure examples of the creative possibilities of using massive form in unusual shapes by themselves. The mind intuitively observes an Arp shape and knows from many encodings, like its smooth texture, the elongated or extruded volume, that it is nothing in nature. Henry Moore, on the other hand, seems to create forms that are part of nature, "rolled round by nature's force," as Kenneth Clark quotes Wordsworth.[20]

A resemblance to the sculpturesque human being is the traditional area of concern for the sculptor. He usually has put the human in a natural pose, and any partings or holes in the work like the hole under an arm on the hip, are not particularly important or novel. It was necessary that the figure grow abstract before a hole could take on new sculpturesque meaning, as they did in Henry Moore's sculpture. Michelangelo contained the power of a mythical human being in solid granite, and in a massive proportion appropriate to his concept of the human being's powerful qualities. Painting the same form did not suffice for the encoding of strength he desired, as witness the fact that his paintings are merely sculptures rendered as plans for work to come.

The potential for the literal use of the human figure is more than we would suspect, as Kenneth Clark's *The Nude*[21] suggests. Yet an abstract form in sculpture is also quite easy to accept—we are used to many abstract forms, and even to organic abstract forms, living as we do all of our lives with, for instance, trees. It is most easy for us to accept Alexander Calder's mobiles, especially when their forms twitter like trees and plants, or bend and spin with the wind. It is quite easy to respond to the suggestions of movement in kinetic sculpture, since it immediately suggests something organic or natural. This is of course not a necessity of sculpture, which can support completely pure abstraction as well.

When the sculptor Jean Tinguely creates an object we are not always reminded of things, especially when he adds paper which it proceeds to articulate as a drawing before our eyes— we are aghast to think that it could even vaguely resemble a painter at his drawing board, and therefore do not dare make the jump in our mind to this conception—or do we? The inspiration of Tinguely is to suggest a connection between a mobile sculpture and a drawing; and his famous "self-consuming" machine has possibilities for parody which are by definition lost.

The electric era in which we live will no doubt see many other similar attempts to weld seemingly inappropriate arts together, probably to an extent that would cause Richard Wagner to blush. We live in a gimmicky period of art, comparable in painting perhaps to that period in the history of dance when the idea of lifting a dancer off the floor first became popular, suggesting ethereality. As this idea intoxicated choreographers to use levers and wires to lift their delicate ballerinas into the air, so modern media and technical innovations are obviously intoxicating the modern artist.

Nowhere is the gimmicky inclination of a modern fabricator more rampant than in the building of buildings. The architect has discovered for the first time in his history that his materials need not limit his imagination. Modern materials and construction methods take the craftsman, whose materials used to dictate the form of his art, and turn him into a typically romantic artist. Practically, however, due to the restrictions of clients, the demands of society, the need to fit a new building into an overbuilt area (as if he had to fit diamonds into clay mosaics), the true artistic creativity of most practicing architects is limited. The visionary architect becomes largely a visual artist whose creations are renderings on paper or sculpturesque models. If they could learn to apply the intricate and highly refined printed-circuit etching techniques, or perhaps a photochemical reduction process, to large physical scales, making it possible to etch or develop an architectural structure directly from plans or renderings, architects would be relieved of the problems of the builder.

The truly new creative architectural construction comes to physical fruition only rarely. And when it does, as for example in the Louis Sullivan-Frank Lloyd Wright progression, it is generally a cumulative and collaborative thing. The architect is more intimately connected with society than most artists, and this, combined with his need for a solid technology, restricts his creativity. The greater structures, complexes of cities which have become a megalopolis, will require that the architectural imagination operate on an even larger scale in the future. No doubt his creativity will continue to be restricted to projects on paper and to models, except perhaps when we land on the moon or a planet and the government awards individual contracts for total cities. We can conceive of the prefabricated marine city of the Japanese architect Kiyonori Kikutake floating around in the Atlantic or the Pacific, but Noriaki Kurokawa's wall or helix cities[22] are too colossal economically to imagine on earth—unless some natural or unnatural holocaust (or city planner) devastates the cities we already have.

The complete artistic meaning of gigantic structures would require not only that man live in them, but that he also be able to fly over them, see them as total complexes and sculpturesque forms (as the models can be seen). This is getting close to the fanciful idea of McLuhan's of the total earth as a work of art[23]—the entire earth articulated by architecture—which could only be appreciated from a satellite, spaceship, or the moon. To articulate an asteroid in this way is not inconceivable, and the landed gentry of the future—or the architecture-school projects of the future—will undoubtedly build spherical residences which can be orbited at leisure in any atmosphere in the solar system.

Our electric environment has shifted our principal world, as McLuhan suggests, from a single point—the vanishing point of the Renaissance, or the visual point of the Gutenberg printed surface—to the multiple, simultaneity of disconnected communications. Accordingly art is outmoded when it insists on presenting only the eye's view. Cézanne and Picasso brought in the multiple views of touch along with the simultaneous visual qualities, and contemporary media mixtures have been forcing the complexity of artistic encoding levels to the breaking point. Paintings and sculpture no longer satisfy the forward-looking mind when they emphasize vision as a single optical view; the rational, single-position painting is falling to the multidimensional, irrational, and more communicatively rich images that transcend the literary.

These and other visual encoding possibilities in art are summarized in Table IV.

TABLE IV—LEVELS OF VISUAL ENCODING

1. FACT OF WORK OF ART WITH VISUAL INTENT, created by a human being
2. INTUITED SHAPES (pure perceived forms)
    a. Line (in variety, rhythm, and space)
    b. Mass (in variety, rhythm, and space)
    c. Optics of form-sensing (optical illusions, dual or multiple visual intent)
3. INTUITED COLOR (communicates itself)
    a. Harmonies or dissonances (due to eye)
    b. Optics of color (physical and psychological reactions)
4. TEXTURE (tactility due to means of production)
    a. Shallow (media qualities, surface qualities)
    b. Deep (means of production, added materials, surface destruction)
5. SCULPTURE
    a. Material of medium
    b. Many-sidedness (round)
    c. Multiple views (continuous object quality, floating structures)
    d. Movement (mobiles, kinetic sculpture, dance)
    e. Lived-in space (architecture)
6. RECOGNIZABLE FORMS (familiarity with realistic analog)
    a. Spacial arrangements (illusion of depth)
    b. Story (motion pictures, story pictures)
    c. Realistic analog of human concept (dream, symbol)
    d. Archetypal or fantasy (beyond reality, super or supra, new worlds)
    e. Neoclassic (old styles or techniques implicit in new form)

5

The optics of sensing depend to a great extent on our human perceptual mechanisms; dazzling effects can be created which can swamp our visual sensitivities. These effects glorify our physiological appratus, and they emphasize our abilities to perceive with our eyes. We first begin to sense an indication of the limitations of the eye-brain when given an experience which optically confuses us. The ambiguity of optical illusions which makes us think we are seeing motion in something that is obviously static is either disquieting or amusing, but it is not creative unless that motion somehow brings us some new revelation into form. Significantly the modern Op art movement has deemphasized the means of human production by eliminating brush strokes, cutting the boundaries hard, sometimes even silkscreening them ad infinitum. This is no longer an attempt to communicate even in the old sense, but it is rather an attempt to dazzle and exploit natural phenomena which are part of our visual apparatus. The scientific qualities of Op art are an attempt to transcend the human and reach a new level of order that exceeds human comprehension—although it allows man to sense it at the same time—which is a noble aspiration to say the least.

The perceptual tenet of abstraction which William C. Seitz elucidated in his brochure for the Op art show at the Museum of Modern Art in 1965, entitled *The Responsive Eye*,[24] states that the purpose of Op art is to fool the brain—a *trompe l'esprit*, I would call it. This would suggest, it seems to me, that creativity is no longer the point of Op art. I do not think that some of the older and more accomplished artists using optical phenomena would agree with Seitz. Victor Vasarely, for instance, uses optical phenomena, but he can hardly be accused of sticking strictly to the tenet of optical attempts to fool the brain. When the emphasis of the illusion is on fooling by means of a visual ambiguity, then a superficial eye-dazzling quality keeps the viewer at one boring level of perception. Josef Albers himself has spent years, first at the Bauhaus and then at Yale, delving exclusively into the relationships of gently colored squares, expanding our awareness of simple combinatorial areas whose color relations are extremely subtle.

Pure color combinations can become creative only when they transcend the science that supports them, just as a harmonious chord loses its meaning when isolated. To assume that optical illusions or physiological perception tricks are sufficient to make art is the same as thinking that perfect fifths or triads alone make music. Surely the musician can discover single chords— or electronic beat situations—which would be analogous to the ear as an optical illusion is to the eye, but if he did so he would call it music only if it transcended this impressive quality which would momentarily block the ear or flood our brains with dazzling tone. These tricks are as literal in their way as physiological science is in its presentation of perceptual models to illustrate some phenomena, although they are symbols of themselves.

It is not so difficult to imagine how these tricks could be used validly in art. The optical illusion is like a pun, having a dual or multilevel meaning, and like the pun or play on words, it could be a bringing together of two visual ideas, the origination of a newly creative ambiguity. But to use this idea, of conjoining images as Yaacov Agam did in "Double Metamorphosis II," which is but two paintings brought together on diagonal slots like signs which change back and forth, two paintings which are unrelated and both uninteresting, is to miss the point and to fail to exploit an idea with great possibilities. Some optical artists also place lenticular screens over their pictures to give a shimmering effect and a change of image as the viewer moves, again done so arbitrarily as to lose meaning and value. The only fascination with this and most optical art is in walking by and being amused by the visual change, since change of this nature is not generally expected in static pictures.

When optical illusions are used in pictures which also have recognizable objects in them, they appear very disquieting since we are not accustomed to a mad visual logic combined with a common-sense reality. Gombrich illustrates medieval pictures using a double logic which sometimes leads you up, and sometimes inconsistently down again, as well as other pictures in which foreground people touch background people in impossible ways.[25] These are fun to look at, but seldom artistically rewarding.

A brief survey of the possible perceptual phenomena which science has uncovered indicates that the optical artists have barely tapped the source.[26] Optical illusions can create apparent movement, a depth ambiguity, an eye-dazzling effect, or a perceptual confusion. Time, movement, and causality can be affected by sagacious use of these phenomena (which is the principle of the motion picture). The motion picture is the one case in which an optical phenomenon has been given valid technical development to bring it to the point where it can take on artistic meaning. Do the other tricks of the eye and brain lack but a sufficient technical development for their true realization in some type of valid art form? Consider the moiré pattern, for instance. When grids of repeated lines are superimposed one over the other, they cross at new points and interfere in such a way that a new pattern is generated, depending on the periodicity ratio between the two original

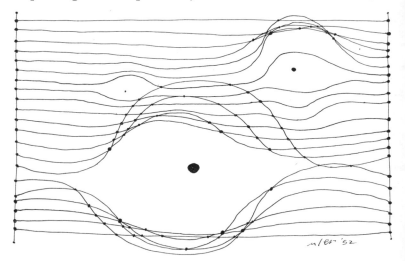

patterns. We sense moiré patterns within our brain also, for instance, when we look at a series of close-spaced concentric circles or a small continuous spiral, due to the fact that the lines impress themselves on our retina and persist, but clash with themselves due to the minute "saccadic" movements which our eye naturally makes all the time (a subconscious moiré effect). This reaction is brought into play in art when parallel lines are used, which in most art is frequent. It is particularly well illustrated by some of the schema in this book, often using fields of parallel lines. But the most impressive illustration of this phenomenon is the fireworks display. We see the plumes of fire, and match them in a more direct way with a successive differently colored bursting plume. But fireworks are of course a more literal kind of visual music since they occur in time much like a nonobjective movie. All our reactions are keyed to the train of events which begins by the initially observed trail of sputtering orange fire from the point of origin on the ground. We hear the *v-room* or the propulsion, and our expectations are initiated; and finally we are rewarded with an almost instantaneous burst of multicolored fire-flowered moiré patterns, spreading broadly in a flashing circle of a many-fingered filigree over a vast expanse of ink-blue darkness; sometimes in multiple or delayed bursts that echo each other; or embellished with little spirals or plumes of twittering colors; finally climaxed with the almost deafening termination explosion and flash that lights up the sky like day. This magnificent perception is never tiring. If the Japanese ever learn to evoke great chords of sound as harmonious to the ear as the flashes of flame are to the eye, coupling them with their fireworks, it would be an artistic and emotional experience which few other abstract arts would be able to match.

Dr. Gerald Oster has studied the mathematics of moiré patterns very carefully, and he has also tried to exploit them artistically by creating circular and linear multilevel pictures which he has exhibited at the Howard Wise Gallery in New York City. Oster also recently presented a series of pictures at this gallery which purported to show the view we see when our eyes are closed. An early draft of this book suggested that rubbing the eyes causes swirls of interesting patterns which might have interesting artistic possibilities—a phenomenon I used to experiment with as a boy, even though the slight pressure to the closed eye eventually causes severe pain just about when the designs become the most interesting. Although his visions do not look like mine, Oster claims to have isolated his swirls, and he paints them and calls them *phosphemes*. Another well-known trick causes these swirls to be manifest in the eye, namely that of using a bright flickering light that is projected onto the closed eyelids at about six to ten flicks per second (although I also sensed nontwirling patterns when I recently tried this). This is related to the alpha rhythm of the brain, and it will induce an epileptic fit in some people.[27] The afterimage, which is due to astigmatic vision or to an eye with color aberration, can also present the illusion of depth in a picture. If you look at a map with a small line of red marching over a vivid green or blue country, it sometimes appears to float out over that color. This is due to the fact that the eye has a chromatic aberration, causing the colors to focus at different points before or behind the surface of the retina. One of Marcel Duchamp's experiments exploited this fact back in 1935, his previously mentioned Rotorelief,[28] and also a filmed attempt to create depth, his *Anemic Cinema*, shot by Man Ray in 1924. This artistic giant who out-opped the Op artists years ago put a disc of clashing complementary colors that defined a form onto a rotating device; when rotated, the object would jump up in total relief before your eyes.

Three-dimensionality is one of those optical phenomena which we have long known about and which no artist has ever actually exploited to best advantage. Perhaps only in the marvelous antique photographic stereopticon views do we ever get a hint of the potential of 3-D. Here is an area which top artists (topological, or primary-structure artists) may well investigate. Modern lenticular lens grids have eliminated the need for glasses like those used during the Hollywood movie craze that used crossed Polaroid polarizing filters to single out the right and left images. Once when I was attending one of these early 3-D movies an interesting thing happened which conceivably could be important artistically: the right eye got out of synchronism with the left! Not only did the images repeat themselves in a curious way, as when a person picked up a glass and then a moment later did the same thing again, but also the two color patterns intermingled and gave unusual color combinations.

I have tried on occasion to apply three-dimensionality to my schema, but the effect was hardly worth the effort, I think. As could be expected, the master of technical artistic trickery, Duchamp, also tried to draw a stereo picture, his "Hand Stereoscopy" of 1918.[29] Stereoscopic pictures may be an apt gimmick for a Dadaist or a Pop artist. I can imagine a Pop art show of dual images, silk-screened in red and green for the separation, like the comic strips used a few years ago, and a gallery director presenting pairs of green-red cellophane glasses to the gallery-goers so that they could plunge into the thrilling 3 D Pop-Comic art! Beyond this we have yet to see optical three-dimensionality used well in serious art.

6

The most successful Op artists are those who use pure color effects, deriving their interest from the clashes and contrasts which are notoriously part of all color-combining. My half namesake George Mueller (whom I do not know) has very successfully used color in optical paintings. One might think that color has been so long in the province of the artist that he would have completely exhausted its potential. The fact remains, however, that the simplest of perceptual mechanisms can sometimes be the most powerful, and potentially the richest for creative manipulation. Color, I think, is such a powerful and potentially creative phenomenon. It can be ornamental, as in many primitive pictures, or it can be representative, as in the traditional schools of painting. The Venetians used color as a substitute for what the Florentines achieved by line, growing their form in color masses rather than tinting line drawings to an appropriate shade. The idea of using color as a pure form grew in importance until the Impressionists used it almost as an end in itself. Gauguin had a mystical attitude toward color, and Monet spent many dedicated hours in intricate color experiments. Aided by their contemporary scientific theorists, the impressionists concentrated on the perceptual possibilities for creating color and exploiting color effects. Modern artists have begun to realize that color has a direct abstract use, in the sense of establishing precise and structurally perfect relationships to which the eye reacts quite naturally.

The relationships of color tones are not as tightly bound, of course, as the relationship of sounds, mainly because of the differences between the eye and the ear as receptors. We have seen how two tones beat together in the nonlinear ear receptor to establish combination tones that build a definite hierarchy of chords. This has led the composer to very explicit laws for harmony and counterpoint in music. Nothing analogous exists in the case of color. Our eye is more perfect than the ear, and because of the nature of light, particularly its point sources, mixing never occurs that can generate related tones that either support or destroy the originals. Nevertheless certain other phenomena which happen when the eye senses color can lead to a rudimentary hierarchy of color combinations—with less obvious artistic value than in the case of sound combinations, itself extremely limited as I have suggested. Every color that strikes the retina of the eye has a chemical effect on what is called the visual purple of the retina, a fluid which pervades the entire surface within our eye. The visual purple absorbs the color impressed on it and turns it slightly toward the opposite or complementary color—so that we see the complement of any color if we look at a white surface quickly after staring at one color for a few minutes. If you look at the complement to a given color instead of white, the visual purple has to make the most extreme about-face in its chemical action, causing the disturbance known as clashing complementaries. We can say then that color complementaries that clash do so because of a chemical action in the eye, and those colors which are adjacent on the color wheel do clash because there is a less extreme chemical action in the eye when the eye shifts from one to the other.

The fact also exists that the visual purple is actually purple, as its name implies; and, being purple, it absorbs yellow-green the most easily. This explains why yellow-green is the lightest-appearing color in the spectrum, and why purple is the heavest. The peak of the spectral response of the eye is in the yellow-green portion of the spectrum, and its minimum is in the purple. Therefore the triad containing yellow, namely yellow-red-blue, is the most intense color combination possible, since triads are somehow strong and since yellow is the strongest. (Why the triad is strong is hard to determine, but some have suggested it may be due to the nature of the eye's receptors for color.) This then can lead to a vague hierarchy of color chords beginning with this triad and descending through larger and larger combinations in a logical way. There have been many attempts to build a theory of color harmony, including a rather thorough one by Arnheim,[30] but none of them is satisfactory to me beyond this simple description. Scientists themselves are not certain how the eye perceives color, and of the effects which colors have on us and on each other; recent experiments by Edwin Land which show that it is possible to recreate all colors, given only two, seem to throw considerable confusion into all the previous tricolor theories of color perception, although some scientists seem to think not.[31]

In any case it is unlikely that a perfect scientific theory of color would be of much use to the artist, since he is less concerned with the how of color perception than he is with the actual effects—and this he can discover himself. The structural relationships of color can be arbitrary, deployed in an almost Schoenbergian color-row way, and we easily learn to accept them and to appreciate them. This is the most cogent way for an artist to exploit color, I think. I spent a solitary year living like Henry James, or Nathaniel Hawthorne before him, in the tower of a Florentine villa, trying to work out a perfect theory of color harmony, equivalent to musical harmony. I had only a superficial knowledge of Helmholtz and Hindemith then, but I realized that there was no physical justification for color harmony; I felt, however, that a personal, intuitive approach might lead me to an artistically viable justification of color theory. I worked out colored wax miniatures, filling notebook after notebook with small nonobjective color images, sometimes twenty to a page. When I found a particularly powerful mosaic of colors I would try to analyze them, then dance around the color ring to see how they worked, using similarly related but different colors.*

The painter has no hierarchy of color combinations, but mixing does occur when light beams of different hues interact—generating instead of a hierarchy as in sound combinations, entirely new colors that are again as autonomous as the originals. Lacking a means to impress a definite structural mode on the viewer through color, and also lacking time as an element in his painting, the visual artist must forever abandon the hope of duplicating music in vision. But if he makes the jump to the abstract motion picture he can build an analog which is interesting if not potentially great. The most famous of these attempts is, of course, Walt Disney's sequence in *Fantasia*, the Bach Toccata and Fugue.

The idea of color music is very old, linking the seven principal colors of the rainbow (ROY G. BIV, as Lieber suggested we remember them[33]) to the seven notes of the diatonic musical scale. Aristotle mentioned the analogy between color and music

---

* From my journals of that time, I now read that I thought I had indeed found a universal theory of color, but I know that it was instead only a very personal feeling toward color. Yet that year's work, during which I made over three hundred small wax paintings and enough oils for my first one-man show in New York City,[32] has established the color tenor of my painting since.

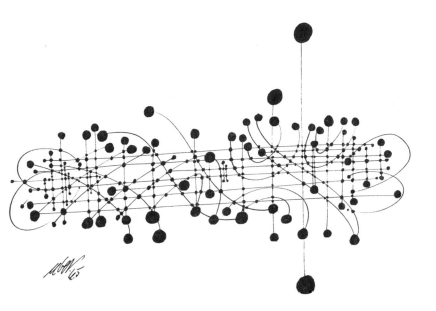

harmony in his *De Sensu*.[34] The French Jesuit Louis Bertrand Castle described the first color piano around 1750, and the idea has popped up now and then ever since.[35] Scriabin, the Russian composer, had what is called *synaesthesia*, a strong color association with musical tones, and he composed "Prometheus: A Poem of Fire," to which an accompanying changing colored light was scored. The Nobel Prize physicist Albert A. Michelson predicted a great future for color music, but to date color music has remained only of marginal interest.

It was soon realized with the development of the color motion picture that such an application was possible, since the motion picture also offered the first chance to present time and motion in an art form other than music which had previously held the monopoly. Artists began to relate color to the sound-track music in a direct way, and although it could exist theoretically as an automonous form, music always supported the abstractions of film. There is a larger body of abstract color film-makers and works than one would suspect; many years ago the Museum of Modern Art in New York City had a series of these films which I chanced to see. The most notable abstract films were created by a German abstract artist and film-maker named Hans Richter (producer of the film *Dreams that Money Can Buy*), who painted slowly on layers of glass, stop-frame photographing the changes as he went along. (He was hired by Disney for work on the abstract sections of *Fantasia*, but I understand all of his sequences went unused in the final version.[36]) Richter and a friend, Viking Eggeling, whose "Rolls," long abstract designs, gave him the idea of abstract film, earlier tried to develop a visual theme in film similar to the sonata form in music. Oscar Fischinger used animated cartooned abstractions in 1929 which were visual accompaniments to standard orchestral compositions. László Moholy-Nagy of the Bauhaus made what he called *Lichtspielen*, or light plays, by casting colored lights over specially shaped objects that were moved by motors.[37] The Dadaists also employed many abstract images in their pictures and demonstrations.[38] The Canadian Norman McLaren drew strips of color on clear 35-mm. acetate which he then projected, and he also experimented with R. E. Lewis with the production of musical sounds by directly drawing the sound track on the film.[39]

Electric images could contribute their particular optical-electronic sensations for artistic use in other ways. For example, it is possible that the infamous use of subliminal images in television could have artistic validity if used shrewdly, as some recent commercials have given hints. Or again, the boundaries of radiation just outside of the visual spectrum could conceivably be captured by a transducer and brought to within our sensual range for other artistic experimentation. Fluorescent paints or electro-optical luminescent colors, or ultraviolet stimulation of fluorescent colors, offer the artists other technical possibilities. The heightened colors which a television tricolor tube can give that are brighter than bright, since the luminosity of color is dependent on the potential of the electron beam which shines on the phosphor, may also be interesting artistically. To imagine a painter using fluorescent paint and displaying his work in a darkroom illuminated solely by ultraviolet light is as far-fetched as it is tasteless, yet it has been tried and must not be discounted as a *possible* art form. However, normal oil colors, used directly in contrasting juxtapositions which emphasize their brilliance, or used with resins or with the new acrylics, allow an extremely wide range of color combinations and color intensities. But they apparently do not satisfy some artists, and perhaps they should not if the artist's creative vision extends into the realm of color. The value of these or all future scientific contributions to color phenomena would lie, of course, in the success which any artistic exploitation of them would demonstrate. As with electronic music, although perhaps slightly more vehemently, we should practice skepticism, yet always keep a ready but cautious eye peeled for potentially exciting results.

7

The most potentially accurate of the visual communicative forms is of course the photograph; it is the culmination of our mechanical age, and the final demonstration of how science can encroach on art. Accuracy—especially mechanical accuracy—does not of course make for creativity, and so the question of most importance in the photographic arts which use a mechanical device, is how it can be original and humanly creative. The camera is mechanical and we might think it is therefore less creatively powerful than other artistic media—but just how mechanical is a camera after all? A camera is part of nature because it is physical, a plastic-metallic-Celluloid-chemical thing; and it uses light itself, also a natural phenomenon. To aim a natural thing at nature, capable of capturing the vivid images of nature in a permanent physical form, is like a fish eating a fish. We must wonder how the simple activation of a mechanical shutter can make the results uniquely human and creative? The images of nature and of life come and go, but a camera can capture and freeze them—the appellation "frozen music" would better apply to photography than to architecture. This capturing of "found images" calls our attention to things we have taken for granted and actually never seen until so frozen in a permanent vision. We all love a photograph, especially of ourselves or a loved one. A good artist with the camera then first of all shows us things which we may have seen again and again, but things which are essentially invisible to our eye until he singles them out and presents them to us for our scrutiny, or he apotheosizes that which we are already fond of seeing. We see humanity, nature, life, more intimately than our unaided eyes are capable of perceiving, in a photograph.

There is a three-dimensional equivalent to this situation in the work of the sculptor George Segal, who has stumbled on an analog to the photographic medium for objects in the round. He pats his friends with plaster-soaked cheesecloth until it sets, and then reassembles the pieces into a figure after "development." We want to catch reality today in all of its dimensionality—perhaps we can guess that our science will ultimately consummate this urge by bringing forth a technical equivalent to Segal's artistic idea; some kind of an optical-chemical device that ends up with a miniature model in complete color after development. The urge of Segal's is to make the "found objects" of nature more vivid; it is a desire to record reality just as the primitive photographer desires to record reality. He often adds natural objects—tables, chairs, playing cards—even fragments of buses. Segal's art is more of a primitive reproductive science than it is a creative communication, but because of our desire to see all things reproduced, because they actually take on a new meaning when they are duplicated and placed in special surroundings like museums, we find them extremely fascinating.

Does the mere capturing of an image, a finding of some part of our visual reality which we have made invisible through overexposure, make the well-exposed image significant enough that we can call it art? Are instant-color Polaroid cameras the ideal visual artists? Certainly photography gives us an instance of one technical device that to all intents and purposes is identical to an art form being carried to perfection—how does it make that art operate after its perfection, and how do we feel about it in turn?

The current feeling about the computer as a helpmate for an artist, and about all potential automated art in general, is an echo of that which was felt along about 1889 when Dr. P. H. Emerson published his book *Naturalistic Photography*.[40] He argued then for the first time that photography could aspire to the condition of art. The machine is always considered the artist's archenemy; mechanical devices are supposed to cause an extremely low entropy imprint on art which drains it of all human significance. The mistake of this reasoning is in assuming that the camera (or the computer, or whatever the mechanical or electrical device may be) is passive, or that is is dominating and uncontrollable. The fact is that the camera no more obscures human needs and expressions than the person who uses it is capable of imagining. The status of the camera as a potential means of creative communication hinges on the fact that an artist can transcend the mechanism behind it, and enter into a new area of visual experience through its glass eye. As Lewis Mumford remarks in *Techniques and Civilization*,[41] it requires that the artist who uses a camera have a "rigorous respect for the limitation of the machine."

A camera encodes more than what the eye sees in all of its naiveté. The camera can be made to encode a larger range of visual experience than one would imagine. Just because historically the camera has been used or envied by painters does not make it their natural enemy. Perhaps it makes the aims of a Renaissance-type painter difficult if not superfluous today, however. The attitude which strives to achieve the eye's optical view to the exclusion of other qualities in a kind of naive realism fails to consider its creative value in art, and it seems to me that it can seldom if ever rise to the level of a meaningful artistic statement. Realism must have something more, and good realists, like Andrew Wyeth or Edwin Dickinson, although painting single-point compositions, add to their view a poetic lyricism or heightened reality which could never be seen in nature. To hinge realism on the technical facility of drawing or skill in manipulating the oil medium seems to me to be a failure in art. The nature which the eye sees, looking as deeply as possible into the available optical phenomena, can best be captured obviously by the camera. However, this is the least creative use to which an artist (even a photographer) can put the natural single-point vision of the world. Its exploitation leads to a science of vision, a science of seeing, a record of historical seeing, in which the optics of life are penetrated and recorded, and as such, the camera is but a tool of science. Photography is capable of perfected *trompe-l'oeil*, but the creative photographer has embarked on a special path that is more rewarding creatively than this obvious pitfall.

The complete realism of magically painted pictures or actual photographs (or any possible realistic addition to the optical arts which science might invent) can bring out the suggestions of a story, or present an archetypal view or a fantastic imagining by using appropriate costumes or constructions in a studio. Realism can also present an echo of an old or neoclassic idea which is revitalized in a contemporary idiom. The means, whatever it is, must be realized, however, by conventional visual artistic encoding devices, and they must bring some creative revelation to bear in a nexus of images or form or idea, before we can justify them in art.

Photography is of course limited even in its desire to be realistic. The human choice is limited in photography, and the photographer must decide what restrictions to accept, and what to try and transcend. The creative photographer must discover how to exceed the found images of his machine, and express human control and discover a new way to use framing, timing, design, mood, and all other devices at his command. Most photography is, however, just an apotheosis that glorifies visual reality, and only frame variations or the emphasizing of shapes through placement do not suffice, I think, for a truly creative work of photographic art. How, then, can the photographer become an artist?

The photographer begins with a camera—but it can be selected from a great many different types, with many different lens possibilities, using many different types of film, from fast to slow, coarse or fine grain, black-and-white to color of many different types. The lighting conditions can be varied from artificial to natural, from conditions of driving rain to moonlight or bright sun. The modern film speeds allow the photographer an extreme latitude of light which he can supplant with flash or strobe light to illuminate small or large areas. The possibilities of double or multiple exposure, hazing or defocusing, contrary lighting, and so on, allow many choices, not to mention the choice of subject, time of day, shutter speed, and many more. Then in the darkroom the photographer can enlarge a segment, select or control different areas, tilt or distort to change perspective or shapes; and while developing he can spot or drip chemicals, rub, dye, or tone, with endless variations. Texture can also be included, either a visual suggestion of texture, or an actual texture of paper or other rough sensitized surface like cloth or wood. The ultimate form of the photographic arts can lead to as many encoding possibilities as exist for any art. In sum, there are sufficient possibilities with the photographic medium to give the artist-photographer all the variety and imaginative images necessary to make a valuable creative communication.

The highest aspiration of photography as an art form is to give us a new perceptual experience which allows us to see with our eyes something we do not in our wildest dreams ever see. This can be accomplished in a gentle way, or it can be done in an exaggeration of vision. Anything can be the subject matter: humans, landscapes, cityscapes, even such frivolous objects as Edward Steichen's tree in all of its seasonal variations, or Alfred Stieglitz's pure clouds, which he called "Equivalents"—equivalent to music.[42] In fact, no scene at all need be used, as when a photographer paints with light—for example in Man Ray's Rayograms, invented by accident in 1921 when an abandoned object cast a shadow on sensitized paper which was inadvertently developed. Carried to its extreme in Lotte Jacobi's darkroom abstractions, they become extremely interesting images, suggestive of deep space and forms that soar in an unfractioned idiom. Her pictures are deliberate shadow images that are precisely controlled by virtuoso hands, and they are as expressive as music or nonobjective painting. These visions are perhaps equivalent to the visual phases of the new landscape of science—only they are not simply orders that are sterile reproductions of a natural order, being generated by a human spirit with an individual vision and broad creativity.

Photography, as a record of experience, can make styles, eras, happenings, catastrophies, or personalities permanent. An artist like Edward Weston who focuses on natural objects has a certain timelessness because those natural objects will always be around and subject to visual inquiry. But unless a picture of either of these types is imbued with some new vision which gives us a creative revelation into form or content when we view it, it will not hold our attention long and neither shall we preserve it long except perhaps for historical (scientific) purposes.

To the extent that photography goes hand in glove with science, at the opening of a new instrument like an electron microscope or a planet-probing satellite, it will naturally reveal new visions for our eyes. The new landscape mentioned in the first chapter and beautifully shown in Gyorgy Kepes's book[43] is quite a revelation to us, but it is not a creative revelation. We are perhaps overwhelmed by the mysteries of nature, and also by its infinite variety; and we can be raised to a very high pitch of excitement by seeing them. We do not, however, experience a growth in our humanness when we perceive nature (except insofar as we respond ourselves as semi-artists and essay to use that vision in art). Pure emotions in our heart are important—and this is what nature does to us in all of its manifestations, but they do not make for art, I think.

The human manipulation of visual forms is not a sentimental desire to be invoked when trying to extol the varieties of life (to which I do not, naturally, deny great meaning). It is significant that Alfred Stieglitz, a creative photographer of the first rank, also valued painting. He introduced the burgeoning new European vision of cubist painters to America with his own new look in photography at his famed 291 Gallery in New York City. He wrote: "Every print I make, even from one negative, is a new experience, a new problem. For, unless I am able to vary—add—I am not interested. There is no mechanicalization, but only photography."[44] The artist-photographer, as with all artists who use machines or artificial aids, transcends the machine. Photography is still an image created by a human's inner eye, however much it relies on a frozen chunk of nature, captured in some automatic device. The importance of an art form cannot be demeaned by the method it uses, only judged by the insight it conceives and captures in permanent form for our visual edification and human enlargement.

8

The "radio theory" of the evolution of abstraction as a significant expression of humanness, which I suggested previously (that the abstracted disembodied sound of radio with which vestiges of humanness is still associated, leads to a further faith in abstraction as a message of humanness), can be supplemented by a line of reasoning derived from the use of visual forms. The invention of a mechanical competitor like photography forced artists to reconsider the nature of representation. Since light has been the main phenomenon by which we have learned about our physical environment, subject matter is easily and naturally associated with visual sensations. Sound generally tells us very little about reality, only perhaps that some large unidentified object is moving across the sky or down the road,

. a crowd is gathering, a bird arguing with a squirrel, . that a great blast occurred off in the distance—hopefully dynamite or an airplane breaking the sound barrier. Even our language, the most communicative of sounds, is meaningless in itself, abstracted and so arbitrary that many different languages and sound patterns have come into use throughout the world. Only one language of sight and one image or visual reality is seen by our eyes at all times, and light is father of them all. If the sun were a source of immense sound energy, then perhaps, as David Pratt suggested,[45] we animals would have exalted sound rather than light, and music would be naturally representational, and painting naturally purely nonrepresentational!

Of course design has long been in existence. We may have exhausted conventional design as pure embellishment, and it may no longer suggest a perceptual phenomenon through which some insight into form can be discovered. Only Leonardo's famous fantastic monsters boded a kind of serious nonrealism which suggested humans, although depraved and distorted ones. Sound is so easily articulated, even when free of the human voice, that it is easy to build up a sufficiently interesting structure with creative possibilities.

Perhaps this delay in exploiting the world of the purely visual abstractions is also due to the fact that our visual world dominates our lives. Realistic objects are part of all our visual experience; and any departure in art is difficult to accept because it is so uncommon to our experience. We are used to realistic sounds getting mixed up, but visual things seldom get broken up, except rarely in a rippling brook or a cracked mirror. It is still quite difficult for people to accept abstraction in the visual realm because of the overwhelming precedence of recognizability. Our most venerable art critics and also some of our contemporary old masters seem to agree that nonobjective art is but a temporary aberration. With what accolades and welcome sighs of relief they greeted the nihilistic Pop art! At last we are back to our normal world of visual truth! Perhaps both Abstract Expressionism or Action painting have discharged their creative energies, but certainly it is foolishness to dismiss the genre of nonrepresentational art as being theoretically sterile and meaningless. This is how the Greeks reacted to the early extravagances of musical instruments, how Peri's contemporaries accepted his innovation of opera. I feel that we are at about the same stage in nonobjective painting or sculpture today that the Italians were when they first gave birth to pure instrumental music without story or singers; or at the point in history when man first realized that his mechanical inventions need not duplicate animal forms, as I mentioned previously.

The visual art forms have not developed larger units like the sonata form in music because of the lack of structural meaning by which larger counstructions might be connected. Only by using a literal theme which carries over from one picture to another, or by a recognizable stylistic similarity from picture to picture, is it possible to have any larger continuity in paintings. It is important to realize that the stylistic similiarity of a particular artist's output makes it important to view a large body of his work in order to detect his true vision. If a body of work rests on some extra-art suggestion to give it a continuous meaning, it is conceivable that an artist can arrive at a new creativity through it, yet every picture must remain autonomous since it is only tenuously connected in this way— eventually to be broken when the pictures are sold or separated into museums.

The multipanel painting allows the only possible extensive form in painting, because here (as in a triptych) two or more pictures that are physically connected and thus inseparable, can treat of the same theme in different ways, or treat different themes in the same way. Like the movements of a symphony they can give diversity in unity. Pop artists who use comic-strip images but leave out their multiplicity miss one of their most interesting qualities. Most artists who have used the triptych form, as for instance in the great icons of the Byzantines, or the triptych woodcuts of the great Japanese artists Hokusai or Hiroshige, the German expressionist Heckel, or the oils of Max Beckmann, have not actually exploited this possibility—each work being essentially one picture merely divided arbitrarily into three sections. The boundary of the triptych is theoretically open to drastic changes as the image goes from picture to picture. I have long been fascinated with this possibility, once doing a thirty-three-color woodcut entitled "Of The Iris Family," in which the left panel is a seated figure entirely in warm colors, the right another seated figure in cool colors, and the connecting panel a still life in both warms and cools, joining the spectrum. From time to time I have also tried to do abstract oils or wax paintings or etchings which exploit the triptych's potential, forming contrasting panels that are related perhaps by lines that connect across the boundaries, or by colors that repeat. This idea has a potential which I do not as yet feel has been realized, although theory does not stand in its way, only the lack of an appropriate artistic vision. This seems to me to be a much more potentially viable and valuable approach to newness in the visual realm, than that of, say, the primary structures which are simply geometric sculptures whose only startling quality is that you mistake them for architectural elements. I have not given up my search for a truly creative statement in a triptych.

The next chapter discusses the semivisual arts, such as television, the theater, and the motion picture. Although they all have important visual qualities, they are basically literary and vivifying, in the sense of describing persons and society. The dance and the puppet theater are also two semivisual art forms which are essentially vivifying. Modern dance is less literal and vivifying than classical ballet, but the fact that the dancer is the prime instrument gives it a human literalness which is difficult to transcend. Puppetry is sculpture coming to life by welding it to word and deed. This small art form is in disfavor in America, although there are signs that a revival is in store. Our communication media demand new art forms and constantly force a reevaluation of those on the current scene, and it seems to me it is inevitable that puppetry will come into modern focus.

The visual arts lie midway like an inchoate sea between two extremely well-structured islands: on the one hand music, which, due to our physical-physiological perception reactions, can build a very precise encoding form; and on the other the literary arts, where meaning is explicit because of common agreement. The visual arts are inchoate not only because colors and forms do not mix, but also because simultaneity can flood our vision; because space is static and vague, depending on how we look at it; because forms in space are not easy to relate; because we are prejudiced against new orders of seeing since our history of seeing is so overwhelmingly in favor of the recognizable. Yet this very inchoate quality is what gives the visual arts a certain ascendency over the other arts, and why I personally am so attracted to them. The visual arts have the possibility of communicating the more perceptually vague and unknown and sweetly mysterious realms of human experience, and of doing so through our eyes, which we intuitively feel are close to the orgin of all understanding.

Vivifying with Words

1

WORDS have a remarkable way of vivifying themselves, so that we sense countless realities when we read them which we do not actually experience. Neolithic man scratched drawings on the barks of trees or the walls of caves, depicting animals and men. The act can be understood quite simply as a morphological rendition of what his eyes saw—he "traced" a bison as he looked with his eye, letting his hand record the impressions one-to-one. But when the same primitive man went into a field and notched a stick to indicate how many bison were grazing there, there is no equally simple explanation; a notch is so highly abstracted from a bison that it is difficult to understand how early man got the idea of letting a notch represent so complex a visual stimulus. And making the jump from quipus or wampum to idiograms is not so simple to analyze either, nor is how the brain correlated these marks with the highly abstracted sounds that issued from man's throat. The use of words and language to build art is extremely difficult to analyze when all things are considered because the mechanisms for the generation of the media itself are so very complex.

In the visual arts it is easy to see how we might value a picture which looks like things we value; or in music, it is not difficult to guess why a sound that is as impressive and tuneful as a bird's could be treasured. These morphological suggestions indicate that their arts give us direct sensations which are either pleasing or not, reflecting or deviating from, or creating natural worlds with an intrinsic sensual beauty. But when words reach the mind and bring an amazing new reality to life we are loath to find a simple explanation for the vivifying process. It is easy to say that a kind of truncated relational morphology occurs when we arbitrarily use marks to stand for things of a more elementary nature, allowing them to grow into abstractions once removed from our senses: this might be a good definition of a symbol. It may explain how we give meaning to scratches, and if we add memory to suggest how we can perceive this meaning at a later date we can complete the con cept of symbolization; but it does not suggest how a series of words can aspire to art, when they only build a beauty which comes directly out of our own memory in an automatic way.

Artistic creativity depends on a system of relational communicants working together to reveal new possibilities. When our sense receptors are involved, as in the visual or aural arts—that is directly involved at the physical level—we can perhaps understand how they might discharge feelings within us. They are being physically effective on us, and there is a direct interaction exchange of energies with our nervous system. We so accept language and discursive communication that we think the communication of art meanings through them is obvious. But does a mark which stands for something beautiful suffice to communicate the beautiful? Nothing sensual is actually communicated directly in the language we use, save the immediate sensation of a little curlicue running by, and this can take on one of many forms. Electronic engineers have shown that there need only be two marks to communicate all literary and language meanings: yes and no, 1 and 0, a presence of something and an absence of something. Does naming something beautiful, impressive, or profound make us respond to it as if it were actually so? Does calling out those inner qualities we value in life and nature, by means of language, suffice to make art?

Naturally not—if so, then it would be simple to make art: one need barely probe for honest feelings or deep emotions, just reach for a thesaurus or a dictionary and set down the words (which is sometimes how literature or poetry may sound, if it is not creative.) Our inner being is a rich storehouse of experiences and emotions which we have recorded in many forms, including some which make sentences, and which we can quite easily communicate from person to person. Communication is not sufficient for art. However much we plumb the inner world of our psyche or range throughout the most exotic of places, it is easy to set down the experiences in words, and accurately communicate what we feel, but this is quite a bit different from turning those experiences into art. The communication of thoughts is intangible and abstract; the words have no similiarity in form or sound to the ideas being communicated, no more to our feelings than to the geography of the earth. How, then, do we rise to art with words?

Language is finite; the words we use are restricted in number and they can be contained in a reasonable-sized dictionary. Since our experience is, on the other hand, very great, language is always ambiguous. Information theory suggests that the act of communication of an idea erases the ambiguity of meaning in one area because it establishes one instance of meaning-choice. At this most primal level of language-encoding the words mean just what they say they mean; there is no ambiguity in simple, common-sense statements. Language at the most primitive level of encoding is a concretizing communication. Much of our day-to-day intercourse uses language to describe simple and direct experiences which we all understand—there are no hidden meanings (except perhaps unconscious Freudian ones which do not concern us generally). However complex this communication can grow, its aim is for clarity of expression, for certainty of communication. The fact might be that an assertive positive statement is wrong, but nevertheless it is nothing more than an inaccurate communication. This is the true limit of discursive language, and it is not art unless by accident.

Language used unambiguously is close to mathematics, close to Leibnitz's universal symbology; true or false, but highly restricted and unemotional and without confusion. This truncated, morphological use of language which corresponds to our experience leaves absolutely nothing to be desired since it is so exact, and is an immediate exchange of ideas from person to person. This is an unusual way to think of language, of course, because to a greater or lesser degree, by accident or design, ambiguity and suggestiveness always manage to creep into even the most prosaic statement. This type of language is the type of language logicians talk about; the type of language a philosopher like Charles Morris tried to grasp, as in his work *Signs, Language and Behavior*.[1] The attempts to rectify language to its most elemental descriptive terms for a computer must be begun at the most unencumbered level of commonsense meaning, and then, after it has been done, and the computer has been taught to manipulate it, it may be possible to go on to higher and more complex language utterances. Mathematical models of language, like those of Noam Chomsky[2] or his teacher Zelig Harris, strive to build an elementary grammar out of which phrases and paragraphs can be constructed. This aspect of language is of structural importance in a linguistic science that tries to understand speech and the human use of words, but its relevance to a theory of art is highly restricted.

Only insofar as a person learns to disregard accepted linguistic utterances and forges ahead to a new and creative use of language is he being poetical—which is antithetical to the current computer-oriented linguistic approach. Linguistic scientists think that syntax and the conventional grammatical meanings of language exhaust their communicative possibilities, but even a poor poet like myself knows these are but a fraction of the possibilities for communicating with words. Carried to its extreme, language is the most complex and sophisticated cre-

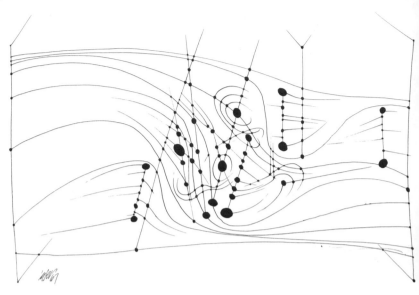

ative communication man has developed, considering the range and expanse of human concern it can summon up, plus the abstract levels of sensual meanings it can suggest. This is both its virtue and its failing, a virtue when its communication can be appropriated without too much human difficulty, while still retaining a creative revelation, and a failing when it encumbers itself with inordinately complex relationships, obscured behind a seemingly interesting verbal or symbolic smoke screen that tries to be creative but never is.

2

At the most elementary level the sensual qualities of words have an aural or visual quality—there is a music in their clicking and snarling in the mouth which the ear appreciates; or there is a style to the calligraphy of the letters and words which the eye notes. Poets have of course carried the musical quality to its highest realization. Sidney Lanier (who was also an orchestral flutist of repute) was well aware of the musical qualities of poetry, and he wrote an excellent code book on the musical use of meter in poetic forms.[3] When a poet is most successful in his use of the sound of poetry it is easily fit to song, as even the extreme modern example of Edith Sitwell's *Facade*, set to music by Sir William Walton, demonstrates. Calligraphy, except in the East, is not easily used because of the restriction of typesetting. Ruskin's colored abstract writing could only be realized in a manuscript culture, or by an artist-poet like William Blake. To transcend the mechanical visual quality of typeset words is difficult. Rimbaud did so in his *Sonnet of Vowels* and in *Illuminations* which used strings of substantives. These interesting visual experiments have been used by many modern poets, the most notable of whom is e. e. cummings. The impulse to spread the poem across the page in unusual ways was perhaps a desire to return to the special mode of presentation which an aural reading allowed—halts and inflections being suggested by jumps and twists of the printed word. Reading poetry, and emphasizing its sound modulations, is the more traditional way of the poet, and modern recordings of poets reading their own poetry have allowed a return to this primary communicative mode which the printed page bypassed.

The finiteness of language allows the poet to use roots or accents or subdivisions which sound alike and permit the establishment of rhyme and meter. A language like Italian, having more redundancies than English, with its ever-present vowels, exerts its musical power by deviation. Dante was well aware of this, and in the *Inferno* the more powerful passages usually diverge most from the mellifluous nature of the Italian language. It is a random deviation from the order of meter which gives these passages an unusual strength.

The internal beat of a poetical sentence and the surprise of rhyming words communicate a subtle order which underlies the chaos of experience that is contained in the meaning of the words. The scansion rhythms of the brain give all rhythmic experiences in communication phenomena a new meaning and importance, either by their falling in step, or by their opposing the meter. Our limit of toleration to various poetical rhythms varies from age to age. The poem *The Raven* by Edgar Allan Poe was tolerated and praised when first written and accepted, but it is too redundantly boring today. On the other hand Poe has been revived on the basis of other encoding richnesses which his contemporaries did not note, his symbolism or multilevel literary encodings. Gray's elegant classical order, for instance, which at first reading is quite pleasing, has gone out of style in favor of the more modern and broken rhythms of Donne. This is, I think, part of the modern age's turn toward the fractured forms which seem to characterize our age's penchant for fragmentation and multiplicity.

But obviously we cannot attribute the artistry of poetry exclusively to the music of the words or to its linear visual calligraphy or typesetting.* The incidental music of the sound of words in poetry accompanies the meaning which is encoded in all other possible levels of literary significance. The sounds of words alone do not, as Gertrude Stein hoped, suffice to make an art form, mainly because of the fact that the possibilities of structural relationships between sounds or visual placements are too weak or subtle and hard to detect. The consonances, dissonances, rhythms, form of word meters and typographical placements of words become important in all poetry, but in and of themselves they do not contain enough structure to rise to art.

Music and the visual arts require, as we have seen, coded elements that: (1) relate internally to themselves, or (2) relate to other encoded elements. Sounds relate to sounds, but sounds and meanings are not quite as easy to relate structurally; their relations are perfectly arbitrary and due almost entirely to convention. As has often been suggested, only a few onomatopoeic words sound something like their meaning (they vary greatly from language to language, like *cock-a-doodle-doo* in

---

* There is no reason, for instance, to discount the possibility that we could not become conditioned to the sequential presentation of letters by means of some electronic display. Books could be recorded on coded tape, then fed to a display which speeds the letters off for us to read without scanning, thus giving us literature without the need to read a page. We cannot assume that this kind of medium would be the same as printing or the same as an aural reading of a text, possibly leading to new perceptual ramifications.

English, *cu-cu-ri-ku* in Hungarian, *kikeriki* in German, *kokke-kokkō* in Japanese). There are few enough verbal equivalents to what Gombrich calls our physiognomic forms for us to be able to detect the physical quality which they suggest.[4] And even if we could build a repertory of such sounds (like clicking consonants that suggest pointed objects, or vowels which seem like rounded and soft objects), it would be difficult to imagine how they could relate to one another tightly enough to support creative relationships. Literary meanings must accompany the sound of a poem in order to structure the music of the word in a creative fashion.

The simplest ambiguity of literary language which might have the necessary structural and meaning significance to suggest a creative possibility is when one word resembles another, or when one word carries two or more meanings. When the context is not sufficiently clear such a word would have a directly ambiguous quality, but when the word has a definite dual meaning, it becomes a very explicit pun or play on words. This metaphorical ambiguity allows for the simultaneous communication of two related ideas, related twice by structure—the identical word and meaning. It can be an original thing when such a word is being revealed to us in its metaphorical sense for the first time. You understand a metaphor the instant you read it, if you are prepared for both of its connotations, and it is usually an insight and thus an elemental art act. Arthur Koestler devotes many pages to an analysis of successful puns, which are less than artistic, although elementary art ideas.[5] The poetic metapor is an idea amplification like the electron vacuum-tube amplifier in which a miniscule voltage on the grid (symbol) governs the greater change of the plate circuit (content).[6] A more complete analysis of ambiguity in language is made by William Empson whose seven categories are: (1) multiple signification of details, (2) multiple details that unite into one, (3) two unconnected meanings given at once, (4) alternative meanings that unite, (5) fortunate confusions with accidental multiple meanings, (6) contradictions which force a new meaning, and (7) contradictions which remain unreconcilable and random.[7]

That a simple metaphor can be a creative act can be appreciated by reading any good poem. The use of a word in this way can be a crude pun, as when the villain of a television serial like "Batman" or "Gunsmoke" says he is going to blow up a bridge, meaning that he is going to blow up an enlargement of the picture of a bridge, or it can be very sophisticated as in a poetic couplet. The word *aristocracy* in Emily Dickinson's couplet,

> The pedigree of honey does not concern the bee.
> A clover, any time, to him is aristocracy[8]

takes on a new revelatory meaning to us. We can only grasp a poetic meaning in context, and they are always meanings we do not find in a dictionary, nor in any other single sentence which is not the poetry itself. No other set of verbal descriptors suffices to carry off the meaning of the word *aristocracy* as used in this beautiful couplet. The problem of translating poetry from one language to another emphasizes the uniqueness of creative communication with words, and it indicates how even the slightest change can destroy the meaning and give it a different effect. In T. S. Eliot's couplet,

> Shape without form, shade without colour
> Paralyzed force, gesture without motion[9]

there is a total sense of frustration and tension about to explode. The contradiction can also be carried to the point of complete nonsense, as in the poetry of Edward Lear or Lewis Carroll. We accept nonsense in poetry as we accept a totally black picture interestingly captioned, but we can more clearly understand the meanings exchanged in a poem because of the context. For instance, the words in Carroll's *Jabberwocky* are clearly

understood although we have never met with them before—
brillig, *slithy*, and *gimbel* seem to have meaning. It is much as
if we sense what the swirls are in a Gustave Moreau painting
because they come to focus on something we recognize. *Jabberwocky*, as John Ciardi indicates,[10] also has other levels of
meaning, since it ridicules a traditional type of heroic poem.
But even without other hidden meanings such a poem can rise
to a vivid revelation of nothing save its own extremes or play-
fulness. In this almost abstract way even a nonsensical poem,
novel, or play can have meaning and pull us into the land of
creative significance. The reason is that we are always eager to
read into the fantastic or unknown something which we understand, and we interpret abstraction or symbolism as codes for
more immediately known things. This is how we attribute
humanness to abstractions, however mad or illogical they are
on the surface.

The poem becomes one of the most efficient artistic encod
ing packages possessed by man. Consider the density of ideas
in a poem like *The Wasteland*, which requires countless books
to analyze it properly, and many pages to annotate all of its
references.* Francis Thompson's great religious and mystical
poem *The Hound of Heaven* has vague reverberations of the
poets Keats, Blake, Tennyson, Wordsworth, Shelley, Byron,
Herbert, and Swinburne, as well as the biblical quality of St.
John and the Psalms. It is also extremely timely today since it
presciences the cosmic forces and space rapture which are
rampant in the modern world. When we become aware of all
the encodings of a tightly packed poem of this nature an
avalanche of ideas overwhelms us and forces us to a new revelation of relationships which we would never have dreamed
possible. That these relationships are new and valid is what
justifies calling such a poem creative.

Syntax change or changed emphasis permit many new meanings to be given to words. If a sentence is reversed from the

---

* The very word *reference* can be thought of as a synonym to *encoding*.

normal order, we sense an unnatural quality, a stilted or poetic quality; or if we give a sentence a different reading, we can completely change its significance. Albert Hofstadter has a brilliant passage in *Truth and Art*, some ten pages long[11] which analyzes the various possible and implied meaning with different emphases and permutations of a simple statement. It is useful to repeat the conclusions here. The sentence "The sky is cloudy" can have the following different significances:

1. The *sky* is cloudy: about the sky;
2. The sky *is cloudy*: attribute of sky;
3. *The sky is cloudy*: statement of objective fact;
4. "The sky is cloudy": observed by someone;
5. Clóudy ís the śky: more personal and subjective, emphasizing cloudy and the rhythm of the meter;
6. The sky is cloudy: objective-subjective duality of a person realizing a fact;
7. The sky is cloudy: the fact of a written language, the score of an aural articulation of our human beingness.

Longer and more complex sentences and paragraphs of course give us countless more meaning possibilities.

A poem opens many doors simultaneously, not only into past literary ideas, but also into many areas of experience, pulling them together in a grand creative synthesis. The poem therefore has the opportunity to fulfill the needs of our electric media which embrace multiple, seemingly illogical fragments simultaneously. However, the poetic vision must always give us a new insight into a multiplicity of ideas, before we recognize it as being creative.

3

The more complex encodings which literature employs begin where poetry leaves off, although they often relapse into a purely poetical use of language in the ways described above. The poetical plus the other encoding levels of literature are summarized in Table V. It is the expanse of the multilevel encoding range which gives literature a great potential for creative revelation. And it has been the preparation of past writers like Proust, Joyce, Mann, and Faulkner—plus the critical schools like the New Criticism which have made us more aware of them and of their methods—which today enables us to apply a "hard-earned responsiveness" to exceedingly complex literary works, as Robert Scholes wrote.[12]

James Joyce, perhaps more than any other modern writer, illustrates the extremes to which literary encoding can be

TABLE V—ENCODING IN THE VIVIFYING ARTS

1. FACT OF LANGUAGE, someone communicating via words
2. COMMON-SENSE MEANING
3. RHYTHMIC AND SOUND PATTERNS (communicates order)
    a. Sounds themselves
    b. Internal rhymes and end rhymes
    c. Meter and sentence beat
4. WORD ORDER OR IDEA VARIATION (poetic syntax changes with resulting changes of meaning)
5. WORDS WITH MULTIPLE MEANINGS (metaphor, pun, comparisons, contrasts, and so on, that unite different ideas in one word or phrase)
6. MULTIPLE CONTEXTUAL MEANINGS
    a. Simultaneous multiple ideas (plot, subplot, etc.)
    b. Mythical or other structural background
    c. Reality structure extending to fantasy or parody, or into a mystical or super-reality
7. MULTIPLE CHARACTERS VIVIFIED
    a. Psychological or real-life clues, inner-outer suggestions
    b. Mortality, life-death structure
    c. Immortality, fantasy, and parody, etc.
8. LARGER RHYTHMIC PATTERNS
    a. Life rhythms, social rhythms, personal and inter-personal, historic, quick or extended
    b. Natural rhythms, reality pulse, tone

stretched. His *Ulysses*, ostensibly about one Stephan Daedalus and his mentor Leopold Bloom, two contemporary Irishmen meandering in and about Dublin, conjures up not only the tale of Homer's *Odyssey* quite literally passage by passage, but also the origin of language itself, and many of the high points in all past literature. The reading of such a work gives you a heightened sense of *déjà vu* if you have even a superficial knowledge of its structure and are familiar with some of its references, and you sense a supreme attempt to call much experience and art to account, which makes it a tour de force in artistic communication.

The fact that very complicated meanings can be encoded in literature leads us to another important but confusing point. When a work of art is so complex that it is either unintelligible or comprehended only after considerable effort, what is the value of the experience? The answer that the value can only be measured by the degree to which a work of art succeeds in some creative revelation, does not seem satisfactory. If we have to become a scholar in order to grasp the elements that go into the creative relationship in some literary work, why should we bother? The answer is that we do not have to bother, but if we do, we will read a communication which can cause a very radical action within our brains, one which serves at minimum the function of housekeeping in our literary house, and at most a true enlargement of our psyche.

The creativity of most art is due to a bountiful use of images, sounds, ideas, metaphors, and subtle relationships, most of which either escape immediate observation, or which are difficult to understand at first. To trace even briefly the insights of a single great poem or a picture can fill a book; to begin to grasp the creative scope of a great novel sometimes requires generations of exposure and consideration. It is the efficiency of the artistic encoding which enables an artist to pack his work densely with many ideas. The value of art is the scope of any given work, and its ability to lift up our perceptual awareness in the experience—making us desire to return to it again and again until we have exhausted it.

The initial reaction to a particular work of art is due to our education in that art, our previous exposure and knowledge before the fact as to the artistic means and the encodings being used. Given the proper familiarity with the elements of any work of art, the creative communication is triggered off—if it is present—even though we may not be aware of all of the elements which have gone into its formulation. The artist must assume that his reader or viewer is perfectly familiar with all literature or art, and with all possible allusions or references which he might desire to use, so that even the slightest innuendo, the barest clue, is sufficient to carry his idea. The problem of attaining a creative view in literature is so difficult (as in all the arts), that if it is necessary for the creator to have to worry about the level of a particular audience, he would no longer be sufficiently at ease to create. This fact, which most artists sense or know, has led many people to criticize them; they are accused of being obscure for the sake of confusing. Actually the obscurity of an advanced artist is an optimistic gesture he is making to the intelligence of his audience. It is inconceivable that an artist could reach the creative insight needed in art to give it a real human meaning if he worried at every step about its reception.

Carried too far, however—and this is of course possible—the multiple-encoding of dense literary meanings can be so very esoteric or scholarly as to become a professional inside joke. But what is one generation's confusion is another's clarity. We cannot say a priori that, for instance, *Finnegan's Wake* or any other esoteric literary work is so very far out as to be forever unintelligible except for the few—after all, the day has come when these works are being analyzed for us by scholars on National Educational Television.[13]

Inside jokes, personal references, all obscurities which we cannot detect, contribute an element of randomness to any work of art. Nonsense becomes defined, confusing side remarks take on some significance, depending on how they are used in context and how sensitively we can read the author's intent. We forgive Joyce when he builds a meaning out of a personal experience because we begin to understand what meaning he had in mind, even without knowing the details of the experience itself. Much as Picasso did when he introduced nonsense into his pictures, we read the whole from the part. Foolishness, if done tastefully and with even the most obscure intent, can help a new clarity emerge. Such is the nature of creativity that we cannot predict it beforehand, and to exclude even the most personal allusions may be to deny one more creative step.

Chaos, looming over the creative fabric of art, serves to push disorder back a little further into the darkness of the unknown from whence it came, if that chaos can resolve itself ever so little. Change and chaos are variable things, and it is not wise to reject disorder a priori, especially in art. The potential of art is to reach into what we thought was chaotic and feel out little orders that grow into great creative truths. The apparent irrationalities of the modern theater, the found-word quality of literature which mocks the newspaper, or the snatching of fragmentary conversations, or stilted forms, of radical images and ideas, suggests a possible art form appropriate to our electric age.

Artists themselves are not always aware of the meaning of their vision, and they do not always understand its possibilities or potential, primarily because they know that their medium can exceed their grasp. The media of art leads the artist into the unknown, almost despite himself. If the artist expects to be creative, he knows that he must trustingly rely on his experience with craft, and his inspiration and talent for combining, to function within his chosen art situation.

Literature can extend into utterly fantastic worlds that have meaning for us right here in the most banal of situations. The visions of W. H. Hudson, T. H. White, or even Arthur Clarke, building fantastic or mythical kingdoms for our comprehension, do so in order to fabricate new creative contingencies, contingencies which would not be possible within normal experiences. Working in an abstraction of worlds, the fantasy writer creates a nonobjectivity of human experience. It has human meaning only if it is creative in the sense of revealing new possibilities for our human-beingness, by articulating new worlds of vision which do not have to be realizable in physical form, but which do have to extend our perceptual boundaries—perhaps into a realm of future moral vision or of human communication and intercourse. We believe anything in literature which we understand, although we do not necessarily admire it; the admiration of flights of fancy comes from a forceful imagination bringing new insights into being. Operating thus it is possible for a writer to create even ideal situations, final forms, ultimate creations, and Utopian dreams; he can explore unlimited human potentialities and emotions in the worlds of "as if." The nature of literary encoding is that it lends credence to whatever system can be imagined, as long as there is sufficient development to carry the reader along into the unknown, implicitly developed or explicitly stated. Since all experience is essentially a vortex of unknown forces, the very greatness of literature is that it gives form to all realities, even hypothetical ones we can never experience.

The writer may be encoding one set of events by entirely different ideas, as when he sets before the reader commonplace ideas which in fact mean something quite uncommon—and this even without ever suggesting his symbolization. The clue for the interpretation of literature always has to come from ourselves, and it does not rest with the artist to make his intent clear in so many words—to do so would be to break the creativity barrier which protects and gives meaning to his communication. We do not need telegraphic-numbered messages clued in throughout Marcel Proust's *Remembrance of Things Past* to sense that he is developing an idea presented earlier; he puts most of the dominant ideas into the first few paragraphs. We do not need to make explicit the dominance of any root idea in literature or in a play or poem in order to grasp its implication. Justice may triumph over lawlessness, evil over corruption, and it may be present in every sentence or paragraph, but the author need not spell it out.

The extra order which the simple root idea forced on past literature or theater is being broken down in our modern age because we require more diversity in our artistic vision. The Kafkaesque novel, the André Breton poem, the Salvador Dali surrealistic picture, all began to fragment reality and build a new order of artistic encoding The recent *nouveau romans* of Alain Robbe-Grillet, Michel Butor, Claude Mauriac and Nathalie Sarraute also tend to transcend the logic of past novels. Their fragmented subplots and ingenious absurdities, woven into verbalized high-speed tricks of illusion and perception, seldom seem to gel into a creative insight. Tending to imitate an interesting experimental movie montage, the *nouveau roman* leaves one unsatisfied and yearning for less complex but more startling novelistic insights into life and personalities. Yet the urge to break down the linear form of the novel is obviously a valid and important one. The single-view solution to life that is our cultural heritage, the rational approach of our ancestors, may have little or no meaning today. Understanding used to operate in the form of parsimony and direct paths and logical links which were explicit, but today this is not the case. Only some great works of literature, like Tolstoi's *War and Peace*, are able to maintain most of their original meaning for us today, because their size allowed the inclusion of many qualities, many complex multidimensionalities of personality, scene, and time. The larger rhythms of modern life can be expressed most easily in larger works, although they can also be realized in exceptional smaller works through leaps in time or by exaggerated experiences.

At present the theater is encompassing this diversity by novel experiments which the general public has great difficulty understanding. An Ionesco innovation, like his first play *The Bald Soprano*, is as radical in its theatrical encoding as Schoenberg's was in music. Ionesco relies on the clichés of absurd situations, frankly derived from the illogic of his dreams. The logic of the absurd is difficult to grasp, but we know, not only from our own dreams, but also from the irregular rhythms of our own disjointed lives, that it is a meaningful logic.

4

The arts of literature, the theater, and the movies are concerned with vivifying people and their social, human problems. In these arts the mind searches for and discovers clues principally aimed at defining personalities. The Greeks typecast their characters to enhance this process, giving them consistent acts and movements—and even masks—which facilitated their definition; the element of predestination in Greek theater rounded out the typecasting of form by including not only people but also all experience. The myth typecast the various stories of the gods, and a brief suggestion or allusion to a myth sufficed to communicate many ideas.

The natural inclination to see the traits of Hollywood stars or television actors in our friends makes it the easier for us to accept them as encoded forms of types which we can understand. We would desire that our theatrical experiences consist almost entirely of *déjà vus*, and the Greeks carried this to its logical extreme in predestination. The star system aids communication by explaining much to us the first instant we recognize a star. We know, for instance, that the image of Humphrey Bogart or Edward G. Robinson is going to give us a "gangster" or "tough guy," and that Gary Cooper is a "cowboy." We are already familiar with the physical characteristics and with many of the mannerisms of the person the star is playing, simply because we know the star intimately and also know his typical roles. We can guess a lot about the plot if we see Gregory Peck or Charlie Chaplin or Bette Davis playing the role. The star system serves the same function as the mask of the Greek theater. A star *is* a mask, unmovable and stylized. We know what to expect when we see the mask of Bette Davis, and we are always fascinated, even before she scowls or puffs frantically at her life-giving cigarette.

The Hollywood gangster movie and the Western are archetypal plots in which variation is made by virtue of the pre-knowledge we might derive from a given, known star, placed into a new situation. When we find a drawing-room star cast in a cowboy movie we are immediately curious to find out how it will all come out. The new combinations and permutations of our recognized stars in familiar plots are much like the Greek situation in drama where the gods were subjected to various agreeable and disagreeable situations of human origin. The revival of many old movies on the late television shows offers those of us who are interested a marvelous opportunity to see just how Hollywood has played this game of character-switching throughout its history. If it is a gangster movie we expect the "hero" to be nervous, sullen and temperamental to the point of distraction, as Robert Warshow suggests in *The Immediate Experience*;[14] but if we find the role cast with a calm personality of our acquaintance, we are disposed to an interest and uncertainty which we must resolve—thus we are trapped to watch it (regardless of the hour). As the Greek audience knew its gods and what to expect of them, including many facts which are not described by the play itself, we react to the communications of modern art forms because of many encodings which we have accrued in our past experiences of looking and listening and reading.

And we are the more impressed by movies that have stars in them who are currently either the topic of some scandalous gossip or are notorious in some way. Sometimes too we begin to sense the emergence of a remarkable new talent who wraps us up in his private cult. I remember how I became aware of the Marlon Brando mystique along with some English friends of mine, emerging from the first London showing of *On The Waterfront* almost overwhelmed by an idolization I had not experienced since my youth. We have all gone through our Charlie Chaplin or Sir Laurence Olivier phases. This is a com-

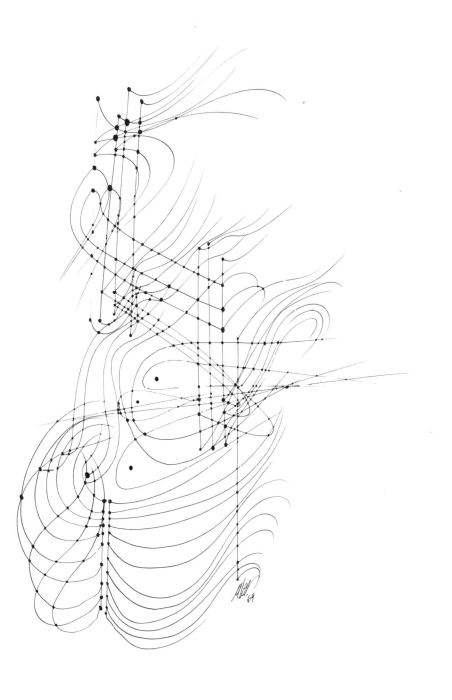

munication phenomenon similar to that mentioned earlier when you come across bits of art created by some world-famous personage.*

Using character types or archetypal plots is to communicate only a matrix of art. The moment-to-moment experience is an immediate event in the vivid lives of people, and we live in the action of the moment; the given matrix is superimposed on the existential reality which art heightens and gives meaning to. We also sense the various effects of the atmosphere summoned up perhaps by words, by set decor or lighting variations. We also react to the montage of images or the changes of motion. The qualities of the total, almost subliminal impressions, given by the movement of the characters, their body shiftings and gestures and facial expressions, add up to the total creativity of the art form—the handling of them all are the director's job. The character type and plot imprints itself on these other secondary and usually delicate happenings, however, and this is the main force and main interest in a movie or play.

Character and plot are all but excuses for the dynamic structure behind the central phenomena of the vivifying arts. In their most important form the vivifying arts are concerned with human lives, trying to discover the meaning of existent man, the possibilities of human interrelationships, and the problems of individualities. The topics of death and nobility, of extremes such as violence and corruption, of unusal characters like circus people or eccentrics, are most interesting for artists because they explore the limits of life. The life situation is best dealt with at the razor's edge of precarious decisions, beset with dilemmas and contradictions, in whose resolution or clarification new potentialities for human choice and action are creatively communicated. Driven either by cogent psychological human motives, or by reference to an archetypal action which history has established as meaningful, or by new and urgently

* Can we perhaps guess that Greek audiences also had a similar reaction to their favorite character, god or goddess?

recognized problems, the characters of a vivifying art enact the necessary trials that lead to a resolution we expect to be original and creative. There is no question that we have gotten the message as we experience this art, because we are so close to life that it has direct application and meaning to us; and if it presents a true creative revelation, it can be an overwhelming experience.

The movies embrace the claims of the natural world more readily than do the theater and the novel, which both have certain limitations of set or physical experience. To this extent the motion picture puts us immediately into a more acceptable life situation. This should therefore lead us to conclude that the film is closer to the ideal art which can best deal with real lives—were it not for the fact that even the ideal arts have limitations, and that the un-ideal arts can sometimes be appropriate for the inappropriate. There is no illusion which we transcend so quickly as the illusion of the movies, passing into the magnified two-dimensional world as easily as we pass into another room in our home. Yet we are continually jarred by this ease of transference, because in movies the world in which we find ourselves is filled with difficulties and falsifications. For example, crossing a street is always a problem, because we cannot look beyond the screen to see if a threatening car is coming along; directors know that this act—and many others—are anxiety-ridden to the viewer, and they must treat them accordingly.

In primitive cultures the natives exposed to modern film react as our unconscious must react and ask: Where do the people go when they go off the screen? or How can a person of normal dimensions in one scene have such a large face in another? or If a person is killed in one film, how can he come back to life in another?[15] The evolution of the close-up in the movie was hampered not by a lack of understanding of the film medium so much as by an inability to accept the reality of the cinematographic fact.

The ease of transference into the film world, however, may

be only a limitation of realistic cinematography. The film's closeness to our real, vivified world is not necessarily inherent to the medium, no more than it is for still photography. Sustained abstraction is difficult to accept in the movies, however, as a viewing of completely nonobjective film seems to indicate, or as some recent experiments like *Marienbad* (which, while not abstract, use the human quite abstractly) also imply. That the transcendent, almost mythological can be built successfully in the film, for instance in Jean Cocteau's *Beauty and the Beast*, attest to its power as a fantasy form. But when Federico Fellini uses fantasy, as he did in *8½* for instance, it is just a more heightened and accurate realism, because fantasy is very much a part of our experience. If the dreamlike or imaginative is elevated to a revelation or archetypal creation, as in many Ingmar Bergman films, we enter into a truly original cinematographic technique that justifies the greatest extremes in experimental visions. How far multiple encodings, symbolism, subtle references to past films or old visual experiences, the conjoining of ideas, or the eclecticism of styles or stories, can be carried, has yet to be determined since cinematographers have barely begun to explore this area. We can assume, however, that since our visual memory is so strong it would be possible to go as far in the film as T. S. Eliot has in poetry. The poet of the film is a poet of visual experiences, and our vision has a remarkable retention of the most fleeting images. Startling juxtapositions, unusual montages or motions, extremes of exposures to reduce or reverse images that give surprising new images that are reductions of reality, all possible tricks of the camera and film, only take on creative meaning when they build a new consciousness of the communication of visual forms. That form can either describe itself quite autonomously, or it can be an envelope of shadows which entwine the visual qualities of our personal and human realities, and expand our awareness of them.

Our abilities to enter into the role of the hero of a film, because of its similitude to our human frame of reference, to project ourselves into new roles as they come and go, can be a pleasant fantasy realization, but it can also be a horrible nightmare manifestation. It is not strange that romantic wish-fulfillment, exaggerated human powers, and maudlinism in the film can be extremely thrilling, and yet so very unrewarding artistically. They cater to very human psychological needs, but they do not build the human potential for perception. A romantic or larger-than-life character, sometimes quite superhuman, titillates us, perhaps, but he seldom moves us. And the technical problems which have allowed the cinematographer to create him often get in our way. I cannot help but play a constant little game to determine how the technical feats of a spectacular movie are carried off; part of my brain cannot for a moment "suspend disbelief," despite the fact that there it is, happening before my very eyes. Of course, being a true cinema-buff, I accept it as it happens—there is a part of my brain which does not know what disbelief is—I am simply being exposed to something which it accepts as a matter of course. My game takes place because I desire a deep insight when experiencing so potentially powerful an art form, and, lacking one, I am forced to search out the technical creativity which has gone into the physical production of the film—usually a considerable creativity at that, but one which the cinematographer has done everything in his power to hide.

It would be impossible for us to support all the horrors of even the most superficial detective novel or movie[16] if it succeeded in communicating the emotional trials its characters would have to entertain in real life. And we would shrivel up and die under the weight of the psychological feelings of a super character were he but human and we grasped his emotions. This is what makes him *in*human, and why he is actually no emotional challenge whatsoever. We can watch heads being twisted off or men's eyes gouged out, buckets of blood flowing, even humans disintegrating into dust before our every eyes—without so much as batting an eye. These paper-thin deaths and vapor murders are not terminations of life in any sense of the word. There has been no chance for us to get to know the character, to become involved with his life, and the death of someone we do not know and care absolutely nothing about cannot possibly affect us, at least in art.

Each of us is capable only of absorbing a few significant events in his life, one or two deaths, extreme poverty only for a limited time, or ecstatic joys and raptures only on occasion. When we realize that in ages gone by people lived more in constant danger than we do, and speculate that the recent precariousness of life—bombing scares, delinquencies, robbings and multiple-murders—are but echoes of past times, we can begin to appreciate the contentment of our lives—and begin to question our complacency in living them without qualms. Our satisfaction in the papier mâché murders of cheap media is psychological to the extent that we all briefly toy with similar murders: we kill our mothers in our minds, our fathers, or our wives and children; we eliminate in one brief moment of glory all disagreeable or trying things in life. We all fantasize new situations for the life of our free souls. These are very real meanings, and they are natural human fantasies—but they have little to do with the communication of art per se.

Simon O. Lesser suggests[17] that escape literature and Grade-B movies avoid arousing anxieties like those of our everyday experience; monsters, supermen, lascivious women, all are extremely interesting possibilities, but they do not occur for our concern (very often). This level of reality in the vivifying arts is like the representational level in pictures, only in the movies it is more powerful to our senses. Curious to behold, movies may give us images which impress or even disgust us, but they actually do not involve us very profoundly. Escape literature or poor literature usually leads the reader into a trance world which, although not as debilitating as a drug world, still destroys the abilities of a person to come to grips with reality. Great art—and this is perhaps one of the reasons it is often difficult to take—turns perceptions toward life's realities, however harsh or disagreeable, and helps man to size up the most pressing problems he might be living with and not appreciate (much as found art or found objects present their aspects of reality for our consideration). In this way the human being slowly begins to feel out his own human limitations, faults, shortcomings, and also potentials and powers.

Yet we must realize the limitation of this approach to art, because art obviously does not serve as an inexpensive psychoanalysis. There is no assurance that a person versed in the arts will be ennobled from any given immersion. Our identification with characters, the analogyzing we might make with theatrical or fictional situations, or the empathetic reactions we might have with a particular action, bespeak a vicarious involvement in art which has definite limitations. When we watch the peregrinations of a Willy Loman in Arthur Miller's *Death of a Salesman* we cannot help but learn the moral that dreams are sometimes too impossible to support, that hopes of success, the aspirations for our children, the few minutes of human love are feeble and barely realized in this life. Most of us return home and continue blindly to have the same illusions.

How art is psychologically meaningful to each of us probably depends on our own personal mental health. We can only experience the Aristotelian catharsis if we are in need of it. Simon O. Lesser writes that "A great work of fiction may give us such a profound understanding of some situation which has troubled us and permit us to work it through with such completeness that the anxiety which it aroused is entirely liquidated."[18] Being human we all have "troubled situations," and literature or the theater which caters to them is certainly more interesting than that which does not.

I know that personally I went through an intense late adolescent period reading the great literature of the world, a period in which I was also trying to solve the problems of manhood. But a work by Overstreet or Fosdick, or Erich Fromm's *The Art of Loving*,[19] would have probably served me just as well. I also began to write poetry during this same time, but does writing poetry, often begun in response to a romantic encounter or an idealistic pressure, serve therapeutically to still the anxieties of the poet? Perhaps so, to a certain extent. There is no doubt that my first few novels also helped me reevaluate my own life, in a pseudo-self-analytic fashion. The objectifying of a person's own experiences in directly autobiographical ways is useful if only to gain perpective. Many novelists begin autobiographically, or remain there in effect, like Marcel Proust or Thomas Wolfe. But a story must go beyond a simple recount of a man's life before we can call it literature. And I think our reactions to literature must generate more than a therapeutic conditioning before we call it an artistic experience. The act of building or responding to literature must enlarge men's sympathies, as George Eliot contends; or form and lead the flow of our sympathetic consciousness into new places, as D. H. Lawrence has said.[20]

The new television medium, superficially like the movies, has certain important differences, as indicated by Carpenter and McLuhan.[21] We cannot yet evaluate these differences since the medium is young and it has probably not yet been used in its most appropriate mode. The masses prefer fare on television which it has come to accept through the movies as archetypal for a moving-visual medium: cowboys, gangsters, horror or the supernatural or science fiction, a list which fills prime time any winter week-evening. McLuhan wrote that as the invention of printing consumed all available manuscripts, so television is also consuming old movies,[22] but this is a misplaced consumption and when movies are exhausted there will be a forced need to learn what to do with television time.*

* Facsimile never caught on as a mass medium. If we had it in our homes, we would receive our newspapers and other reading matter from relatively simple electronic devices spewing out printed sheets. I do not know why the industry never pushed it, unless the newspaper and magazine lobbies were very strong. It would have caused its own silent revolution in our attitude toward books, as some predict that xerography will ultimately do, since we would be essentially our own publishers. House-to-house communication need not have remained exclusively aural either, since facsimile for both print or graphic matter function easily over telephone lines.

A new mode of television, significantly different from the movies, may take some time to arrive. It will probably exploit the immediacy (nonrecorded) quality of television, and also lean heavily the cruder image that is small and tactilely sensual. Carpenter notes that Greek drama is more adaptable to television than film because television's boxed-in quality lends itself to more static drama than the movies. He also says that the histrionic actor is more acceptable on television than either in the movies or on the stage.[23] *

Television is close to the puppet theater in many ways, and both puppets and cartoons, because of their more elementary and clearly articulated features, are easily translated into this medium. The technical possibilities of television, using mixed video signals or inserts, allows the cartoon or puppet to combine with live actors as readily as Disney did in his film *Mary Poppins.* Today this combination conjures up only children's entertainment, but this need not necessarily be their only potential (as I also suggest later for the puppet itself). And there is no reason to eliminate the possibility that a basic television cartoon image cannot be created directly through electronic manipulation. If a computer were given the restraints of specific visual images, it could translate them for manipulation throughout the visual field, sidewise and backwards or forwards. Much as a composer uses a music synthesizer, an artist could build forms of a cartoon or abstract nature out of given visual elements using the computer.

The filmed or televised moving image is the closest to the view of the natural world that we have, next to the view which the theater gives us. A single-point view on film or television is only slightly inferior from the point of view of naturalism to the double-point view of our own eyes, as in the theater. The extra point of view is sufficient to change the image

---

* I know that I often watch a television show on my set as if partially blind. My set suffers distortions and interferences and reduced signal strength on the best educational channel, and sometimes I can barely distinguish the actor.

from an artificial one, which has been recorded or translated to us from a distance, into the real-life situation of the theater. The technical innovation of 3-D film is not a good substitute for the live image not only because it is a recorded image (it is conceivable that live, 3-D television could be perfected), but also because it is poor: it presents not rounded objects, but rather, flat, cutouts to our eyes. If you look carefully through a 3-D viewer you will notice that the individual objects are always flat. Nevertheless, assuming that this flatness were corrected through better technique (which is possible), the 3-D image would still not substitute for the actual image. When the actual image is there, the art loses its separateness from the natural world and becomes a different thing. We have an actual object simulating not some artificial presentation, but itself. This becomes a found image, a found object, and the art mode changes, either back to that sculptural art which the Dadaists originated and the recent Pop artists revived, or to a theatrical situation employing live people representing a realistic situation.

5

The use of live human beings in art, as in the theater, dance, and movies (not to mention live musical preformances), presents many special problems. Artifices of an organic vitality in the selfsame form of a human being suggest a paradox first recognized by Diderot. An actor who is not master of his emotions cannot cause a creative communication; as Diderot said, he must remain unmoved himself, the more surely to move others.[24] Too much realism on the part of the actor makes the audience forget that the actor is an artifice; but too much artifice (or simply poor acting) errs on the side of overblown artificiality. The actor, as with all performing artists, must achieve a creative role in his performance. Musicians rarely play the notes as they are written, but must, as Leonard B. Meyer indicates, achieve a significant and creative deviation.[25] It is this creative deviation which gives the performer control over the medium of his art: himself. He must bring out, as he performs, something not only deviant, but something which is significant in its deviation, significant in that it is a new revelation for the audience. Some rare or vivid or unusual, but revelatory act must accompany a creative performer's actions on stage. Be he an actor, dancer, instrumentalist, or puppeteer, he must make manifest, if we can call him creative, some vivid thing which not only moves us—and that can be done easily by sheer virtuosity or emoting to such an extreme that we cry or squirm or react highly emotionally ourselves in one way or the other—but it must be relevant to that which he is performing in a creative way.

Actors who practice the Method, that school of acting derived from the great Russian director Stanislavsky, and amplified in the New World by association with psychological realism, sub merge the self in a new realism derived from their concept of the characters they are portraying. The obvious danger of this psychological realism is that there is too great an identification with the personality, which may lead the actor to a kind of faulty drama which is beside the point. The mind must be aware of the unreality of all art before it can alert us to the new possibilities beyond itself. Otherwise we would be just as

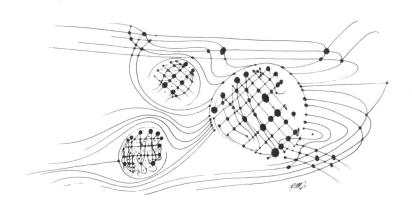

content attending a session of Moreno's psychodrama, some-times interesting and very moving because we know that it is a real-life situation played by the characters who have lived it. Method actors usually fall short of their own ideals, however, and we cannot help but sense that they are human beings who are not perfect simulations of the roles they portray.

The other dominant modern school is usually referred to as the English school, derived from RADA training (the Royal Academy of Dramatic Arts) or the school of hard knocks—on the boards or in stock or repertory for years. George Arliss has written that all acting is a bag of tricks, and that half the fun and half the art of the actor is to act artificially while appear-ing to be natural.[26] The actor learns many tricks to give the illusion of emoting—to cry, for instance, he turns half from the audience and shakes his shoulders. This histrionic method has built up movements and gestures which psychological or character traits seem to indicate. A fortuitous combination of these two schemes is perhaps the best compromise the actor can make, as when a RADA-trained actor or actress joins the New York theater world.* It is difficult for the one kind of trained actor to understand the other, in most cases. Lou Gil-bert, a Method actor, remarked to me[27] that the experience of seeing a performance of Laurence Olivier from the first row was too much for him—the "artificiality" of the acting forced him to leave in the first act. Olivier is obviously an old trouper, and he must intuitively give his stage performances one kind of acting, and his film performances another. Generally his vital-ity is in his individual style, which he brings to all roles, be they princes or punks. We sense, for instance, when he is playing Hamlet, that we have discovered a new dimension of the Bard's sense of tragedy. Simone Signoret is another great per-former, and in *Room At The Top*, for instance, we understand the poignancy of what could be a cliché part, raising our view

* The English actresses Rosemary Harris and Christine Pickles (my sister-in-law) are actresses who seem to marry these two acting styles successfully.

of such a woman to a new level of perception concerning humanness. This particular form is so intimately connected with the actual conditions of humanity that its perception is direct and unencumbered by abstractions or artifices; perhaps this is why the stage—an encounter directly with an artified human being who is right there, alive, performing for our benefit—is such a powerful and important medium. We all seem to appreciate and desire to perpetuate theater in our lives in one form or another—amateur theatricals, children's shows, road troupes, Broadway, all give us this experience to a greater or lesser degree.*

An actor or an actress struggles to find some way to make a role more than a simple reading of lines that reflects a certain meaning. The director can of course aid in this discovery, and since he is apart from the actor, he may more objectively be able to evaluate a given dramatic idea. Often we see imprints of directors which do not wear well with the particular actor or actress. The wiser directors, like the wiser symphonic conductors, I think, let the performers interact in their own ways, trusting that they have chosen artists whose level of imagination can lead to the desired over-all effect. This is how group effort takes on a new creative meaning, and how a new vision can arise out of a group effort—by the members of any group all being uninhibited virtuosi. I think this applies to all group creativity. Few dictatorial directors have managed to give us other than a single performance in many guises. But if this is the desire, and I can see where it is valid (in the case, for instance, of Charlie Chaplin's wonderful efforts to bring his own brand of *gesamtkunstwerk* to life), it seems to me that the medium should be other than live actors—puppets, for instance,

---

* Theater at a professional level will inevitably be the first art to receive Federal aid, and to become an accepted part of our social community. The next will come music, that human art form in which meaning has been made less explicitly human, but in which it is still kept at a human level by virtue of the use of live performers.

or a form like dance in which the movements are so highly codified that a director-choreographer is able to get his instructions carried out to the T.

6

The movements of dance, the repertory of elements, are so strict, even in their modern forms, that it gives the director almost complete control over his product, even though he uses human beings subject to their own whims. The dancer spends years of constant and strenuous learning to control his instrument so that he can make it do what he wants, and he also learns an ensemble of movements according to the particular school of his inclination. Those great innovators in modern dance, like Isadora Duncan or Martha Graham, not to mention the developers of ballet in the sixteenth century, worked out their movement ideas and spent years impressing them on a group of co-dancers. These movements form the repertory of visual ideas out of which dance is shaped. Years of working with one *maître de ballet* or choreographer is difficult and can lead to a certain stagnation, even for an audience used to the performances, but it obviously also permits a high perfection of control, something that is essential in all art forms, especially a performing one. The modern movement broke with the rigidity of classical ballet at a time when an entire generation of artists were getting tired of classical forms, bored with the order of the previous age, and ready to make radical departures. This is but another manifestation of the last generation's initial break with the rational, one-viewed approach of logic. But the new forms were amorphous, and soon the creators found themselves having to generate a new set—although slightly more liberating for the body, ones they felt to be more honest and not trying to strive for either the ethereal heavens or to break down the earth's gravity. Dance requires that pure movement be apotheosized, that the human body be subjugated and given a new release of movement. It is almost impossible to hide the human body, although Alwin Nikolais tries by enveloping it with large colored webs or behind props. Story is natural to dance since the body moves, and pantomime is traditionally part of the encoding mechanism, all supported of course by music which is essential for rhythm. Dance without music is done on occasion, but it usually builds a percussive rhythm of its own by stomping feet, or a strong visual rhythm by wild movements.

Modern choreographers have limited story-content, and some have transcended it altogether. Martha Graham brought in ritualistic, psychological movements, which were general although literal. She tried to objectify a contrasting movement which captured a sense of understanding and tightness, releasing itself in an almost universal worship on the verge of mysticism. But when the form is completely devoid of story, as with the choreographers Murray Louis or Beverly Schmidt (who worked with Alwin Nikolais); or James Waring whose abstractions are sometimes humorous but always moving; or Merce Cunningham whose near-ballet technique is strong and personal, danced always to the music of John Cage; they give us a new sense of the possibilities of dance, so long considered to be dying in the torpor of misplaced rigidity. The influence of these moderns has also been felt by all classical dance companies, whose choreographers think nothing of using some startling and strange movement which would have been anathema to a traditional ballet choreographer.*

Dance encodes not explicit hand signals as in Hawaiian or Balinese forms, but rather the intricate formal movements of the human body. In the hands of modern choreographers the dance becomes a form almost as abstract as nonobjective film, yet, however, firmly planted in the human figure which serves as its focus and counterpoint. It is removed from, yet dominated by, actual physical humans, differentiated as to sex, and mean-

* The modern dance usually employs electronic music, and some painters, notably Robert Rauschenberg, have joined the troupes in a search for overlapping multi-dimensionality in art.

ingful as a play of human forms against each other, and with respect to the field of the dance floor and whatever props or lights are used.

We have a great sympathy with dancers because it is such a strong, universal urge within us all. It can be a social and a physical release, whether it be the waltz, the Frug or Watusi or Jelly Belly or what have you, or a ballet or modern dance to which we passively react. The dance of life, as Havelock Ellis called it, is within easy reach of us all. Although we may not be balletomanes or sympathetic enough to modern dance to go out of our way to see it, we cannot help reacting to the human body in motion. When such an opportunity does arise, however, chances are we will see only bodies in motion. As with all the arts it is necessary to have long familiarity with the form and technique and practice, before it is possible to transcend the literal facade and direct the attention where it is most rewardingly served.* Alwin Nikolais has been influenced by Hanya Holm and the theoretical writings of Rudolf von Laban, but his studies into space and the psychology of movement have gone well beyond his influences into a valuable extended form of his own inimitable concoction. Drama is his keynote, although it is abstract drama; and it is futuristic in that the mechanisms sometimes inundate the humans, turning the dance experience into a new creative manifestation of moving form and color. This is one of the few art forms which I consider to be appropriate for our electronic age, although it may sometimes err on the side of technique and bravado.

It will be interesting to see if the new drugs, which athletes have sometimes used unlawfully to break records, will help the dancer reach new physical or creative heights in their movements. Certainly the almost hypnotic ritualistic exercise that dancers must subject themselves to might be obviated, with

---

* I was fortunate in that my wife Diana was dancing at the Henry Street Settlement House under Alwin Nikolais when I married her. This gave me an opportunity to study the problems of dance firsthand. Most important, my exposure helped me realize that dance is a spacial-temporal art as vital as music or the motion picture.

some medical assistance—naturally however it must be expected that nothing physically harmful will be employed, and that all such experiments will be under strict medical control. There is no record to break here, and we have everything to gain in our artistic experiences by making the experiment. The mechanism of dance, since it rests on definite physical possibilities, could conceivably derive new and graceful or powerful, or sustained and complex movements from some chemical aid. But dance is a temporary form, and its experience fades after the one performance. Only the immediate audience would absorb the experience, as with a virtuoso musician giving a concert to an extremely limited audience. But art need not be democratically general to be meaningful; the word gets around, the new synthesis works its magic in unknown but powerful ways, and we all are ultimately the benefactors.

7

Drugs of course have a negative connotation today, because they seem to suggest addiction or mind control; this need not be the case, however, if the proper moves are made by the authorities. It is to be assumed, for instance, that the current publicity over the deleterious effects of LSD will force its artistic exploitation off the current market, which may or may not be salutary. It probably can be assumed that most of the good effects of all such psychedelic mind-expanding drugs could also be reached by the mind on its own, with sufficient inspiration or motivation; but such an assumption may not be correct. If the goal is mastery over the human body for the purposes of exploiting it to the fullest, then we will have to wait until we understand better the bad effects, and go on to experiment with the good ones.

In the meantime it is possible to realize a rather perfect art form of humanoid figures without resorting to such extreme but interesting conditions. The urge for complete and perfect control over the human form is in fact realizable in the puppet theater. A miniature *gesamtkunstwerk*, the likes of which

Richard Wagner would not have been able to imagine, the puppet allows the artist complete control—if he is sufficiently versatile to realize it by himself. He cannot only conceive the play, stage the production, control the lights and scene and all action, but he can also fabricate the personalities, execute their voices, and control their every action.

The puppet theater has a long and distinguished history which Marjorie Batchelder outlines in her *Rod Puppets and the Human Theater*.[28] Although we generally include the puppeteer with the circus performer or street entertainer, serious puppetry has existed in the past in many countries, and it still does today in some. Batchelder notes that Ben Jonson used puppets in his plays, and Marlowe probably also did. Shakespeare's *Midsummer Night's Dream* and other plays were reputed to have been written for marionettes. Goethe wrote a puppet play in 1769 and his *Faust* was strongly influenced by the classic *Doctor Faust*, still on the boards of the puppet theater of his day. Haydn composed five operas for the puppet theater at the castle of Eisenstadt between 1773 and 1780, none of which are extant. I saw both his *Philemon and Baucis* and Mozart's *Bastien and Bastienne* successfully done with rod puppets, and they were undoubtedly similar to Haydn's actual puppet operas. Bertolt Brecht conceived of his plays as receiving their optimum presentation in the puppet theater, perhaps due to the trouble he had with actors.[29] The director and scenic designer E. Gordon Craig conceived of the *Übermarionette* to take the place of the actor.[30] Gertrude Stein wrote *Identity* for the puppet theater. Even George Bernard Shaw wrote a play for puppets, although it is a poor one. Shaw said that puppets served as object-lessons to actors, because although they were stiff and wooden, always with the same overcharged expression, they moved an audience as surely as the most experienced, muscular, and intense actor could.

The puppet is related to the animated cartoon, because, as Hanns Sachs suggests in *The Creative Unconscious*,[31] they can be created entirely by the artist, and also because they can bring anything to life in a primitive animism. The cartoon is more appealing to children because it requires so little visual effort to grasp the images. The puppet theater has received but scant attention in our Western culture, perhaps because it is traditionally not a single-point, simple art form with a sequential logic. This is also why it will obviously play an increasing role in the art of the future: it is multileveled, diverse, capable of great fractionings, and it demands a larger grasp by the audience for them to completely understand both its technique and its message. This multiplicity of awareness begins with the initial perception of the theater of little sculpturesque people, standing for real people; then you sense the space in which they perform, with its miniature sets and lighting, soon amplifying in the mind of the viewer to a large-as-life situation; and then you watch the play that is being performed, with its simplifications, exaggerations, and extended to ways not so characteristic or well known in the theater; and finally you realize the fact of the performers and manipulators working the puppets by string or at the ends of their hands in real time. These various levels contribute considerable insight into artistic form which is not easy to grasp with a single-value logical approach that demands unity.

In the East, especially in Japan, the puppet is and long has been a serious art form. As McLuhan notes,[32] the East has been long used to a complex, multiviewed attitude toward its media. The Javanese *Wayang* (drama) *Kulit* (shadow puppet) is linked to the other Javanese arts in a continuous spectrum: *Wayang Beber* (an unrolled scroll accompanied by recitation), *Wayang Golek* (relief puppet directly visible), *Wayang Topeng* (actors wearing masks), and *Wayang* (actors and dancers.)[33] The theory is that theater began with the shadow, originating in a religious ancestor cult, evolving from its artificial plastic form to the realistic dance-drama. The encoding of the characters in the Javanese *Wayang* is as strict as the Greek drama or the Hollywood star system. The two extremes of good and evil are the *alus*, a puppet with almond eyes and no chin, representing supreme spiritual beauty; and the *kasar*, with bulging eyes and a coarse mouth, representing the base and evil. The native who witnesses the Javanese play does not understand the ancient language, but he knows the characters, realizes that a moral idea is being expressed—the triumph of the spiritual over the base—and he follows the communication and perceives its creativity when it occurs in performance. In a similar way the Sicilian peasant probably today watches the Charlemagne tales which his puppet theater employs—battles between the Saracens and the Christians, though he may have forgotten the origin of these Norman adventures.

Both the Javanese and the Sicilian puppet theaters are tight, stylized communications, whose encoded puppet characters are well understood by both young and old. The novelty of this form—creativity is perhaps too high a word for this earthy and wonderfully primitive form—may have seeped out of the constantly repeated actions; but if you or I watch them, we are impressed by a singular vision.

The crowning example of serious puppetry in the East is of course the Bunraku puppet theater of Japan (recently seen on a New York tour). This stylized doll theater is a strange contradiction between the realistic and the artificial. We may have difficulty transcending the gap between a crew of men operating a puppet in full sight, a master puppeteer whose face we also see, and two black-hooded assistants who work one puppet hand and both the feet, but if we do, we enter into a new experience that is difficult to describe. The puppet suddenly comes to life, as surely as does a live actor when we overcome the fact that he is a human with his own traits and problems. Realism is tempered in the puppet theater only by the characterization, and the Bunraku puppet is as codified as the puppet in the Javanese or Sicilian theater. Unless we have had long familiarity with these puppets, however, I imagine that this falsity is difficult to overlook. The stories of Bunraku plays are remarkably like Italian operas in plot, and Bunraku in translation (available by means of a transistor receiver stuck into one ear) becomes a natural experience within a few minutes. Perhaps this is one way we will be able to close the gap between countless ages and difficulties such as languages.

A playwright's dream, the puppet is capable of being exactly like the conceived character. Only the mask can duplicate the perfection of characterization of the puppet, which is why it is sometimes used with puppets. The puppet not only looks the part perfectly, it moves correctly, and performs exaggerated movements or subtle movements to any degree. In a good European marionette production, as, for instance, that of Professor Anton Aicher's Salzburg Marionette Theater, you are immediately fascinated by the borderline between reality and artifice. This tasteful company does opera, and the puppet is most charming when it walks in this land of Mozart's singing. The dances also achieve a grace and airy quality which would have been the envy of Taglioni. The idealized figures have a strong power of illusion which is a makeup artist's dream. Only the motion picture can exceed the technical possibilities of the puppet theater, but the two-dimensionality and secondhandedness of the movies throw it back into a more artificial mode, despite its attempts at realism; and the movies too are but a record, whereas the puppet is an immediate performance, in which the performer is alive, although hidden.

Puppet shows are perforce live performances, even when the human motive force is invisible. It is not necessary, as with the Bunraku, for the manipulator to be hidden or obscured, because we soon forget the mechanism. Peter Arnott, who gives his shows in direct sight of his audience (Greek tragedies done with marionettes), suggests that the audiences are never disturbed by his presence—perhaps they are all the more impressed by his godlike size and dominance over his predestined creatures.[34] The puppet operator or operators not only move the puppets, they also lend their voices—which can add another multidimensionality to the act. It is through this human support that the puppet can derive its most creative aspect, I think, rather than through the medium per se—I say this because I think that it is the performance which differentiates puppetry from, say, kinetic sculpture.

Tape-controlled puppets, such as those at the I.B.M. exhibition at the 1965 New York World's Fair, or the amimatrons of Walt Disney at Disneyland, are, like all automatons, failures as art—unless their construction is so consummate that they become modern kinetic human-appearing sculpture, programmed however in a repetitive way. The robot moves mechanically, which is to say jerkily; he must be the antithesis of the random, tentative human being; he must be certain, well-defined, but never heroic. At most, the robot must evoke our fear or perhaps our pity, as in *R.U.R.* where Rossum's robots pitifully inherit the earth, becoming humans *manqué* (Karel Capek who wrote this play also invented the term "robot.") Puppets on the other hand are transference modes into which we can project vivifying features and humanness, expecting to be rewarded for our efforts by the insights of a creative communication.

It may be difficult to imagine, but one can become a virtuoso at manipulating puppets. The control of a marionette is no simple feat, and the artistry goes beyond the problem of keeping the feet on the ground. Hand puppets have the added possibility that they can present two figures under a single person's control, and thus enable a person to play a duet with himself.*

Puppets share the feature of animism with cartoons, as mentioned previously, showing us how vivified inanimate objects can relate to each other creatively; but puppets are not flat and merely a recording like the cartoon. A puppet cannot be made

---

* If you were to spend a week at a state fair, operating hand-puppets every hour on the hour, you would discover, as my wife and I did a few years ago, that every performance reveals new subtleties of movement, new ideas in form and performance modes, which sometimes culminate in something as exact and skillful, and even as inspired, as that of a virtuoso violinist. The only trouble is that the American puppet audiences, geared only to an occasional puppet in a television commercial or children's program, could detect none of this, and therefore no communication, much less a creative one, was possible.

to distort like a piano cartoon, change its form to grin its ivory-key teeth at you and smile out its music. It may perhaps be a virtue of puppets that they cannot too far transcend the normal limitations of physicality, because cartoons sometimes become an overwhelming infantile fantasy which destroys any artistic power they might be capable of attaining. Our anxieties are not played on with puppets as they most readily can be and often are with the cartoon. We can see Mickey Mouse cleaved in half and both sides run away, to coalesce bloodlessly a few frames later on.[35] To make a naturalistic cartoon of a person is a very difficult achievement, which makes all of Walt Disney's people hard to stand. The puppet on the other hand can easily idealize people, and also form a realistic person which is quite acceptable although diminutive—we forget within a few moments that they are diminutive, and are most surprised afterward when the puppeteer-giants take their bows. For these reasons a puppet is quite a bit different from a cartoon, although they are both the vivification of inanimate form. Only some traditional folk puppets such as Punch and Judy (and their equivalents throughout the world) actually play on the abandonment of our anxieties as do the cartoons.

As Alexandre Bakshy observes: "The puppet can never live unless it acts, as the man can never act unless he lives;"[36] the puppet is always taken as a puppet, whereas live actors are always people acting like other people. When Audrey Hepburn played Liza in *My Fair Lady* to someone else's singing voice, she was actually being used as a type of human puppet—which is one of the remarkable intermedia possibilities of the motion picture. The artifice of the puppet is never so perfect as the actor in his role, and no extraneous encodings, such as a person sneezing or scratching his nose out of character, will mar the perfection it is possible to attain. The puppet is always equally sincere, funny, horrible; there is no possibility of confusion in the communication situation with the puppet, and its creativity comes through an intensification of the theatrical experience.

Although puppets are potentially ideal dancers, here the limitations of technique are most immediately seen in practice, especially when the puppet attempts to imitate a human. Professor Aicher's dance sequences, while adding a certain whimsy to ballerinas by enabling them to perform impossible feats (not only of flight, but also of double-jointedness), are the weakest links in his almost perfect chain (like most walking marionette movements). The grace of an actual human form dancing is almost lost when a marionette tries to match the human physicality at its height. The hand puppet, an extension of an actual human hand, while it does not have legs to move, can more readily translate human movement into abstract form, as can obscured figures in abstract costumes, for instance, Picasso's "stage hands" in the ballet *Parade* by Erik Satie and Jean Cocteau, or Nikolais' dancing forms.* The human is also self-programming and has a creative contribution to make to dance movement. But on the other hard, as an abstract moving form, the puppet can easily outdo the kinetic sculpture. The Dadaists are unrivaled in their use of puppetlike sculpturesque forms, and they made several remarkable films that are essentially puppet ballets, the most famous being the *Ballet Méchanique* designed by Kurt Schmidt with F. W. Bogler and Georg Teltscher; or the marionette productions of Jean Arp's wife, Sophie Taeuber, an ex-dancer of the Laban-Wigman troupe.[37]

The puppet is a manifestation of the vivifying instinct at its extreme, most precarious limit. A facsimile of men and women, and also of their most far-out imaginings, the puppet theater communicates its meanings not through an exactitude, but from an inimitable sense of new vitality which is a counterpoise of the human situation. The puppet has many unique features: an immediate presence, an incredible mobility, perfect characterization, a sculptural and fantasy inventiveness of great potential, a strong kinetic force, and extremes of color

---

* This difficulty may have motivated Nikolais to give up marionettes and turn to choreographing humans.

and illumination possibilities. This makes puppetry a medium of multifaceted potential which would readily meet the demands of simultaneity and disconnectedness.

There are few practicing imaginative puppeteers today, however, since most are confined to traditional or mass-entertainment forms. F. J. Peshka's *The Standwells*, Burr Tillstrom's or George Latshaw's television skits, Larry Berthelson's children's productions, are some of the superior traditional puppet shows in America. But we have little evidence of puppeteers devoted to the form as an art medium as some past puppeteers have been, in the sense of using beautiful shapes and movements and original theatrical drama as did Richard Teschner or Gera Blattner in Europe, or Paul McPharlin or Remo Bufano in America. The most well-known American puppeteer Bil Baird has done mostly eclectic ventures for industrial shows which reflect Disney-like characterizations, just as Serge Obratzov, the Russian puppeteer, has restricted his government-supported adult shows to theatrical parodies or repeats of classics. James Henson's muppets are about the most original puppets on the current American scene, capturing a uniquely mad quality in the dancing, singing, extraterrestrial creatures that attain an unexpected but consumating climax. Peter Schuman, a young German living in New York City who began the Bread and Puppet Theater, has also created remarkable giant rod puppets and masks, which he uses powerfully in human-puppet pageants for civil rights or anti-war shows and demonstrations.

Puppets carry the connotation of a children's diversion today, but this is not an intrinsic part of the medium. When serious artists begin to ignore this stigma and devote more creative energies to the puppet form, it will perhaps emerge as a viable contemporary expression. Puppeteers must also try to enlist serious playwrights, artists, and patrons; and they must experiment with all kinds of theatrical combinations. Puppets are perfect "absurd" people, and their artificiality would obviously make them useful in the Theater of the Absurd, with the added effect that a puppet in a human role shocks you all the more into seeing the ridiculousness of the human situation.*

The recent Associated Production Artists (APA) production of Erwin Piscator, Alfred Newmann, and Guntrum Prufer's *War and Peace*[38] suggests how puppets might also become a part of the standard theater. In this show there was a sequence of the Battle of Borodino for which I created puppetlike figures that the live actors manipulated on stage; but unfortunately my job was only construction, and no suggestions as to a more active puppet role was accepted for the figures.

In the Piscator-Newmann-Prufer play the puppets emphasize the futility of war and the almost predestined immobility of the participants, which does justify unmoving statuettes. They were used like giant chess pieces, Napoleon and General Kutuzov engaging each other in battle, and a live actor playing Levin rescuing the puppet Pierre when he was wounded. Puppets allow great dimensional changes. As projected views or movies are sometimes used for the backgrounds of plays, the puppet could afford an unusual new diminutive situation on stage. In contrast to live actors the puppet scene can become a long shot as in the movies, or it can turn into a marvelous fantasy sequence.

The abstraction of peopleness in puppets is easy to accept, and the deus ex machina becomes valid, even though naturally you realize how it is formed. The puppet gives consistent exaggerations, extreme motions, and sudden transitions that are more vivid than in the motion picture because they are live, and it also maintains a perfect personification, which can also extend throughout an unimaginable variety of size or form. The puppet, I think, is the ultimate in the mechanization of matter which strives for the condition of art. It is not real nor does it try to be an automaton; and neither is it artificial since we easily identify with it.

---

* The modern English composer Harrison Birtwistle has written an opera, *Punch and Judy*, with a highly stylized and inventive libretto by the American Stephen Pruslin, which would make an excellent contemporary puppet opera.

8

The vivifying arts must end, like life itself, but that ending is all important, as it is in life. "If death did not exist," Schopenhauer has written, "there would be no philosophy—nor would there be poetry."[39] When we finish reading some sweeping novel we are almost dazed that it is over—experiencing in miniature what an afterlife would be like were it true. Great art seems to have an extra meaning because we have, godlike, survived it. Since art is a closed system, its self-containedness makes it comprehensible, and even if it is a disjointed or fractioned work of art that is like the page of a newspaper or a Rimbaud poem, we sense an order. If we nostalgically wish to reenter into this world at a later date we can do so easily—but the act is not one of admiring that work, only exhibiting our own romantic shortcomings and human limitations. Art, although rich enough to ennoble us again and again, must be ennobling in and of itself, rather than a call to nostalgia. Romantic escape in literature is a mirrorlike reflection of our inner insecurities, not an emphasis of a creative growth which we have not yet grasped.

When we first find some true vitality in art and begin to sense, as, for instance, in our first gripping novel, that something vital is going on in there, something important and dominating, we are initially quite confused and unable to assess the value of the experience. A new revelation of life is usually treasured for the wrong reasons. This vitality of art derives not from its accurately engaging us with real life characters, but rather from its accurately building the experience of perceptual and moral understanding through which we measure future experience. When we realize this fact we can settle down to experiencing the true nature of art, and accordingly grow through it. Art's imperishability is important, but so is its ability to enlarge our view.

Art is one answer to the question of life, but in itself it is of course not the same as the reality of life itself. Experiences, adventures, boring times, tragedies, day-to-day events which have happened to us all in our childhood and adult life—including sex experiences, getting to know and partially understand people, our wife, parents, children; learning to solve or live with our economic problems; these comprise the true experience of life and are colored by the kind of individual humanness we ourselves generate. But out total heritage of art creativity, imbibed from the time of our birth until the present, both consciously and unconsciously, determines not only the specialized modes of our intellectual reason, but also the total structure of our experiences and what we derive from them, both positively and negatively. Language is the earliest accretion of the art act, providing us with perhaps the most basic human creative communication; literature and the other vivifying arts, depending as they do on language, therefore become meaningful to us for very basic and deeply ingrained reasons.

To assume, however, that the communication of art is more important than the communication of life is to miss the entire point of these discussions. Art is for life, art *is* life, and experiencing art is for living. Even in this communicative age we feel that we have lost contact with our fellowman. Art is how man can regain contact with humanity, in fact it is the primary invention of man whereby he gains contact not only with his humanity, but also the humanity of other people and of other ages of peoples. The difficulty of any intellectual exchange between two people forces them to art; the loneliness of the intellectual self is heightened by the complexities of all man-to-man exchanges. We resort at most to trivia today, and to go any deeper is difficult—usually the excuse to do so must come from some article about art, or through some art experience we have shared. Art is a bridge which enables us to get into the souls of our fellowmen, to grasp the essential humanness and the most sensitive and creative qualities of our fellowmen. At one point or another everyone has probably had the urge to sit at the feet of those great men he knows or realizes are within easy communication distance, but it is generally a useless and romantic gesture without reward. Those great men communicate best to us through their greatest work, and personal contact is often anticlimactic; the personal contacts we have with our most intimate friends are obviously more rewarding. Thanks to the vivifying arts it is possible for unknown humans to give us meaningful human relationships, even though the intermediary of art separates us from all physical human contact. Unlike personal experiences the creative communications of art not only give us these personal contacts, but make them eternally available for our repeated experience.

8

The Computer Apprentice

The Limits of Robot Artists

1

I T IS quite easy to fool people into believing that a mechanical device is human. We look for signs of humanness in everthing, personifying nature, animals, and machines. Automatons were the rage in the eighteenth century. The early drawing or musical automatons of Vaucanson or Maillardet still reside in the Neuchâtel Museum or the Benjamin Franklin Institute, playing their flutes or pianos, or drawing charming cherubs or frigates at the turn of a switch. We are no less fascinated today by attempts to simulate human beings, or by the mechanization of some human attributes. Walt Disney's animatrons in Disneyland play on this age-old human hope; and so do computers, when they are programmed dramatically to answer questions ranging from hints on cosmetics to matchmaking, as they were at the recent New York World's Fair.

But there is a limit to our credulity. When the phonograph or telephone was first invented its human voice was too close to home, and many people thought it was a trick, with a ventriloquist hiding somewhere to throw his voice into the small contrivance. We take the reproduction of the human voice for granted today, but when a machine tries its hand at another human quality we are just as suspicious. A chess-playing automaton invented by the Baron von Kempelen confounded the world in the 1700's. Chess is thought to be a game in which only the most brilliant human minds excel. When a machine beat most masters (except Philidor or Légal) it seemed to refute the fact that the intellectuality of man had no equal in the machine. This invention turned out to be a human hoax, of course, a chessmaster midget hiding in the magician's box which supposedly housed the mechanism. Edgar Allan Poe, who had an interest in such subjects, applied irrefutable logic to deduce that this machine was not a *pure* machine. The manner in which the human agency operated confounded him, but he recognized that it must exist. He deducted that a man named Schlumberger was the human agent, since when this midget was ill or over indulged in wine, the machine would play a sloppy game or would be "out of order."

If Poe were confronted with a modern computer he would have more difficulty in proving that it is a pure machine, and even less chance of guessing the manner in which the human agency was effected. This is due to the fact that the modern computer, although it does not look human, can be programmed to achieve what many people before had thought strictly in the human province. Chess-playing computer programs in fact have been written which give the amateur a run for his money, and this without a midget hiding in the machine.[2] But to what extent is the humanness but a hoax, and how far can computers of the future actually encroach on human reason and intellectual or artistic activities?

The computer is about a million times faster than the human being, and probably more times as accurate. It has an infallible memory, with perfect recall, and although it is limited in its space and access time to the data within its memories, this is being improved with each new generation of computers. The so-called potential for "artificial intelligence" of computers has led some computer enthusiasts to predict that human thought will be completely anticipated by the computer of the future.[3]

Self-directing motivations used to be the criteria for measuring the behavioral patterns of organic mechanisms, but simple feedback mechanisms readily exhibit this quality. Learning also was once considered to be the quality which no machine could accomplish, especially learning to profit by experience. Computer programs can be quite easily programmed to learn from experience in an almost human way. The final criticism of the inhumanness of the computer was its creativity gap—it could not make a creative contribution to its calculations. But, as Ulric Neisser points out in a fascinating and important article in *Science*[4] entitled "The Imitation of Man by Machine," it is quite easy to introduce novelty into the computer program so that it will perform the unexpected. Lengthy programs for computers often arrive at conclusions that are original in one important sense of the word. He says: "The results of 200,000 elementary symbolic operations cannot be readily predicted from the knowledge of the elements and the programs. The sheer *amount* of processing which a computer does can lead to results to which the adjective *novel* may honestly be applied. Indeed, complexity is the basis for emergent qualities wherever they are found in nature."[5]

Neisser continues his discussion by indicating three characteristics that are fundamental and interrelated aspects of human thought which are conspicuously absent from existing or contemplated computer programs or hardware. They are that human thinking: (1) takes place in and contributes to a cumulative process of growth and development; (2) begins in an intimate association with emotions and feelings which is never lost; and (3) with all human activities serves not only one, but a multiplicity of motives. These three characteristics of human thought also apply a fortiori to the cognitive processes which underlie the creation of art. But I think that Neisser overlooked the most important distinction between human and computer "thought," namely that a human is most concerned with the *form* of the communicative embodiment of his thought. No computer ever concerns itself with the media on which its outputs are placed, nor does it concern itself with perceptual needs or means for grasping inputs, simply because of the fact that it does not profit in any mechanical way from the fabrication of its communicative meanings. There is no reason for the computer to print out its calculations after it has made them because they can just as well reside in its memories at a particular location on its tape or discs.

But computers can accumulate a repository of operations and data which enlarges their abilities to act on new instructions and data, much as we humans do when we accept a creative communication and profit by it. The computer specialist has learned that he can instruct a computer to do a certain complex operation, such as computing a logarithm or the sine of an angle; and then he can put these operations somewhere specific in the computer's memory. When he wishes to perform this operation again he need not reinstruct the computer, since he can simply refer it to the memory location containing all of the instructions. If he wishes to he can build up a large series of complex operations which are all located in memory, and give a new complex problem which uses them, as, for instance, if he wishes the computer to compute the trajectory of a rocket to Mars at any day or hour in the year, he can instruct the computer to perform the operation with a single instruction. Limited only by the space in the memory of the computer the programmer can in this way build up exceedingly complex operations, and the computer *compiles* its individual steps from its repertory of memorized simpler operations. This is in a way analogous to the type of encoding which humans perform when they react to art, although it is a sequential operation which loses all grasp of structural interrelationships.

One reason the computer specialist desires to build up such complexes of instruction within a computer is for the very purpose of improving its communicative powers. A computer can be programmed, for instance, to respond to natural-language instructions by means of such compiler systems. A computer instructed in English to compute the trajectory of a rocket fired at such-and-such an angle, at such-and-such a time and day, with so much initial velocity, would first determine what the English words meant in one of its memory locations, what the various operations are that would enable it to make the calculation in another memory location, and then proceed to compile the routines necessary to make the calculation, and then perform it and print out the answer—also in English if it has been programmed to do so, with a nice, easily understood sentence giving the answer. The computer does not actually understand English, but it has been given the means to grasp what the words mean in terms of certain programs which reside in its memories. A wealth of such computer-language interpretive abilities is being developed for the express purpose of facilitating the man-computer communication link. When a businessman wants to use a computer he would rather be able to type his specialized demands into the computer input typewriter in a nomenclature which is familiar, than in a highly specialized mathematical computer language. A specialist in computer languages develops special programs in all such cases which interpret whatever is placed into the computer and automatically begin the computations.

The computer-language compiler system that brings about this added computer ability to communicate in easier and more human terms is a rough mechanical analog to the present theory of creative communication. Above all the compiler illustrates the potential for multilevel encoding in any mechanism. The power of the compiler system is only beginning to be understood by computer specialists. They are erecting a Tower of Babel out of their computer languages, and they have not yet begun to understand the level to which it can ultimately rise. Hopefully, it will be possible to build a computer whose memory is sufficiently large, that will discuss practically anything in a natural language like English. Short of this goal it is beginning to be realized that a computer is powerful in proportion to its ability to compile systems of languages, whatever they may be. The modern designer of computers takes into account not only the vast growing body of specialized computer languages, but also the potential for comprehending those new languages which may be invented in the future.

Nevertheless we can only conclude, at this stage of the development of the computer, that as an artist the robot computer is another human hoax. This is the case mainly because it has not been designed to truly exploit the communicative phenomenon on which it operates, and because it does not grow its own patterns for perception out of the encoding means by which it communicates. We human beings want products that are part of our very perceptual apparatus by which we can relate, store, manipulate, and in turn communicate again. The computer just the same has certain obvious advantages which might become potentially useful for the artist. If we can discover what they are we can render unto man the things that are man's, and unto robots the things that are the robots', to paraphrase Norbert Wiener's paraphrase.[6]

2

The mathematical background of music makes it a most obvious art candidate for the robot artist. Its sequential, harmoniously logical basis, although intuitively codefied and manipulated by musicians, has long been recognized as being close to mathematics and therefore a computational logic. Once standard forms of preferred structural combinations were developed it was possible to imagine a directly computational music of a rudimentary sort. By the time of Mozart, composers realized that this ordering could be achieved by chance, and in fact Mozart himself wrote his *Würfelmusik*: waltzes, rondos, hornpipes, and reels, the elements of which are decided by the throw of a dice.[7] The spirit of these experiments was much as if modern artists would collaborate in a series of number paintings for general enjoyment. It was not taken seriously by anyone as a substitute for creative composition. But not until quite recently has any serious study been made into the statistics of music with a mind toward the reproduction of the creative processes of music by a computer.

The most interesting and complete summary of these recent attempts is the book *Experimental Music* by Lajaren Hiller and Leonard Isaacson,[8] who also composed a string quartet by means of an Illiac computer, and accordingly called it the Illiac Suite. This book outlines the problem of creating music by mechanical means, and also quite interestingly discusses both the philosophical background and the practical problems. Hiller and Isaacson began by taking the classic book on counterpoint, Fux's *Steps to Parnassus*, and programmed the Illiac computer so that it would perform Fux's first species of simple counterpoint. They also included certain instructions in their program about the instruments to be used, the tempo and dynamic variations, wisely deciding to end up with conventional instruments that played notes composed by the computer. Without unduly emphasizing the mechanical or electric quality of their work, which would have been the case had they employed electronic sounds, it is possible to evaluate the creative possibilities of a computer without undue prejudice against the means. We are immediately at home with the string quartet sound, however radical the composition. The results of their work is not particularly imaginative, and it has a certain looseness of form which is rather characteristic of the student's work. Hearing the music you place it in the historical framework of the history of the string quartet; you judge it accordingly, and it does not stand up favorably. Nevertheless you realize that the work is remarkable if it is a mechanical product, although you suspect that you are listening not to a computer so much as to Hiller and Isaacson once removed on a computer and disturbed compositionally by some indefinable mechanism that prevents their really expressing themselves.

In the future when higher and higher species of counterpoint are programmed it is clear that the results will merely be advancing closer and closer to the type of sound which enabled

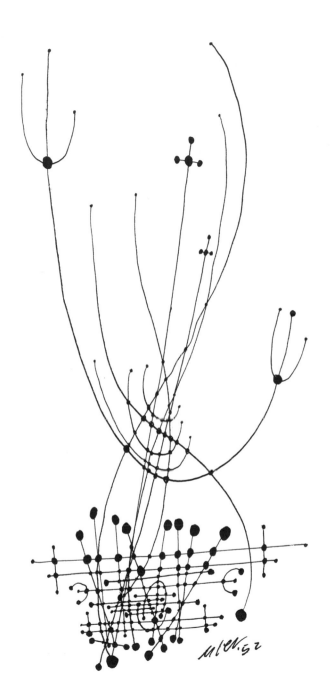

Fux to formulate his particular kind of counterpoint. We would arrive finally at a mechanical way to compose a classical string quartet. The most obvious limitation would be the same as that encountered by programmers trying to make computers into chess masters: the amount of information-processing becomes prohibitive when you want to increase the complexity of the choices beyond a certain point. The layman assumes that the computer is ever so vast and able to memorize everything we desire of it, but the number of possibilities in chess at the beginning of the game are so large that no computer can ever be expected to trace the contingencies of any given first move. A computer must be programmed to make guesses which are the results of "weighted" rules, according to which it will move on the basis of the programmer's experience. Mass-memoried computers are obviously not very equipped to decide on these "weighted" moves, and the programmer must decide them for him. But the limit of computational complexity of a computer will probably be pushed along as the state-of-the-computer-art advances, obviously always this side of infinite, and always less than the human—which makes all the difference between its being able to compute music which is artificial or humanly meaningful. This is obviously not the only limitation, but it is the most obvious practical one

However, in music there are areas other than composition in which the computer can serve the artist. The analysis of music, either for the purpose of determining what past musicians have been accomplishing from a statistical-mathematical point of view, or for the purpose of helping a composer organize his own past output, could function as a positive value for the artist. The logic of serial music, for example, is strict and easily computerizable, although the permutations of the tone row need a human insight for meaningful arrangement. As a crutch whereby the composer might be given ideas, which he would then proceed to supplement or reject, it could serve as a considerable help. The ability of the computer to go through a vast number of combinations could save a composer considerable labor, and, much as an inventor searching for some novel arrangement, it could provide print-outs which he personally would go over, in search of a creatively meaningful combination.

Hiller and Isaacson suggest that the computer would be most helpful in translating musical notations, say figuring base, or working out counterpoint given a theme, or making complex orchestrations according to some predetermined scheme of the composer's conception.

The ability to program a computer to profit from past experience would enable a composer to get his device to make compositions closer and closer to any desired style. We are assuming that the computer program has been written to give the computer this ability, and that it would accept suggestions from the composer who would make adjustments in the printouts in an attempt to "match" a given style. The ability of the computer to "match" a function is quite remarkable, especially when there is a give-and-take with an active element that adjusts its mistakes. Of course if another composer sat down at the computer console he would find that the computer would not so readily adjust to his own style, and any compositional attempt he might make would be "in the tradition" of the previous composer-programmer. For this reason it is conceivable that the computer would be a marvelous adjunct for individuals desiring a "group art." It would most readily serve as a repository for the combined styles of the composers or artists who use it. In this case the computer would build its group tradition, and much that has happened historically would take place almost instantly. We know that most composers of any era compose essentially in the style of their given tradition. Mozart wrote music like Haydn because the influences were very strong and any slight deviation was considered to be poor art—except when Mozart advanced to the point that he was a creator in his own right. The computer is our electric chance to turn tradition to almost immediate account, which would make the word "tradition" completely meaningless.

Mozart transcended Haydn out of a creative difference, and this is what even a computer-using composer must search for when working with his robot apprentice. There seems to be little difference then, except for the speed or perhaps the possibilities for amalgamating human styles, between a computer-compositional situation and the normal historical one. The computer does not help at all in the problem of finding truly creative and perceptual significances in music as a communicative function, but it does seem to have the potential for speeding up the process of finding them.

3

The many and various attempts of computer specialists to program their robots to make visually interesting pictures have usually arrived at orders within orders. They are like snow-flakes and kaleidoscopic or natural forms, quite impressive in themselves as are all manifestations of order to the human mind; but they are all quite without the necessary exchange value from which we profit on the entropy or information market. The journal *Automation and Control* has a yearly competition for computer works of visual "art," and some of them are quite beautiful. This is part of the new landscape which Kepes describes,[9] and it can, if we let it, perhaps inspire an artist to a significant addition to our communicative creations. They are mathematical orders which usually exhibit certain qualities dependent on the transducer by which they are formed, as, for instance, the oscilloscope which displays them, or the stylus system that draws them, plus the characteristics of electrical circuitry. The various permutations of these media possibilities are as interesting in their way as are the various manipulations of some new art media. We are curious to behold the transcendental functions, the capacitor-inductor decay or impulse characteristics, or the various oscillatory functions pulled together into one symmetrical display, but what we are seeing is not art so much as it is a compressed and unified mathematic of the electronic elements employed. As I have suggested, order does not recommend itself as a criterion for art because it only *impresses* the mind, whereas the communication must *change* the mind before we call it art.

Bela Julesz has made studies into the varieties of the picture plane as a statistically growing system, beginning with a perfectly random area divided into countless tiny squares. His original studies were made for the purpose of considering how visual textures affected our visual perception.[10] He concluded that the recognition of all familiar shapes is not needed for the discrimination of texture and for binocular perception. Like that of Gerald Oster this scientist's work began to fascinate certain sectors of the modern art scene, and he was accordingly given a show—again at the Howard Wise gallery, and he was acclaimed by some as an apostle of science as art. Julesz was probably innocent of these machinations; his published work is devoted to strictly scientific considerations (which has not been the case with Oster). Julesz was trying to discover how visual orders were arrived at, and as his surfaces massed together into specific arrangements, both on a two-dimensional surface and in three-dimensional binocular vision, they became increasingly interesting to the beholder.

The versatility of the computer as a design assistant is just being tapped today. Using either special computer languages designed to facilitate the interpretation of graphic details or special graphic input equipment by which actual visual data is "seen" by a computer, it is possible to program a computer to modify or alter any design in any preconceived manner. For instance, a computer could give an isometric from three inputs in profile, or vice versa, altering the output at will in aspect, angle or size.[11] Architects can now solve previously insoluble construction problems with the aid of a computer, eliminating guesswork or overdesign. The user's feel for the aesthetics of form, coupled with the computer's vast potential for details (as well as its ability to work out new forms given a few constraints, either visual or mathematical), will obviously play an increasing role in the art of the future.

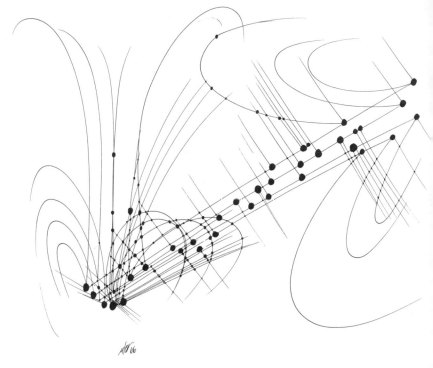

AW 66

The problem always reduces to that of formalizing the mental processes by which a mental activity arrives at a new design. In the act of this formalization it is usually discovered that even complex intuitive ideas contain many easily described elements which are thus computerizable. This formalization usually pushes man a little more toward a deeper level of creative understanding by revealing just where the imaginative new ideas must lie. Today's unchartered creative human frontiers are tomorrow's computer formalizations, to be replaced in turn by new human ideas and values.

The fact that computer specialists and scientists who work in the visual realm have little or no detectable knowledge of the tradition of artistic visual work makes most of their work entirely without artistic meaning and completely sterile visually. In time it is conceivable that they might derive a tradition of their own, built on oscillatory functions that are distorted in novel ways, but if they insist on working in the direction of purely design orders, it is not easy to see how they can make anything of more meaning than natural orders like the snowflake. It would be more fruitful, I think, if the research institutions that use computers would hire one or two good artists—or even art historians—to serve as critics of their productions. Why, asks the computer specialist, should I concern myself with art? What practical results would obtain, useful to me in my specialized research into computers? The answers to these natural and important questions are that perhaps some of the areas of the computer specialist, at present, such as those in the "artificial intelligence" or natural-language processing areas, are being approached quite incorrectly, and need a richer knowledge of structure and the human mechanisms that give them meaning, than can be arrived at in scientific isolation. Art may be the means of breaking down the barriers which prevent the computer specialist from realizing all of his desires on his remarkable gadget, if he will but let its methods influence him.

Traditional artists or art historians would insist on impossible things from the computer specialist. In the area of the visual arts they would demand recognizability probably, instead of only abstract orders. It would be useless for the computer specialist to explain that recognizable forms cannot be taken apart and reassembled in a meaningful way. The artist would ask, why take it apart? Why not find some way to preserve the meaning, to manipulate the visual elements directly—in other words, why not invent a new way to process images, a new type of machine? The specialist would counter with the fact that the visual arts are so intractable. You note that television requires a scanning operation which reduces the picture to lines of dots that build into a given picture at any given moment of time. This restricts all computer visual manipulations to pictures which can be stripped up and meaningfully reassembled again—restricts the manipulations only to those elements which can be traced or recorded if its parts are torn into shreds. Figures or faces or landscapes cannot be disassembled and meaningfully put back together again because like Humpty-Dumpty their aspects become shattered beyond recall once they fall into pieces in the memory of a computer. Nonobjective forms like those created by Mondrian or Albers, strictly geometric forms, are very easily worked with on computers, however. Most art of the nonobjective type, particularly the more geometric, is a natural for computer manipulation. All symbolic associations however are lost, unless some ancillary program is written to associate these meanings with the visual ones.

Visual computer-processing is then restricted by present-day computer hardware, and the visual arts are even more restricted because their complexity does not allow for the simple reduction to a digital basis. To take a scanned photograph or a television image and perform reductions on it can lead to many visually interesting accidents, broad two- or three-toned images, completely black-and-white reductions, or even to pure line drawings, but never to a single creatively meaningful revelation about our vision's organizing abilities. Images become reduced in a computer, and our strict and exact world of sight becomes sketchy and abstract. We easily accept the abstractions, but until some artist learns what to do with them from the standpoint of converting them into new systems of components whose elements reveal something new to our perception, we will merely look on them all as more of the many curiosities of modern science.

4

Language analysis has long been the subject of computer research.[12] To judge from newspaper accounts, language-translating machines are near-realities, and the computer is about to take over the function of the librarian. This is far from the truth however, since there are still many very formidable problems to be solved before a computer can be considered to be a useful language processor. I worked at RCA for two years in a group trying to teach a computer to make simple sentence diagrams[13] and perhaps ultimately to make good abstracts of a given paragraph. The problems are enormous. Obviously to expect a computer to be creative with language when it has barely begun to speak the tongue is optimistic to say the least.

The processing of ideas by dismembering them and indexing them is useful to a retrieval system, and retrieval can become a discovery when this system grows exceedingly large. It is possible to imagine then that a computer could creatively *aid* a writer, if only as an interesting partner in research. When literature is complexly encoded it is possible to imagine that a computer would help tighten the encoding by providing new references which could have escaped the writer's attention— subject to his acceptance or rejection, depending on his sensing whether or not it was a creative reference and meaningful to the encoding. A writer friend of mine[14] presently uses a punched-card file system to help him in his literary encoding bookkeeping, introducing motifs and generalizations on the cards which are useful clues and stimuli for creative ideas— sort of a mechanical brainstorming system. If he had a computer available it is conceivable that he could improve the efficiency of his self brainstorming system. The job which James Joyce undertook in his writings was to amass considerable data which he clued in by literary references sometimes very esoteric, but sometimes directly obvious, building a fabric of multilevel literary encoding that was a tour de force of inter-relationships and structural creativity. Melville did a similar thing in *Moby Dick*, although the backdrop of information about the whale and whaling industry is less obviously a creative support to the over-all form.

The computer could contribute to the complex fabric of artistic meaning in any literary work by building an iconography or symbolism so complex as to be barely discernible by a human being. The process must, however, build the human perception structure so that a human being exposed to it can finally grasp its scope. We must realize that there is a limit to the human comprehension of data, and to exceed it in an art form is to dehumanize art; at the same time we must not underestimate the human potential for grasping or growing to comprehend the most complex of artistic encodings, however arrived at. This is how the mind proceeds to build up its very consciousness and intellectual understanding. Perhaps the fabric of the mind of the future will depend on this complex structuring, which a computer-artist symbiosis might provide, in order to give him the necessary world view to meet the requirements of future living and thinking.

If one imagined further that sense-stretching gadgets were coupled directly into our very nervous system it is conceivable that man could literally transcend himself, entering into new types of understanding and organization and artistic perception. I once wrote a letter to the editor of Science[15] that suggested that artificial-transduced sense expansions might give us an actual psychic enlargement of our consciousness, but I think that my concept of consciousness was mistaken. Art causes the very expansion I was imagining then, no need to add extra physical transducers to our corporeal selves to enlarge our awareness. The value of all such physical sense-stretching would be to increase the potential for manipulation by an artist, which only then could perhaps "supplement our faculties." Their actual realization, even through their extrahuman physical forms, would have to occur as creative-communicative forms to preserve new insights as tangible and therefore repeatable experiences.

The intangibles of a literary work of art reside in the many different levels of meaning which are encoded, and in their relationships, which are recognized by us as being significant and novel. In order for the computer to be most useful as an active artistic robot apprentice, a human consciousness must be present at all times to sort out the ideas and to indicate when the combinations which the computer quite innocently and automatically forms are, in fact, significant for human perception. The computer is an expensive device to use, and the money outlay demands a justification beyond that of merely expanding our humanness—at least for the businessman, or perhaps also for the scientist who does not see the importance of this expansion. It may be, as the final chapter suggests in detail, that all such expansion of our humanness has more practical justifications than we all realize. The very creative enlargement of our humanness is at stake. The restriction of this creativity will restrict man himself, and prevent him from attaining his next logical intellectual development.

The robot as an artist turns out to be a hoax in which, like on Von Kempelen's chess-playing automaton, there must be a giant and not a midget in the machine. The artist will be performing his natural function, more remote from a brush or a pencil than he would ever have dreamed, hiding behind an unusual type of "mechanism"—acting as a Maxwellian demon in the program—quietly bringing into being significant art.

There is a paradox in man's desire to make robots. Man wants to turn the inanimate world into equivalents of his inner world, and at the same time give them inner worlds of their own. James T. Culbertson's mammoth book, *The Minds of Robots*,[16] seems to beg the question of consciousness by positioning a robot behavior pattern which synthetically influences its structure, jumping to the conclusion that an interaction between behavior and internal states is the equivalent of human consciousness. Yet despite its limitations this approach obviously will provide many useful insights into the mental processes of man, if not actually lead to the creation of a robot equivalent of the human being. When the computer is given a more active participation in the communicative situation, building its logic and structural organization out of the very communicative elements it receives, it will be ready to make an evaluation about the originality of new sensations in terms of its own internal structures. Until that time, however, the computer will serve only as an artistic robot apprentice.

9

The Modern Artist

The Scope of Creative Media

1

IT IS written that there is nothing new under the sun. New things are, by this view, but camouflaged old things, old wine in new bottles. All attempts to discover the new are vanity, and therefore there can be no "modern" artists—only eternal artists. Considering art as communication there is some truth in this adage: all successful encodings must be accomplished in terms which have existed in the past in order for their meaning to be understood. Yet as a *creative* communication, art is new, new in the sense of a revelation which brings about an association through old things which is new—old wine, not only in new bottles, but refermented as well. So those who make the creative refermentation by which mankind brings itself into a new expanded reality should be called modern artists. But since mankind does not quickly react to the true creative innovation in art, since many factors prevent the world at large from grasping the immediate significance of new art, there is usually quite a delay between a really new creation in art and its acceptance. The arts of the turn of the century, the innovations of cubism, surrealism, functional architecture, atonal music, unconsciousness in poetry and literature, are just now gaining general acceptance.

We see that today, however, the delay between an art movement and public acceptance is less. Also, art movements come and go much more quickly. The public has become conditioned to look for the unusual, and the unusual itself has been made synonymous with the creative. The newest fad becomes creative, and the very word "creative" takes on a new meaning and becomes the watchword of a kind of cult. And the rebel is considered to be the most creative person because his rebelliousness is part of the cult of fad art. Modern society loves a rebel because he is satisfying the desire of everyone to experience an unusual reality; and when the rebel takes society itself over the coals by satirical or critical means, the society loves it all the more. The artist is suggesting that what society has realized in its heart is a deadening, nonexperiential living is after all somehow more exciting and dangerous than it ever dreamed possible. This is why books that tear the affluent, conformist society to bits are so popular—they satisfy the need for a sense of excitement, in the very midst of the commonplace.

The subtle pressure by modern society for the new and the risqué is felt by all contemporary artists. In the first place the artist has to give society viable experiences which substitute for a lack of excitement in the world, and secondly he must satisfy the need for newness and critical negativism, so that by contrast society feels excited. It used to be that an artist lived continually with a mild sense of guilt because he was giving in to what society called childlike enjoyments, as Marion Milner writes.[1] Today, however, the shoe seems to be on the other foot: the remainder of society feels guilty because they are not artists! The fad artist who practices the unusual is highly rewarded, whereas the artist who does not, who sticks to some esoteric or traditional form, becomes the guilty-feeling party today.

Art destroys logical rationalities that insist a thing is one thing alone; a thing can be itself and something else at the same time when it is art. And the artist constantly suggests that things are more than they seem because they have meanings which are not immediately obvious on the surface. The irrationality of art was quickly transferred from the artist, who maintained it was part of the essential quality of the art object he fabricated, to the artist himself, who has been traditionally considered irrational. Today when the irrational is in vogue, so is the artist.

What society demands, society usually gets. Artists of the unusual, fad artists, eccentrics who call themselves artists and perhaps actually fabricate objects which appear as art objects on the art market, always appear on the scene, and always with the desired degree of unrespectability. And if the artist is expected to use the newest technique and medium, he does, be it acrylics, synthesized music, depersonalized dancers, strange buildings as far-out as an amusement park, the absurd in theater, "happenings," underground movies, what have you. The role of the fad artist is to be a controversial figure, and he must search for the most unusual forms and fashions to be so. Technological innovation must be his helpmate. He must embrace the completely new—within certain limits, however. If he begins to toy with forbidden drugs such as marijuana or LSD, and if he carries the unacceptable a little too far, he can be ostracized or even prosecuted, and put away into a little, closed system of his own: a cell. A Le Roi Jones, Allen Ginsberg, Lenny Bruce, or Jim Dine is acceptable until he becomes too outspoken or obnoxious, too wild or uncomfortably close to the most delicate truths of human existence. Pop art is welcome when it plays on the sense of futility, destroys ubiquitous commercials, and pokes fun at our synthetic world by taking our packaged society to task; but when it becomes blatantly obscene it is banned.

Or if the art sides with an unpopular ideology, the populace (or the authorities) do not tolerate it. Art is first of all a communication phenomenon, and when it teams up with a political message it exerts a force that a simple message cannot match. This is why art attracts many political ideologists; they unconsciously know that their message comes across loud and clear in art, and that it can shake societies most profoundly when it is packaged as a powerful art insight. In fact many artists feel that the modern artist has a direct responsibility to be revolutionary in the sense of stirring up society, or that the artist must always be destructive and try to shatter traditional values in order to help give birth to new ones. Günter Grass, in his play on Brecht, which reads like a modern, aesthetic, Germanic, *Waiting for Lefty*, suggests that the integrity of art is no release from the artist's revolutionary responsibilities to the world at large.[2] Even a purist abstract painter like Victor Vasarely can write with reason: "It is constantly being said that the artist can be apolitical, reactionary, or even worse, that he need not keep up with the news.... It is inconceivable for an authentic consciousness not to be sensitive to everything that is being done and undone around us. Art is inseparable from life and authentic creation can be only a revolutionary act."[3] Obviously, however, Grass and Vasarely mean totally different things by the word "revolutionary," since the one writes social satires and the other paints highly refined geometric pictures, at least as far as the manifestation appears directly in or through each of their arts.

The revolutionary condition of art must be tempered by the notion that the apparent illogic or radicalism of new and creative art is after all quite logical, although it is a logic we do not perceive until we have assimilated it. However radical an art, it is always the conservative art of the future. The most powerful art always builds our modern sensitivities into new fabrics, and forms for us what we call our humanness—which tomorrow will become yesterday's idea of what the humanness of man actually is. McLuhan notes: "The arts both as storehouse of achieved values and as antennae of new awareness and discovery make possible both a unified and an inclusive human consciousness in which there is easy commerce between old and new, between assured success and tentative inquiry and experience."[4] We grasp experience through our most creative modern art forms, but once the experience is integrated into our mental fabric, once it is part of our purview of life and of experience, we must go on to greater and more inclusive art forms in order to continue this never-ending expansion of our humanness. That this kind of art is considerably different from a novel or fad art—although it too can be novel on the surface—is quite clear; and a true modern artist does not necessarily manifest this novelty, either by using new materials, or by exhibiting modern novelties. The truly modern artist does, however, work in such a way as to bring out new creative insights into form or media or messages, and these creative insights enlarge our future modernity and establish the path of human intelligence, including the social and political intelligence of the future.

2

The source of art is direct experience, but art only comes into being when formulated. Man immersed in a reality that is impressive and immediate is the initial situation for art generation. The artist makes his creative formulation of the perception of that experience in a communicative media. The message *becomes* the media, it takes on its meaning in and through the media. I agree with McLuhan that the medium itself has more influence on us than we realize, but this is a social influence; and it may also be true, as he shrewdly observes, that the contents of a media like television only serve to hypnotize the viewer while the media wrecks him: the media is the massage—like a masseur the media works you over.[5] But before it can be called art, there must be a nexus of direct experiential happenings with a communicative formulation in some medium. The nexus transcends both the experience *and* the medium if it creatively broadens man's perceptual world.

Traditional art forms have become complacent in their media, and artists who use them have concentrated mainly on the experiential world which sustains them. The modern artist who lives his hidebound existence close to mass media which inundate him with a secondhand and highly distorted kind of experience is therefore in a very difficult situation if he sticks to traditional forms. Experience is constantly being watered down through the many filters of modern communication. A superficial use of Madison Avenue advertising gimmicks, Batman or other current campy characters or fads in television, trying to lift traditional media into new expressions, more often fails than it becomes interesting. A "happening" in which an actor watches television, presses a transistor radio to his ear for the Pop music, fingers the foldout nude in a *Playboy* magazine, places his feet on an air-conditioner while his body is electrically warmed with a blanket, drinking at the same time a no-calorie soda, presents a reliable picture of today's reality— attainable and most desired throughout the world.

Of course, art need not give us this picture to be viable today, unless we think that art must reflect reality to be important. If we do, however, we must not leave out the obverse realities: discrimination, bigotry, senseless wars, blind unreason, and man's general inhumanity to man. One way to get around all of this is for the modern artist to embrace media alone, and go into a creative eclipse. The fact that abstraction has become particularly acceptable has led some to conclude that it is just such an embracement of media, pure and simple. I have tried to suggest, however, how abstraction is *not* merely a turning away from reality's ugly or beautiful face, a hiding of the artistic head in the sand.

Nevertheless experience is still the source, even of abstract art. The modern artist, lacking a viable existential reality, one in which he personally is involved, grappling with noble experiences such as death, heroism, passion, must gain all of his experiences secondhand. Unless he is engaged in a peace movement or in a civil rights protest, where he can actually come to grips with some degree of the traditional realities of the human situation that he so desires; or unless he can afford to buy his adventures on the Matterhorn or in the jungles of Africa; or unless he is one of the few individuals trained and chosen to venture into space; he has to gain most all of his experiences via the mass media.

Television, books, the movies, newspapers, magazines, and radio are actually quite boring, however, if a person is mad for real adventure. We all know that news coverage today does sometimes bring real adventure directly into our living rooms, and we crave these adventures, however grotesque or tragic. Man seems to need the realities of experience, whatever they may be, which perhaps partially explains why he does not discourage nations in absurd wars, why he overlooks unforgivable poverties and cruel inhumanities. The race for space is about the only moral equivalent we have for the desolating experiences of the past. It is no wonder, then, that in the face of modern synthetic living any semirealistic thrill is coveted: an illicit love affair, the practice of graft or petty stealing, any or all falsifications of life that are secretly and therefore dangerously possible. This is more of an involvement than spending all the waking hours, not at the office, playing American roulette with the "big eye."

America is discovering also that a little adventure can be had through the arts—witness the growth of community art centers, the increased purchase of classical music, the mass printing of the classics. This is probably a reflection of the fact that everyone is catching up with an already outdated artistic viewpoint, the Western heritage of the eye-oriented and most reasonable world view which gave most past art its sensible meaning. The sensation becomes an important experience when everyone begins to grasp its meaning, both unifying and clarifying as well, which is a bonus that comes along with the experience.

The modern artist of the last generation, then, is helping to lead the bored modern man of today out of the morass of secondhand living. Since art is actually not a secondhand experience when successful and correctly perceived, it can be

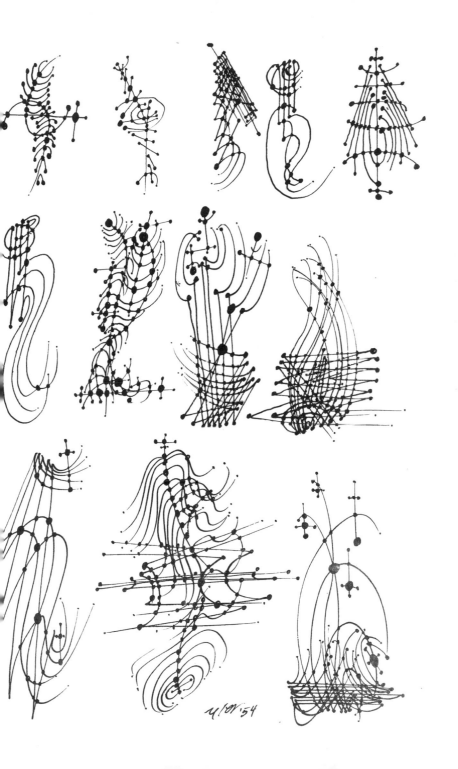

an important substitute for experience, unlike a simple communication medium which only acts as an exchanger. Art by this view could be releasing from alienation since it builds instead of reflects an existential reality. Art does not eliminate itself, and it makes all reality actually more meaningful because it enlarges our psychic mobility within reality; we learn how to move about in the world of our perceptions through art experiences, and therefore we value art *for* experience.

3

If you attend a contemporary art exhibition, go to any concert of modern music, attend an experimental theater or movie house, or read a review of an experimental book, you see immediately that many artists are trying to be modern in some sense of the word—but mostly trying to be unusual and different. The media itself is taking the upper hand in most of the modern attempts to be new. I do not rule out these art investigations as being noncreative, but I do wish to suggest that media investigation per se is insufficient justification for art. It is more than simply a question of the contemporary artist having a wide choice in media due to technological advancements—this most ages have to a greater or lesser degree. The current preoccupation with communication, as I have suggested, has become perverted by misunderstanding and has shifted the emphasis from creative communication to using new media simply for the purpose of deriving unusual communications, which are not necessarily—but can be—creative. This is very confusing to the public, but what is worse, it is also very confusing to the current art students—those individuals on whom we depend for all our future artistic expansions.

When a student begins his studies, he usually does so at some academy, perhaps an academy or school whose instructors practice art close to his vision of what art should be, or perhaps in an academic style which is acceptable and therefore the current fad. But whatever the reasons, assume that the art student gets carried away with his choice, actually learns how to manipulate a given academic medium (realizing of course that today the academic is not the realistic); and also assume that he has some talent. By the time he has finished his course of studies and become strongly entrenched in his particular style, the fad has changed! The student goes out in the art world only to discover that his art has become old hat. It requires that he be a very strong and dedicated person before he can continue to practice his art in a world which rejects it. This is of course an old story. Fortunately artists seem to survive these trials of fire—probably only when the fire within is sufficiently strong to counter fire with a stronger fire.

And as the science of our society and technological improvements become more and more rampant the artist is given more and more media out of which to forge new art forms. It becomes a kind of overkill: at what point does a given society have sufficient art expressions for the purpose of deriving all creative communications within its power? The number of creative insights which can be derived from any given media are obviously quite large, and even in the case of the simplest of media, the potential is almost theoretically unbounded, as I have indicated before. As the history of art has proved again and again, surprising new insights suddenly occur in means once thought to be exhausted. There is no theoretical need for an artist to hunt for new media because of an exhaustion of old ones. To carry this to its logical conclusion: the most minimal means of any type of art can provide sufficient choices for an artist to be modern in all senses of the word.

Practically, this means that a musician could, as I have indicated before, use say a single flute, and still compose modern music that is a true creative communication; or a painter could restrict himself to lines and dots alone and still arrive at a contemporary insight. This is actually not such a difficult proposition to accept if you are familiar with many of the art forms of the past which still very much attract artists today, or if you discover a very meaningful art from some ancient time. By this reasoning the concept that the traditional novel is dead for instance, is quite inaccurate, however much the new or fractioned or esoterically encoded novel is valuable and being praised by contemporary critics. It may be just that the current writer has been unable to capture the messy modern condition and turn its elements into a creative novelistic statement, or that we have been unable so far to recognize it in any given work. This is either the writer's or the reader's limited imagination, I think, rather than a basic limitation of the medium. And the string quartet is viable today, as Eliot Carter has proved, or the violoncello unaccompanied, as Vincent Persichetti has demonstrated; as viable as when Beethoven or Bach wrote for them. There is still strength and imagination in a line drawing by Chagall, that same line which the cave dwellers scratched on their walls eons ago. Or when the traditional poetic forms, even the trite one of the sonnet, comes from the pen of W. H. Auden or Dylan Thomas to shatter some smug convention, or to build a modern sense of the beautiful, we still realize its potential for modernity. It is always the pleasure of the original artist to show us the life hiding in an archaic art form.

4

New media clearly offer the artist new possibilities, however, and their extended scope for perception proliferation admittedly broadens the total art potential of man. The question of its contemporary meaning is another thing, because how do we truly know that a new medium can serve as the most appropriate creative glue for past ideas? Having only barely exhausted the possibilities of old media, is it not conceivable that new media could clog the very wheels of creativity? The human ability to grasp the human meaning of increasing abstractions in art may not yet have grown to a sufficiently high level of absorption to entertain new media. Edmund Wilson wrote, while reviewing André Malraux's *Voices of Silence*, that we only follow the line of reasoning which justified higher levels of abstraction due to the growing dependence on new media at our human peril. He decries essentially the piling of meta-abstraction on abstraction, or advancing to a more distantly removed level of encoding in which an abstraction stands not for something human, once removed, but for something which is itself an abstraction of something human, and therefore twice removed, and so on The danger, as Wilson sees it, is that we are approaching a precipice of abstraction and are about to throw ourselves over it, which would put art in the position of denying that art is a "vindication of human dignity."[6] Personally, knowing how far we can go in symbolic abstraction, I intuitively feel that the human mind is capable of going just as far, if not further, in art, even including new media developments that complicate things unimaginably. Yet I agree that the removal into abstractions will most certainly sacrifice something. At the end point artists are in danger of being totally independent of humanity, or of the realism of "the sacred" or "the divine," as Wilson says, and they become essentially rebels without a real cause, artists without messages, only media. And along comes a prophet to substantiate the idea that the medium suffices, that the medium *is* the message: Marshall McLuhan. I do believe that as pure communication a medium has its singular strength which always influences us incommensurately with our knowledge of the message it contains, and McLuhan's point is well taken. As a *creative* communication, however, the medium becomes integral with and creatively part of the entire exhange, being submerged as a psychological influencing factor in proportion to its success as a work of art. He himself realizes that the value perception of art exceeds the medium itself,[7] but it is easy to misinterpret his hyperbolic method of writing. If I am not mistaken, McLuhan will be invoked by modern abstractionists to justify media alone as art. I do not do it here. The distinction must be clearly made between new media which may alter our awareness of areas in which art can be embodied, and the actual successful use of a new medium as art. The artist must realize how media can be used, and, as I have tried to show, media can shift the artistic import, as when radio taught the value of abstraction as an exchanger of the human condition. In whatever artistic media man can creatively encode that which to him represents humanness, at whatever level of abstraction, another man can learn to decipher those conditions and deem them valuable in proportion to their ability to call out new perceptual awarenesses.

The problem of using new media is that the artist must be so much at home with them that they seem to be old ones, and this always requires considerable technical experience and a fresh imagination, tuned to the media requirements. The example of electronic music can be cited as an art form in which insufficient medium experience has been gained to allow some imagination to take fire. An electronic virtuoso musician-composer will probably have to acquire his early exposure to his craft in almost subliminal ways—the classical or folk musical exposure may come through conventional channels, but what about the electronic? Television perhaps will unknowingly supply this need. For instance, my own children, Erik and Rachel, not only hear live chamber music at home, listen by preference to classical music, and learn traditional instruments (as well as learn Hungarian folk songs because it is half their heritage), they also hear a good deal of electronic music every day of their lives: the sound effects and mood music of their space-age cartoons like Astro-Boy or other favorites.

This everyday exposure to art may be necessary before a person can really build up the proper reflexes to use abstract media for significant human encoding in art; it may not require many years of exposure, but perhaps they must be early ones. This would seem to indicate that the current educational system that makes music and the arts only peripheral activities is severely lacking, limiting the development of human beings with potential for great art or profound intellectual achievement. Again television may unwittingly save the day. Culture—which I would give a minimum definition of as being aware, to greater or less degrees, of the various encoding means of the arts as they have been developed historically—has in the past come primarily from the family unit. The remarkable fact that bright people usually emerge from cultured homes does not seem to have penetrated into the educator's scheme of things. European families have always seen the need for culture and general knowledge and it is generally part of their heritage. Some ethnic groups, as for instance the Jewish, produce a higher percentage of bright children and intellectual adults than others. A child who is exposed to good music and who has parents interested in the theater, painting, and good books, has many advantages over one who lacks these influences. Why not bring this attitude into our schools, instead of concentrating on old logical systems with questionable futures. The new math, a return to fundamentals instead of particulars, may be a good sign, if that math is as basic as the mathematician assures us. Of course heritage, background, early training, education, none of these necessarily make the true creative genius, since he often emerges from the most unlikely situations.

Although novelty for its own sake is not valuable in art, neither is the traditional necessarily valuable simply because of long familiarity. When a work or style repeats itself again and again it can be eliminated, both from the standpoint of information theory and of common sense. Yet we must be cautious. Signature painters, musicians whose style is preponderate or classical authors whose novels continually explore similar themes or insist on being conventional, may be probing for delicacies of meaning in the minuscule that in the end will turn out to be massive. They may be depending on fragile meanings for subtle creative insights which we can only understand after long exposure. No a priori denial of signature styles or repeated themes or even conventional art forms can be made because the elements of creativity often hang on slim threads. It may take an artist many repetitions before he can advance a single iota into a significant creative act. The small differences between the works of the original creator and his followers suggest that very little change makes all the difference.

Repeating the style of an admired master can be important for two reasons: first it gives an intimate acquaintance with the details of another person's art encoding, and second it provides a possible code for future, deeper encoding (that very artist's work). Of course if the admired artist employs essentially a random technique, if he, for instance, delves into his own subconscious and emerges with creative but highly personal revelations, the value of a repetition by another artist is less. Imitating the random is not profitable, because we all house our own reservoir of randomness. Insofar as artists tap subconscious and random sources, as did the surrealists, all artists are surrealists[8]— and so by this consideration all people are also artists, if we can believe Freud that we all tap our subconscious sources in our every act!

Complete variety, short of randomness, is another way out of the trap of exhausted expressiveness, but variety lies where you find it—all media have new varieties that are untapped, and there is no need to search for a new medium. The dancer need not create a robot; his only inventive approach is to dance, dance until he finds a new movement, almost without know-

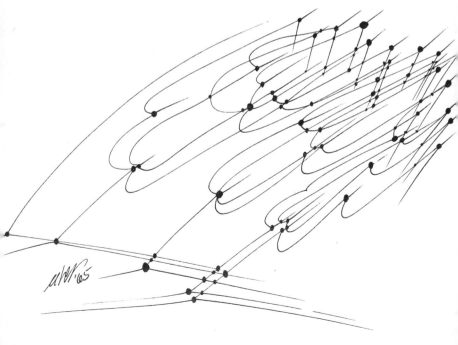

ing it, and almost despite his instrument, the human body. As Jacques Maritain writes: "The great mistake . . . has been to search for an escape through the discovery of a new external approach and new technical revolutions, instead of passing first through the creative source, and thus taking a risk, but having a chance to find a real solution."[9] It is this risk which the modern artist must always take in order to remain modern. He must allow himself to improvise in his medium, and ignore the temptation of going to a new one. A new medium is always a setback—a beginning again, as Kierkegaard would say—and as with all new beginnings, it initiates an entire new set of problems unsolved.

But the personal reason why some artists begin again in a new medium can on occasion be a healthy reaction to a stagnation in an old medium, or it can also be a sincere recognition of some creative possibility which only the hybrid can allow. When an artist sees new contrasts and analogies of his old medium in a new medium, resulting in a new life after the transference, then he can create a new and rarified art atmosphere by such a marriage. Picasso's experiments in pottery have this value and success, as do the compositions of Edgar Varèse or Darius Milhaud using electronic means.

The sudden shift of many semirealistic painters into an abstract mode when it became popular suggests, however, that it is easy for an artist to be tempted by the new for new's sake. The school of Abstract Expressionism swept across New York as surely as Impressionism did across Paris, yet only a few innovators in both cities carried the full meaning of the new and subtle encoding to fruition. The traditionalists with any sensitivity could not remain unmoved in either city, yet if their personal creative vision had any true validity for them personally, the new styles did not change it, only deepened it. As Haydn's later works seem to be fresher after the younger Mozart's operas were played, so we detect in Cézanne some of the unconscious novelty he fathered in the cubists, a novelty which could not have originated with the masters, I think, without this subliminal pressure by their student's work. I have watched more than one new art style grow and die on the New York art scene, heard some of my teachers complaining about Abstract Expressionism, and their abstract expressionistic students complaining about Pop or Op art. Yet the artists who have seen the folly of denying this change, and who have taken what is valuable from it and assimilated it, are the artists whose search is for a true creative insight, regardless of the source. My teacher and good friend Gregorio Prestopino, for instance, who originally derived from the ashcan social-realist school, let the new experimentations flow through his artistic veins until his present pictures pulse with a startling creative vitality, still essentially realistic, although hardly social-realistic. This is always socially redeeming, however.

On the other hand I am hard pressed to find the true abstractionists who have managed to maintain the humanity of abstraction called for to justify their efforts. Picasso never left off from a recognizable image, although in many cases it may be difficult for the uninitiated to detect. Painters like Hans Hofmann or Arschile Gorky, however, show us the extent to which the visual form can be stretched in an abstract way and still provoke our curiosity about form as an abstraction of humanness. However, I admit that it requires considerable familiarity with the codes of plastic form to be able to get the communication of the human creativity, and perhaps some experience in the act of painting itself before the humanity of the act is clear. Sunday painters or students at many of the art centers in America will undoubtedly get this experience, hopefully due to the good guidance of artists with imagination and experience. The increasing numbers of these classes, the growing sizes of art classes (in two years the classes where I have taught painting in Princeton have doubled), suggests that we may someday approach the general level of painting awareness which we now afford good music. Then the average man or woman will be ready to pull himself or herself to the higher levels of painting appreciation, much as he can today with little effort learn to appreciate string quartets.

5

The modern artist, then, is one who keeps the artistic search focused on a new synthesis of one's current sensitivities, regardless of the media. If the artist is a person of this world, if he has a talent for finding creative communications, however old-fashioned his media, he will then be a modern artist, and his art will have modern meaning. The price of modernity, chased to the exclusion of artistic integrity, is beyond the ability of the artist to pay, because it leads onto a path that withers more quickly than an artist can walk. The modern artist is born, not made—which does not mean he is born with any particular potential, but merely that he is born into a situation which will lead him to making his art modern. You cannot of course say that some art grows richer with the ages, or that other art grows poorer—encoding is a fickle thing, and reevaluation of ancient forms comes at surprising moments in our history, usually for unpredictable reasons.

A modern artist can only strive to create a myth of himself for the purpose of gaining the world's eye or ear or mind, and, once gained, he must have something to say to deserve the world's continued attention. The personal equation which makes one person great today and obscure tomorrow in the eyes of the world is always subject to drastic revision. The myth of the artist must be extremely powerful to survive the ages with a poor art—he must have flaunted kings, enraged nations, or be beloved of millions. The myth often grows through innocent admirers who unconsciously add their own art to the tale of the archetypal genius, having a ready carrier and a surefire vehicle for their additional ego. The sycophant inclination is that of a relatively impotent artistry attaching itself barnacle-like to a powerful streaming artistic ship that is well underway to immortality. The same motive partially impels the art patron, the benefactor of the arts, and even the owner or concert-goer or gallery-looker. Looking at or experiencing a work of art is in a way perpetuating that work of art, giving it sustained life and tacit approval. The more we play Beethoven, the more meaning we give him; the more we pay for a Rembrandt, or a Van Gogh, the more important they become—even in the long run.

Little fads here and there can, like sparks, be fanned into raging fires. It is true that many rediscovered artists have been retrieved from the stream of art for the wrong reasons, and often older artists with value for us have been lost undeservingly. Only recently, for instance, we thought surrealism a distant curiosity, but along comes a new school of artists (the Pop artists) who blindly rediscovered the same techniques and insights, and forced us to reevaluate the surrealistic methodology and production. There is a constant shifting of the audiences to which art is directed, especially when communication media begin to exert an influence. What were previously arts directed to individuals become arts which the masses can experience because of their multiplication caused by television or radio.

The interpretive arts, spanning as they do two or more ages, one foot in the age of its creation and the other in the age of its re-creation, have a greater chance of remaining modern than the other arts. The technical innovation which allows us to crystallize an interpretive art in some permanent form—as when a particular orchestral performance becomes a record item, allowing us to rank the artistic worth of specific conductors or virtuoso instrumentalists—serves to make these arts less modernly vital than if they were left in their vague, dissipating form, which every age interprets in its own way. The notation of music is necessarily vague, and it allows succeeding generations to bring to bear new ideas. If that notation were made too tight, then music would be a different thing to us than it is. Dance also lacks any significant notation scheme which preserves enough of the original creative idea so that it may be re-created at a later date; film of dance, or even Labanotation, does not suffice, the one because it is too complete, the other because it is too crude. We can only guess about those original performances of Mary Wigmann or Isadora Duncan, accepting hearsay adulation, or accepting their force as influences which have seeped down to us as residual deposits in all modern dance. Old records only give us very inadaquate preservations of the famous singers, but perhaps this very inadequacy contributes to the myth—had we a hi-fi recording of Caruso it is not easy to guess how we would actually react to him and what role he would have played as an influence on virtuoso singers. The way a new reading of a Mozart symphony or Bach fugue is carried out can give the well-worn works a new vitality, which perhaps exceeds the exhausted creative communications which they may actually represent—and of course Mozart or Bach get all of the credit. We do not know how the original master would react were he to hear one of these latter-day interpretations—how, for instance, Mozart would like the vibrato contemporary violinists give his concerti.

In the long run, however, the truly modern artist provides the creative means of helping the intellectual meet and surmount his personal tragedy: asking questions he cannot answer, trying to solve the unsolvable, struggling to know the impossible, fighting to matcralize the immaterial. The artist invents the images, conceives the root ideas, imagines the archetypal bases that can help the intellectual turn perplexities and torments into harmonies and delights. Nietzsche says that the artist rejects and defies reality; but rather, I think, the artist re-creates the world in which man finds himself, making it sufficiently large to contain all of his fondest dreams and desired insights. Modernity cannot be courted without realizing that a marriage to it may be meaningless and perhaps death. To ape the desires of society by handing it the communications it calls for, is to stand in the way of its final triumph. Since our future depends on the building of sensitivities which exceed our present abilities to grasp them, the modern artist must consider not social pressures, but only his own inner intuitions of form. The true satisfaction which an artist derives from originating creative communications comes from a realization that he is making something which is bigger than his own private world of perception. An artistic creation is a new, large window, out of which the artist gets the first glimpse; but it passes on, and if it is sufficiently large and wonderful, a whole century or era can look out with renewed pleasure and meaning. I think that artists who are seeking fame, trying to be new or contemporary, have never felt the thrill of a creative discovery, and therefore need something else to sustain them in the most lonely and frustrating of professions.

No true modernity is possible without critical knowledge of historical art precedents. As Barzun says, "If Romanticism worked out its possibilities through Realism, Symbolism, and Naturalism, then our Modernism is a second coda to the great movement in four parts which began a century and a half ago. The coda recapitulates and in so doing it brings out many particular beauties not sufficiently felt before but it adds nothing new except its unmistakable sense of a full close."[10] But this close is really the beginning of a new view, the truly creative view of the next evolution of modernity, taking advantage of this exhaustion of old means to spring with renewed energy into new artistic forms with their concomitant insights and human articulations.

10

The Artistic Vision

The Meaning of Art for Science

1

O**UR GLOBAL** culture hinges on universal science, understood and agreed on by all humanity since science knows no cultural or political barriers. Obviously, however, science has failed to reach universal agreement on many points which are extremely important for humanity. I do not mean the political questions of atomic control, or proper governing schemes, which are of course urgently important today, but rather the more fundamental but less hazardous questions concerning the physiological-psychological actions of individuals or groups of individuals. It is not so simple to derive the universal truths which explain nature and teach us how to liberate man from himself. There is a certain irrationality barrier, hiding our Maxwellian artist-demon, beyond which science is unable to go. This barrier separates the truths we know, but are less interested in, from the truths we desire to know, but can only guess about.

Science, sticking to its traditional methods, has proved remarkably inappropriate in many areas of investigation. It has been unable to generate sufficient imagination to produce psychological and social concepts on a par with its physical concepts (many of which are also breaking down today). It seems to me that it behooves the scientist to make a serious reevaluation of his methodology and outlook. Karl Popper devoted his life to this reevaluation, and *The Logic of Scientific Discovery*[1] is a milestone in the philosophy of science too few scientists have studied. Mario Bunge, whose *The Myth of Simplicity*[2] considers one of the fundamental assumptions of science, edited a series of papers in *The Critical Approach to Science and Philosophy*[3] which interpret many of Popper's ideas. These beginnings are barely known by the scientific community, who could most profit from their insights. While we may believe, in an idealistic mood, that science is explaining nature brilliantly, giving us a complete control over our surroundings, and perhaps partially revealing us to ourselves, a great wave of pessimism sweeps over us when we consider the state of the modern world. The failure of science to give us even a few verities on which we could build a meaningful theory of man does not seem to bother the average scientist. The researcher is so wrapped up in his own particular world of discipline and study, so fascinated by what are obviously interesting and astounding intricacies, that he does not dream that he may be pushing mankind further and further out on the proverbial limb—and providing the saw to cut if off. Before we plunge into the yawning abyss it seems to me some means must be found to support that limb. We must learn how to prop up the ever-weakening intellectual supports which are threatening to fall out from under mankind. I believe that a closer bond between the two cultures, as C. P. Snow called them,[4] is one of the most urgent needs to help bring about this support. I would word it slightly differently, however, to suggest that it is not so much a rapprochement between the man of letters and the man of science that is needed, as it is for the man who believes in the value of an irrational artistic approach and the man who idolizes the logic of science to learn to understand one another more, and to realize how fundamentally the other's approach affects his own.

The most obvious dangers of the atomic bomb are surrounded by countless other critical ills that are threatening to explode even sooner. We have severe population, pollution, pesticide and pill problems, which science seems hoplessly inept at solving. The computer, coupled with the mass-communication media, threatens to remove the existential reality of each of us into the most remote and alienated existence conceivable: instant information-retrieval on any subject, from specialized data to daily news. It would lead us to a total processing of all problems, mathematical or syntactical, and predictions and choices based on this knowledge would have to be made so quickly that there would be little or no time to review them, and less of an opportunity to change our minds. The control and automation of human work functions has already begun to create a gap in the meaning of all human activities, to the extent that man finds himself breaking down traditional values with no substitute. The rapprochement then must tie together the man of science and the man of art those two fundamental human outlooks which have traditionally separated the heart and the mind.

I do not think the example of Leonardo da Vince is typical of the man who allows the fantastic and the imaginative to creep into the scientific, because he was an unusual phenomenon, even in his own culture. He was a true loner—probably the most lonely individual in the history of mankind, as Martin Johnson suggests.[5] Possessed of a greater awareness than all of his contemporaries, closer in many ways to the modern viewpoint than Galileo, he was obviously not understood by his contemporaries. It is easy to see why in his art he plunged into an analog of the most modern abstractions: employing, instead of formalities, fantasy and caricature. Nature seemed to be beyond all comprehension to him, so complex did his experiments and analyses find it. Like Einstein he realized that there was an order beyond his powers of comprehension, but an order which he must have thought was theoretically comprehensible. This is probably when he became aware of the

powers which must destroy him, and when he began to symbolize them by the strangely prescient catastrophic drawings,
simultaneously experiencing the severest of mental conflicts.
He could not accept man's pollution of the pure orders of
nature—his one constant in a changing world—by the omni-
present human ruthlessness and deliberate human unreason.

Science proceeds at such a fast pace that it often puts the
scientist in a position where he is unable, like Leonardo, to
measure up to the human responsibilities it entails. If he is a
particularly sensitive scientist he responds, when he realizes
what is happening, by searching as creatively as he can for a
solution at the human level. Einstein, for instance, knew the
earth-shattering implications of his labors, and he reflectively
devoted his later years to deepening his and the world's awareness of the moral and human situation which resulted from his
theorizing and science.

There are too few opportunities for the imaginative scientist
and the creative artist to get together nowadays. Scientists
usually see no value in a collaboration,[6] and the artist does
not understand why he should bother discovering what the
scientist is up to. Occasionally the artist—who is really the lame
duck today because he lacks the organized support and the
group importance to command attention, even if he understands the problem—is invited to be a guest at one of the large
scientific conventions or symposia. The artist receives a certain
respect in our society—if he has a name—and even the scientist
will respond to this respect. Although an artist who is called
on by the scientific community for his counsel is perhaps some-
what flattered by the high-priestly position he finds himself in,
I feel sure he comes away depressed at a total lack of comprehension of the situation of the artist and his goals and potentials, for the scientist as well as for the rest of humanity. On
the other hand, the creative scientist is seldom invited by
groups of artists to expound on his activities, unless of course
he has turned coat or is computerizing or opticalizing some
phase of science which gives him artistic pretensions. I do not

think the artist will suffer much from this lack of collaboration, but both the scientist and mankind will. There are educators, however, who are trying to introduce the opposite discipline into their curricula, as, for instance, Jacob Landau, who is bringing the attitudes and opinions of scientists to his art students at Pratt Institute,[7] and Robert Preusser, who is introducing his students to visual creativity at M.I.T.[8] Both the artist and the scientist who is aware of the problem must counter this prevailing pressure, and the responsibility extends out of their immediate areas of action.

2

Art was the primitive's total science. He concretized supernatural powers through an artistic attitude, helping himself to cope with the realities which they simultaneously embodied and explained. A magical record of things absent, in elementary terms communicating a creative reaction to experience, art gave man his first tool to control the important business of his daily life. The magical mode is a result of an exclusive dependence on interior events, as McLuhan notes,[9] but when it is made manifest externally, it disappears and is replaced by the human mode. All animals live in a purely magical mode, but humans qua human have given it up for a greater awareness. In time, however, art-science divided into their separate disciplines, until today they are almost at the opposite poles of existence and human activities. Art does, after all, proliferate man's awareness of man and of mankind—why not also the awareness of the workings of man's soul and of his humanness? Psychologists knew that many of their insights were anticipated by literature, and indeed they drew some of them directly from the works of Tolstoi, Dostoevski, and Nietzsche. Art can perhaps aid the scientist by helping him generate a different approach to his truths, by enriching the creative wellsprings from which he draws his insights. The scientist has to learn to be creative with creativity itself, and this the artist can teach him.

Art abbreviates past events, condenses time, creates a broader reality that has new relationships which man never knew. Art is more than a media by which man can extend himself, because it offers a creative broadening of the idea of humanity, not just a communicative expansion of information. Man lives many a full life through his art, and its richness derives from the expansion of man's mortal years throughout the immortal experiences of countless sensitive artists. We may take it for granted, but what we perceive, even in our smallest act, leans on the art expansions of the past. Art enriches experience through a perception expansion, an insight binding, wrapping up many sensations and perceptions into one package.

Theodore Reik contends that the myth is a distillation of prehistory and he proceeds to unravel some of their various meanings, as, for instance, the fall of man, the importance of a godhead, the matriarch-patriarch duality.[10] So art is a small package of concentrated experiences, encoded by different schemes, brought to life by a synthesis which we can intuitively sense. The power of art derives from its ability to encode the many in the few, to compress and contract and unify what had been loose or disparate. This enables the packing of more and more human awareness into our lives without our ever feeling the strain. To unravel art sometimes requires considerable analysis and effort, sometimes the efforts of generations; but it is worth it. We cannot actually begin to judge just how great an expansion our soul receives from its exposure to art. The brevity of the art experience is no measure of its scope and impact.

Art is the original psychedelic experience—one which is but temporary and transient in the drug situation, but which is permanent in art. I do not mean to imply that drugs can substitute for or ever lead to art when I borrow this term "psychedelic"; nevertheless many artists, poets, and philosophers have recognized that the experiences of religious or mystical persons, of hypnotic or adolescent discoveries of the self, are related to the insights of art. William James in his *Varieties of Religious Experience*, Eric Ericson in his *Young Man Luther*, Weston La Barre in his *The Peyote Cult*, or David Solomon and Dr. Timothy Leary in many books and articles discuss various aspects of such experiences.[11] The unusual shifts in man's "fields of consciousness," to use James's phrase, brought about under natural but extreme conditions, or through artificial drug or even electro-probe situations, evoke a shift in the cumulative self-awareness a person can achieve, causing a sudden shock to the psyche, which some deem the mystical experience. The suddenness is what is surprising, but its naturalness is what makes the mystical experience meaningful. Taken in art we are not so shocked by a shift into a new frame of perceptual awareness, because we can only experience the communication, the effects of the exchange, if we are prepared. When it does occur in a drug or hypnotic experience, we cannot hope to grasp its meaning, nor can we legitimately profit

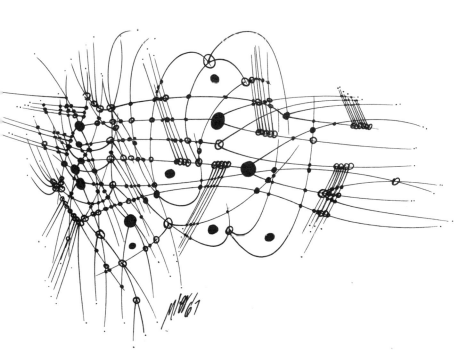

from it intellectually or emotionally, except perhaps under certain well-prepared situations, as when it is part of a consistent psychiatric therapy. Drug experiences are transitory and unsupported by communicative rationale which can sustain their effects in the future—they do not have a notation, and we need perhaps a Guido d'Arezzo for our LSD experiences before we can ever hope to profit from them artistically. When the drug experience is part of a ritual, as in the peyote cult of Mexico, or when it becomes part of a new cult which may be in the making by modern experimenters, it has the potential for a meaningful effect. Drug, hypnotic, and religious experiences all are in desperate need of some human concretization in order to bring them back to the quietness of normal study and effect.

It is interesting that today there is a simultaneous interest in Marshall McLuhan, who indicates how symbols and our technical perception mechanisms condition our experience, at the same time that LSD proponents are suggesting an automatic release from them—almost like reading two ads in the same newspaper which would satisfy each other's needs. If Robert Graves is correct that the hallucinatory mushroom was instrumental in the origin of the Tlalóc or Greek myths,[12] then we should give our current hallucinatories an opportunity to suggest contemporary myth structures. The multisensual interactions of new modes of thinking require a rather drastic shock to overcome the torpor of years of conditioning to a single sensorium, and perhaps LSD can provide it—short of insanity. The mosaic approach of all the senses and powers of reasoning requires that we widen our doors of perception. I am not totally convinced that drugs are the answer, but, as with all new possibilities, I feel that we must not rule them out. Past blindness to potential artistic or scientific media or methods should teach us to entertain all new things, that is if we wish to continue in the ever-growing expansion of our unique humanness.

Art freezes the fleeting feeling relationships man experiences with nature and with other people, and builds realities in which our emotions and even intellects can operate. It is almost as if experience proceeds at such a fast pace that art was a necessary invention in order to preserve the meaning of human existence. Art locks time, gives time its human and psychic meaning. A great work of art not only preserves or restores some valuable human experience, but exceeds the original impulse and brings out something new that broadens the human existential situation. The artistic vision does not try to transcend life by freezing human experience; art does not try to remake that which one loves in order to capture it for eternity, as Shakespeare suggested in his sonnets; and neither can you say that art "cheats mortality," as Marion Milner or Albert Camus argues, by making up for the discovery by man that death is the greatest disillusionment of life.[13] Art instead broadens our total experience of life by extending the human dimension more than can be contained in the space from birth to death without it. Art includes more time, space, sense, and psychic experience than man could have imagined possible in a single, finite life span. Tap this source and you have one of the most profound sources of human experience, one which contains not only the realities of instant-to-instant living, but also condensed and rarefied realities which are more dense than matter itself. Tap this with the scientific attitude and it may be possible to approach the problem of an objective understanding of the human equation.

3

Since art broke away from science, eons ago, its practitioner, the artist, has always been suspicious of the desire to transcend man with an "objective" attitude. This may be due to the artist's having a deep, unconscious residue of fear that derives from the ancient magical urge which gave his office its birth; or it may be due to a legitimate insight into the limitations of science.

Even today most artists are prejudiced against science and its desire for objectivity; they distrust the urge to understand everything by reason, the desire to know without taking into account the uncertain and frail human with all of his feelings. The very irrationality of human subjectivity seems to most artists to be more important for understanding than all possible logics. There is a certain artistic pleasure in the scientific limitation described by Heisenberg, although it is insufficiently descriptive of human interference and man's pivotal situation to satisfy the artist's more inclusive demands of human insight. Yet most artists are realists enough to be influenced by the modern forces which science has unleashed. They are no longer frightened by modern science, however, and they have turned and are ready to face the dragon, come what may. But this modern monster usually proves to be a reluctant dragon, as most artists soon realize who have sought in vain there for traces of ferocity with which to kindle art experiences.

It is not science, an artificial procedure, but rather man himself, whom the artist confronts when he turns to science that interests him the most. He finds within the scientist a relative of his friend, the Maxwell demon-artist. And that demon-scientist can be a fallen demon, who opens the gates the wrong way and causes too sudden a reversal of entropy: a demon who without knowing it sets up things that are too precarious to remain stable for long. This may be, as Wiener suggests, quoting Leibnitz, just because the demon is falling into "a certain vertigo" due too many small decisions.[14] The picture becomes clouded and the artist begins to blame the scientist for putting unimaginable forces into the hands of unpredictable and irresponsible demons. The problem of the scientist as collaborator in the process of building man's humanness remains unsolved, and the artist is always forced back into his ivory tower where he can create his pleasant, disillusioning worlds within worlds.

It remains for the dilettante, as Abraham Moles suggests, to pull everything together, and even to begin new sciences and arts.[15] Leonardo began new sciences and originated new artistic visions because he straddled many intellectual-artistic worlds. I think that this commingling of scientific and artistic origins does not arise out of a need for diversity in creativity, so much as it is a need for art in science; for a person imbued with the most vital arts who can enlarge the current perceptual and imaginary worlds sufficiently so that they invite "revolutionary" jumps in scientific theory. As Butterfield says in *The Origins of Modern Science*,[16] "in both celestial and terrestial physics . . . change is brought about not by new observations or additional evidences in the first place, but by transpositions that were taking place inside the minds of the scientists themselves." The artist who breeds new arts can also profit from this exchange, since it gives his perceptual elaborations more scope and more room to expand in.

It is a cliché that the scientist often bases research on hunches. Michael Polanyi calls it the "tacit dimension," an intuited reality which allows the scientist to search for the evidence that supports his intuition. He sees in scientific knowledge a skill involving connoisseurship, habits, and traditions, but does not realize that these residues of experience are generated not only in the discipline of science.[17] The general beliefs, the assumptions behind the greatest scientific achievements, may not have such a mystical origin as has generally been supposed. And simultaneous invention, ideas like those of Liebnitz and Newton which gave birth to calculus; or Malthus and Darwin who independently conceived evolution; ideas which previously have been explained by such phrases as "being in the air," or "pregnantly ready for birth," can be pinpointed to the prevailing artistic winds blowing throughout the minds of a given age.

Man is finding it increasingly difficult to communicate with his brother, despite modern technology inventing new and different communication devices every day; the spread of true cultural values seems to be on the verge of being stifled, and this despite communication and mass media. It is all the more urgent then that we develop and learn to respect those fundamental human channels for communication, which man developed long before his electric communication media. Art is the spark that in prehistory started the communications explosion we are feeling today, and it can help us bind together mankind if we can but learn how to harness its indescribable, almost atomic pressures. Although the modern ease of communication has apparently driven many artists into the most esoteric of communications, it would seem logical to assume that there exists here a potential for better art communication than in the past—a potential that can only be released when the artist himself truly learns how to use new media for old art, or new media for new art.

Morse Peckham argues in *Man's Rage for Chaos*[18] that art is man's answer to the need for a more stimulating environment than the order-directed social one in which he finds himself due to governments and laws. He dismisses the perceptual reality of art as being completely artificial and deceiving. There may be a certain wisdom in this nihilistic position, but I feel that it is overlooking the true communicative meaning of art and of all human activities which are packaged for exchange. Man does not desire chaos in art as a palliative, since one glance at a newspaper or snap of a television or radio switch clearly indicates that there is sufficient chaos in life to satisfy any inner need for randomness and precariousness that man may possess.

The interpersonal communicative possibilities of art are important, but they are not so important as those resulting from art as a creative expander of our perceptual human world. If a large portion of our intellectual community cuts out the art experience as a meaningful and important experience, they are making it more difficult for themselves and the rest of humanity to develop a new creative humanness. Mankind remains at the level which his artistic consciousness sets for him; expand art and the human emotional-intellectual volume also expands.

The artist still carries around a socially imposed feeling of guilt because he seems to be defying common-sense reality. The scientist has given him some support lately, however, because even science is discovering that nature demands theories which are contrary to common sense. But the layman is not always aware of the latest theories of science, and even less does he appreciate their larger implications. The artist appears to be a neurotic, and a negative connotation is usually associated with the various artistic manifestations we see in the world today—although they are not always undeservedly so. It is not easy for the general public or the scientist to understand why the artist obscures his communications so—why does he not just come right out and say what he means? But to ask this of art is to beg the question of its very means for communicating. Enigmas explained are no longer important. Art is not being enigmatic for confusion's sake; instead it is enigmatic because this is the only way in which certain creative ideas can be communicated—their very ambiguity fuses into their creativity.

As Rudolph Arnheim noted,[19] the penchant for piecemeal scientific analysis is countered with the artistic urge to see the whole. The biochemist, for instance, is blithely concentrating on the structure of the DNA molecule, isolated even from the gene. There are some who argue that this narrowing may prevent an actual determination of the true force of the hereditary-determining characteristics in man, suggesting that an explanation may demand a more traditional wholistic approach.[20]

Perhaps also in physics the traditional approach of reasoning from the particulars of elementary particles to the generality of theories has failed. Mary B. Hesse has begun to sense the common areas of science and art in her *Models and Analogies in Science*,[21] although she still misses the importance of art as the structural preconditioning for science. It is conceivable that some form of artistic encoding could be employed to describe physical reality, even atomic structures, since it is at very least a structural articulation. Susanne Langer suggests, for instance, that music is ideal for symbolizing time (subjective time in the sense that time is something we hypothesize from experience).[22] Hiller and Beauchamp also indicate that music would be the ideal abstract material for the analysis of language structure, because its structure is more complex and has a larger information content than language, but at the same time it is

coded more efficiently.[23] The mathematician has resorted sometimes to art when he plots equations or makes topological
forms. He knows that the best way to describe and to understand space is visually (although his formulas also always
"describe" space in their abstract way).

But the real value of art is never so directly appropriated by
science, because it is more than a conditioning force on the
brain to help it form its Kantian structures for perception since
it conditions the very reality it creates. As I have suggested,
each art has its appropriate contribution to make to some phase
of science, although it is difficult to be more explicit than to
suggest that music may be related to mathematics or logical
theories or that literature can help build archetypal structuring
for theories of the human psyche. These articulations of art
which influence science are so ingrained in our system that we
can only separate them out with great difficulty.* It is obvious
that the relations which new art forms generate must be perceived at a very profound level of mental awareness, and that
it only begins to have its effect by dint of considerable mental
conditioning. It may be that this conditioning must always
begin early in childhood in order to have a lasting significance
and permanental mental formative effect. In this way a potential scientist becomes disposed to many symbologies and structural refinements, and he is psychologically prepared to accept
them. Table VI lists some of the influences of art on the scientist
and his scientific methodologies.

The value of art does not lie in the subject matter nor in
the form, making the content-form problem unimportant; the
content can be noble, the art poor; the form powerful, the art
inadequate. Nor is the value of art in a mystical union between
the two, with form reinforcing a noble content. It is instead the
transcendent form-content problem, the releasing of the objec-

---

* Perhaps a test could be made to determine, for instance, if it would be
possible to aid the development of mathematical brains by subjecting them to
long sessions of listening to the more advanced serial or electronic musics; but
I leave this to the psychological testing laboratories.

tive-subjective difficulty that gives art its meaning.* The scientist, looking for insights into nature, reacts to his experience much as the artist does, and in order to build up a theory he must learn to take that experience and reflect on it in the light of his own consciousness—and this is the province which his art awareness has built. Science is concerned with the act of building a communicative form which resembles outer reality. On the other hand art is a creative communication that extends

TABLE VI—WAYS ART INFLUENCES SCIENCE

1. ENCODING CONSCIOUSNESS
    a. Perceptual awareness
        (1) Spatial
        (2) Temporal
        (3) Psychic
    b. Sensual articulations
2. GENERATING MENTAL STRUCTURES
    a. Abstract (mathematics, logic)
    b. Aural (musical, sounds)
    c. Visual (painting, graphs)
    d. Tactile (sculptural, architectural)
    e. Literal (language)
    f. Fantastic (literal or abstract)
3. ARTICULATING HUMANNESS
    a. Moral (individual)
    b. Social (groups)
    c. Political (world situations)
    d. Ideal (mythical, Utopian, archetypal)
4. NURTURING CREATIVITY
    a. Unconscious modes of thought
    b. Structuring potential scientific ideas

* The progression from art to science can be illustrated in miniature by the simple example Harold Lanier provided me when I proposed my theory to him. Man first draws an ellipse because it is artistically pleasing to him. Then he finds the mathematics of that form. Then he discovers that the planets also take that form in their paths around the sun.

man's inner reality so that he can have sufficient forms available for the needs of his scientific communications. Artists see a coupling and a unification between these inner and outer worlds, the inner world of man and the outer world of experience, whereas the scientist sees only its division. Marion Milner writes that ". . . the artists, by embodying the experience of illusion, provides the essential basis for realizing, making real, for feeling as well as for knowing . . . the external world . . . art creates nature, including human nature . . . the artist . . . refuses to deny his inner reality, but also and because of this, is potentially capable of seeing more of the external reality than [the scientist]."[24]

The artistic attitude is potentially able to see more of external reality than the scientific because it not only uncovers more of man's actual experientially felt and sensed reality than impersonal science but also helps to create more of it in the very act itself. Personally, for instance, all of the reports of outer space experiences, both from Russian and American astronauts, have been extremely anticlimactic to me because I have sought in vain to get at the true emotions, the true *being* for a human in the infinite void and terrific loneliness of outer space. The most socially valuable and approaching an artistic insight yet uttered by an astronaut was made when James Lovell suggested that the most startling thing about the world spinning under him was the lack of boundaries that distinguished nations. Until we get a few more such artistically inclined astronauts out in space we will have to content ourselves with the imaginings of artists like the Hubleys who create a more real and beautiful animated view of the universe than the actual ones of the scientist—which are therefore much more meaningful to us in all attempts to "understand" the human situation in deep-space. If the scientist realized that "understanding" space also included putting it to human use, in the sense of giving our very being a new dimension, then he might concentrate on these more important human demands, and perhaps also get more of our sympathy with his endeavors.

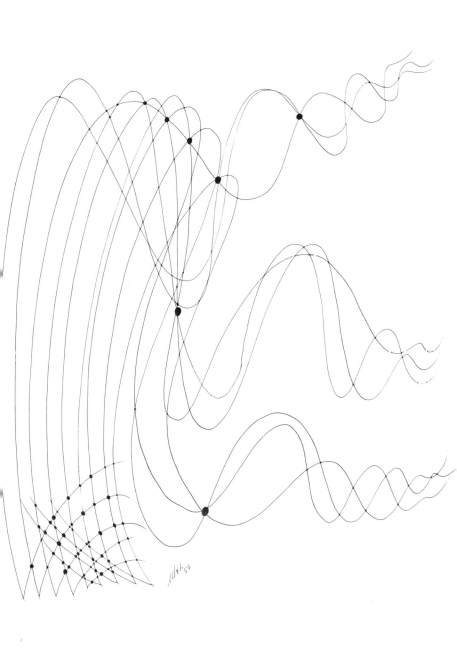

In many ways, I think, the scientist is delaying his own understanding and development in science by discouraging, not only the artistically inclined members of his clan, but also the artistic urges within himself. He is actually overlooking a very practical and urgent need, dismissing it as childish or irrelevant. The so-called scientific method, a sacred pronunciamento in some circles, is being too fanatically defended. We have to admit that we probably owe our modernity, our affluence, and fabulous know-how (as well as many of our present ills) to the scientific method in its strictest form. But to advance more from now on, I think, it will be necessary to alter this dictum. Science has been too anthropomorphically centered, which is why today we find that the culmination of that anthropomorphism is so threatening.[25] The computer is trying to automate all human functions and to lead to a total mechanization of the anthropod. What new and truly abstract analog will drive science on when this current fashion in science has been completely realized? The answer to this question can only lie in an artistic intuition which creates something new and startling out of it for our consideration.

4

To maintain that the mathematization of all human experience is the goal of science seems to me to be a highly arbitrary assumption. And the natural desire for scientists to develop a so-called aesthetic solution to their problems, one elegant formula or system of ideas that wraps up experience in one neat package, also may be false or misleading, as Mario Bunge and others have argued.[26] Einstein's final general field theory which attempted to unite gravity and electromagnetism does not seem justified today by the facts of physical discovery. Neat theories like Newton's dynamics or Maxwell's electromagnetic phenomena are gained at the price of detachment from fact, and clinging too steadfastly to theory is a single-minded folly which prevents progress in science. Heisenberg's wisdom was in granting the uncertainty of measurement, which is ever-present in all sciences due to the means man has of communicating with, and ever so minutely interfering with, the facts of nature. Our multifaceted electric environment and the natural world it reveals may be too complex to be explained by tidy and simple theories.

Symbols often become a screen that obscures the view of the reality they symbolize, and mathematics as applied science can obscure the reality which it was inductively invoked to describe. The tacit assumption is easily forgotten, the relationships can be inaccurately realized and quickly overlooked, and an ambiguity can be lost in a mathematical theorization that accounts for only some of the observations in a physical, natural realm. This freezing in theory can prevent creativity because it allows for no new inroads to the imagination. Single-sense restrictions—like the demand for meter readings—limit science. In a similar way language itself may have frozen our ideas too quickly. McLuhan suggests that the dismembering of language, which scientists are doing for the purpose of putting ideas into the retrieval systems of computers, may have a salutary effect on art (and science) by giving us a new look at the inner roots of ideas we thought were indestructible.[27] We call something by misleading words, or we take a name too seriously and forget that for which it stands. This is the argument of the general semanticist.[28] As Rimbaud called for verbal recklessness in poetry, so creativity in all thought requires a certain logical recklessness. The Greeks called their smallest particle an atom, which meant something indivisible; Rutherford saw through this inaccuracy and had the courage to attempt to divide the indivisible.[29] An act of irrationality is necessary in order to break through the rigidity of a symbol system. As Arthur Koestler says, "true creativity often starts where language ends,"[30] which can also apply to mathematics and all symbologies. Irrationality establishes the basis for deeper scientific truths, and the artistic penchant for irrationality makes art a perfect tonic for the scientist. As J. Bronowski argues, and as the remarkable proof of Kurt Gödel demonstrates in logical terms, all logical systems are incomplete, and our understanding is carried into new systems only through illogical jumps. Bronowski says that the imagination in science aims to impoverish itself, suggesting that the grand view is the miserly view because a rich model of the universe is one which is as poor as possible in hypotheses.[31]

The incredulity of the scientist when he is confronted with parallels between physics and modern art, recorded by Siegfried Giedion in *Mechanization Takes Command*,[32] suggests his inability to comprehend the psychology of his own pursuit. The purist in science has justified his activities by claiming to build his theories out of nothing save the logic of the realities he is investigating. The creative potential of this method of science has never been a subject which scientists have felt to be limiting, and therefore it has slyly escaped consideration. When mathematical symbolization has a surfeit of pure mathematical concepts to come to the aid of pure science, when pure science seems to have everything it desires for its theorizing, there seems to be no need to question the basic validity of mathematics as a primary tool for science. To paraphrase McLuhan, however,[33] it seems to me that it is absurd for the scientist to live involuntarily altered in his thinking at the most intimate intuitive and scientific levels by a technical extension of his inner self—his logic system—when he should instead reevaluate this logical motivation to determine if it is in fact immutable.

Earlier scientists knew the sterility of relying only on the mathematical, and if you read the original works of James Clerk Maxwell or Sir Isaac Newton,[34] you are constantly impressed by the fecundity of their minds. Constant asides and seemingly unrelated insights are strewn throughout their work. Galileo and Einstein reflected their broad culture in their writing, as in their lives, and their sciences as a result were the richest products of the human spirit. But turn to any modern scientific journal and you find essays that are the height of sterility, because of an impeccable devotion to a single logic.

The narrow-minded specialist today wonders why theory is so difficult, why no grand scheme exists in which to fit all modern facts. This could be due to the complexity of modern nature as revealed by an electric experimenter, but it could also be due to a lack of sufficiently creative world-views by which the scientist could light up his theorizing. It is analogous to the artist's complaining that the modern world is too confusing and the communicative media too diverting to allow him to rise to truly great art.

The artist too is culpable, of course. Part of the contemporary difficulty is that he has succumbed to the mass communication media and joined the establishment. Art becomes pure entertainment or pure cultural snobbery, depending on the needs of the artist, and all serious explorations into creative communication are given up because they do not fit easily into the living room on the "big eye." A creative communication is by definition hard to grasp because it requires a shift into a new mode of awareness, forcing the audience to make a new jump into an unknown area of humanness. It is as if art, like science or research in the business-oriented world, is refused a position because its meaning is not immediately obvious, and because it is not immediately, practically rewarding. The world loses the imagination which is so necessary to sustain its creative vision into all life, just as the business world stagnates when it does not allow pure research. Fortunately the urge to creativity is so strong in man that there are always underground creators, hidden artists, even in totalitarian states. Yet is even this optimism justified in the face of modern thought-control and mind-bending and mass-communication hysteria?

The view that maintains that the attitude of the eccentric individual is a tonic which gives us perspective on life or on new developments, is, I think, an insufficient *raison d'être* for creative communication in art. The importance of freedom is not to encourage idiosyncrasies, but rather to allow the psyche the isolation and uninterrupted concentration that is necessary to bring forth creative relationships in perceptual as well as other phenomena. This is why groups that try their hands at joint creations, either in art or in science, produce only the simplest and most sterile results; why also, I think, the recent attempts at group science-art are complete nonsense. The jumps of imagination required of the human brain when it ranges into creative territory demand that it be unfettered and on its own, without even the feeling that someone else is looking over the shoulder.*

The understanding of science derives from mental processes as yet not understood, but it seems clear that they result not from a single power or function which can be attributed to certain immutable brain activities. The ongoing development of reason is a growing of form like a web that an industrious artistic spider weaves to catch nature's insects as they happen to fly by. The scientist must adopt the notion that qualitatively nature is infinite, that theory is never-ending, and that no final Aristotelian form exists which encompasses all.[36] And the artist must pursue his craft assuming that the soul is infinitely large, and that it can harbor an ever-growing artistic awareness and an increasingly refined artistic vision. These two infinities seem to meet in some theoretical never-never land to justify each other. The scientist and the artist emerge as opposite sides of the same human process and spirituality—the human condition scientifically striving to know, and enabled to grow by the complementary artistic imaginative enlargement of our human awareness.

Man's science comprehends nature best in perceptual areas that art has proliferated deepest. The scientific mind has but regained from nature that which the artistic mind has put into nature, to paraphrase Eddington.[37] As Barzun indicates it was William James who "swept away forever the machine-inspired image of man as 'a conscious automaton,' and reestablished the mind as myth-maker and artist."[38] Neither the artist nor the scientist seems to appreciate this fact today. Either the failure

* I have elaborated on the pitfalls of group creativity in science and in art in my book *Inventivity*.[35]

of modern science to come to grips with its new experiential reality is due to a lack of comprehension or assimilation of modern art forms, or it is due of a true failure of the modern artist to provide sufficiently powerful images and perceptual awarenesses and psychic attitudes with which the scientist can rationalize his new landscape. Which is the case, only time will tell.

Every age, and especially an age so aware of itself as ours is, must build its own heightened appreciation of its existence and values, using both past art and new scientific insights. We must enlarge our moral perceptions through our art, and expand our humanness in all ways with the generation of a new and meaningful art. The new realities of the future can only be entered into with equanimity and appreciation when our art has adequately prepared us for the experiences they contain. When we have a strong awareness of art at our disposal we will be able to experience the even more unimaginable scientific realities of tomorrow as if we own them—which in fact we do because we create them ourselves through our art.

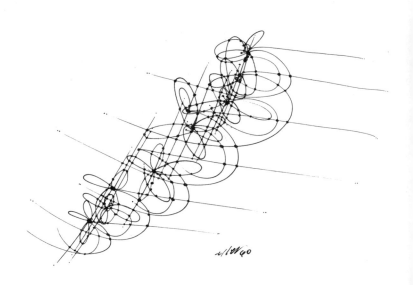

References

Preface

1. Edmund Carpenter and Marshall McLuhan, eds., *Explorations in Communication* (Boston, Beacon Press, 1960); Edward T. Hall, *The Silent Language* (New York, Doubleday, 1959); William M. Ivins, Jr., *Prints and Visual Communication* (Cambridge, Harvard University Press, 1953).
2. John Canaday, "Art: Preview of Seattle World's Fair," *The New York Times*, April 17, 1962.
3. R. E. Mueller, "Science as Art," Communications Center, *International Science and Technology*, No. 42 (June, 1965).
4. Gyorgy Kepes, *Language of Vision* (Chicago, Paul Theobald, 1939); *The New Landscape in Art and Sciences* (Chicago, Paul Theobald, 1962); *Vision and Value* (New York, Braziller, 1965–1966), 6 vols.
5. Norbert Wiener, *Cybernetics* (New York, John Wiley, 1948); Claude Shannon, "The Mathematical Theory of Communication," *Bell System Technical Journal*, 27:80–84 (April, 1950).
6. H. H. Lanier and R. E. Mueller, U. S. Patent No. 2,449,558 (Sept. 21, 1948).
7. R. E. Mueller, *Inventivity* (New York, John Day, 1964); *Inventor's Notebook* (New York, John Day, 1965).
8. T. Munro, *Towards Science in Aesthetics* (New York, The Liberal Arts Press, 1950).
9. F. Kainz, *Aesthetics and Science* (Detroit, Wayne State University Press, 1962).
10. W. B. Honey, *Science and the Creative Arts* (London, Faber & Faber, 1945).

11. J. P. Dabney, *The Musical Basis of Verse* (London, Longmans, Green and Co., 1901).
12. Sidney Lanier, *The Science of English Verse* (New York, Scribners, 1898).
13. Abraham Moles, *Information Theory and Esthetic Perception*, trans. by J. Cohen (Urbana, University of Illinois Press, 1966).
14. Karl W. Deutsch, "Scientific and Humanistic Knowledge in the Growth of Civilization," in H. Brown, ed., *Science and the Creative Spirit* (Toronto, University of Toronto Press, 1958), pp. 21–41.
15. David Hawkins, "The Creativity of Science," *ibid.*, p. 161.
16. C. P. Snow, *The Two Cultures: And a Second Look* (New York, Mentor, 1963).
17. E. H. Gombrich, "The Tradition of General Knowledge," in Mario Bunge, ed., *The Critical Approach to Science and Philosophy* (London, Collier-Macmillan, 1964), p. 431.

Chapter 1: Art and Science

1. Jacques Barzun, *Science: The Glorious Entertainment* (New York, Harper & Row, 1964), pp. 110–112.
2. Aldous Huxley, *Literature and Science* (New York, Harper & Row, 1963), p. 79.
3. David Hawkins, "The Creativity of Science," in H. Brown, ed., *Science and the Creative Spirit* (Toronto, University of Toronto Press, 1958), p. 135.
4. P. A. Coggin, *Art, Science and Religion* (London, George Harrap & Co., 1962).
5. Philipp Frank, *Einstein, His Life and Times* (New York, Knopf, 1947).
6. Bernard Friedman, "What Are Mathematicians Doing?" *Science*, 134:362 (October, 1966).
7. Martin Johnson, *Art and Scientific Thought* (London, Faber and Faber, 1945), p. 15.
8. Marshall McLuhan, *The Gutenberg Galaxy* (Toronto, University of Toronto Press, 1962), p. 35; William Ivins, *Art and Geometry* (Cambridge, Harvard University Press, 1946).
9. Stefan Toulimin and June Goodfield, *The Discovery of Time* (New York, Harper & Row, 1965).
10. George Kubler, *The Shape of Time* (New Haven, Yale University Press, 1962), p. 48–49.
11. Edmund Carpenter and Marshall McLuhan, eds., *Explorations in Communication* (Boston, Beacon Press, 1960), p. 182.
12. Harold Rosenberg, "From Pollock to Pop: Twenty Years of Painting and Sculpture," *Holiday*, 39:96–105 (March, 1966).
13. Barzun, *op. cit.*
14. A. N. Whitehead, *Science and the Modern World* (New York, Mentor, 1948).

15. Marshall McLuhan, *Understanding Media: The Extensions of Man* (New York, McGraw-Hill, 1964), p. 18.
16. Erwin Panofsky, "Style and Medium in the Motion Picture," *Critique*, Vol. I, No. 3 (1947).
17. Maurice Grosser, *The Painter's Eye* (New York, Mentor, 1955).
18. E. H. Gombrich, *Art and Illusion* (New York, Pantheon, 1961), p. 338.
19. Arthur Knight, *The Liveliest Art* (New York, Mentor, 1957), p. 18.
20. *Ibid.*, p. 13.
21. Alex Comfort, *The Novel and Our Time* (London, Phoenix House, 1948).
22. McLuhan, *Understanding Media, op. cit.*, p. 294.
23. Edmund Carpenter, "The New Languages," in Carpenter and McLuhan, *op. cit.*, p. 162.
24. Gyorgy Kepes, *The New Landscape in Art and Science* (Chicago, Paul Theobald, 1962).
25. H. Bruce Franklin, *Future Perfect* (New York, Oxford University Press, 1966).
26. Norman O. Brown, *Love's Body* (New York, Random House, 1966).
27. Aldous Huxley, *Brave New World* (New York, Harper & Brothers, 1946).
28. George Orwell, *1984* (New York, Harcourt, Brace, 1949).
29. Marshall McLuhan, *The Mechanical Bride* (New York, The Vanguard Press, 1951), p. 4.
30. Marcel Jean, *The History of Surrealist Painting* (Paris, Grove Press, Editions du Seuil, 1950).
31. John Canaday, "Art: Preview of Seattle World's Fair," *The New York Times*, April 17, 1962.
32. E. Jahnke and F. Emde, *Table of Functions* (New York, Dover, 1945).
33. Honoré de Balzac, *Le chef-d'oeuvre inconnu* (Paris, Ambroise Vollard, 1926).
34. Barzun, *op. cit.*, p. 215.
35. Carpenter and McLuhan, *op. cit.*
36. André Malraux, *Voices of Silence* (Garden City, Doubleday, 1953).
37. Alexander Korzybski, *Manhood of Humanity* (New York, Dutton, 1921); *Science and Sanity* (Lakeville, Conn., International Non-Aristotelian Library Publishing Company, 1933).
38. Norman O. Brown, *Life Against Death* (New York, Random House, 1959), p. 67.
39. Barzun, *op. cit.*, Chap. XII.

Chapter 2: Cybernetics and Art

1. J. R. Pierce, *Symbols, Signals and Noise* (New York, Harper and Brothers, 1961).
2. Abraham Moles, *Information Theory and Esthetic Perception*, trans. by J. Cohen, (Urbana, University of Illinois Press, 1966).

3. Norbert Wiener, *I Am a Mathematician* (Cambridge, M.I.T. Press, 1958).

4. Norbert Wiener, *God and Golem, Inc.* (New York, John Wiley, 1965).

5. Northrop Frye, "The Instruments of Mental Production," *Chicago Review*, 18 (1966).

6. Norbert Wiener, *Cybernetics* (New York, John Wiley, 1948).

7. B. F. Miessner and J. H. Hammondy, "The Mechanical Dog" *Popular Mechanics* (November, 1924).

8. W. R. Ashby, *Design for a Brain* (New York, John Wiley, 1960); W. Grey Walter, *The Living Brain* (New York, W. W. Norton, 1953); Claude Shannon, "Presentation of a Maze-Solving Machine," *Cybernetics, 8th Conference* (New York, Macy Foundation, 1952).

9. Morse Peckham, *Man's Rage for Chaos* (Philadelphia, Chilton, 1965).

10. Wiener, *Cybernetics, op. cit.*

11. Claude Shannon, "The Mathematical Theory of Communication," *Bell System Technical Journal*, 27:80–84 (April, 1950).

12. L. Brillouin, *Scientific Uncertainty, and Information* (New York, Academic Press, 1964).

13. L. Szilard, "Über die Entropienerminderung in einen thermodynamischen System bei Eingriffen Intelligenter Wesen," *Zeitschrif Physik*, 53:840 (1929).

14. Werner Heisenberg, *Nuclear Physics* (New York, Philosophical Library, 1953).

15. Wiener, *Cybernetics, op. cit.*, p. 58.

16. Colin Cherry, *On Human Communication* (New York, John Wiley, 1957), p. 241.

17. Brillouin, *op. cit.*

18. "Language Analysis and Mechanical Translation," in Colin Cherry, ed., *Information Theory* (London, Butterworths Scientific Publications, 1956).

19. W. Fucks, "Mathematical Analysis of Formal Structure of Music," IRE (IEEE), *Transactions on Information Theory*, Vol. IT8 (September, 1962).

20. G. K. Zipf, *Human Behavior and the Principle of Least Effort* (Cambridge, Addison-Wesley Press, 1949).

21. Peckham, *op. cit.*

22. Rudolph Arnheim, *Art and Visual Perception* (Los Angeles, University of California Press, 1954).

23. Gyorgy Kepes, *The New Landscape in Art and Science* (Chicago, Paul Theobald, 1956).

24. Northrop Frye, "The Language of Poetry," in Edmund Carpenter and Marshall McLuhan, eds., *Explorations in Communication* (Boston, Beacon Press, 1960).

25. Kenneth Clark, "The Blot and the Diagram," *Encounter*, 20:I (January, 1963).

26. Shannon, "The Mathematical Theory of Communication," *op. cit.*

27. N. Nyquist, "Certain Factors Affecting Telegraphic Speed," *Bell Telephone System Technical Journal*, 3:324 (1924).
28. R. V. L. Hartley, "Transmission of Information," *Bell Telephone System Technical Journal*, 7:535 (1928).
29. A. Kolmogoroff, "Interpolation und Extrapolation von stationärem zufälligen Folgen," *Bulletin of the Academy of Science*, U.S.S.R., serial mathematics 5:3–14 (1942).
30. "Philology by Machine," *Scientific American*, 197:64 (October, 1957).
31. Shannon, "The Mathematical Theory of Communication," *op. cit.*
32. Moles, *op. cit.*
33. Richard C. Pinkerton, "Information Theory and Melody," *Scientific American*, 94:77 (February, 1956).
34. Fucks, *op. cit.*
35. Arnold Schoenberg, *Structural Functions of Harmony* (New York, W. W. Norton, 1954).
36. George D. Birkhoff, *Aesthetic Measure* (Cambridge, Harvard University Press, 1933).
37. Hans Tischler, "The Aesthetic Experience," *The Music Review*, 17:189 (1956).
38. C. K. Ogden and I. A. Richards, *The Meaning of Meaning* (London, Routledge and Kegnor Paul, Ltd., 1949); D. M. MacKay, "The Place of Meaning in Information Theory," *Information Theory, op. cit.*, p. 215; D. K. C. MacDonald, "Information Theory and Knowledge," *Journal of Applied Physics*, 25:619 (1954).
39. Philip Solomon, *Sensory Deprivation* (Cambridge, Harvard University Press, 1961).
40. J. J. Jasper and others, *Reticular Formation of the Brain* (Boston, Little Brown & Co., 1958).
41. G. Révész, *Psychology and Art of the Blind*, trans. by H. Wolff (New York, Longmans, Green & Co., 1950).
42. Georg Von Békésy, *Experiments in Hearing*, trans. by E. G. Wever (New York, McGraw-Hill, 1960), p. 332.
43. Max Wertheimer, "Laws of Organization in Perceptual Forms," in W. D. Ellis, ed., *A Source Book of Gestalt Psychology* (New York, Harcourt, Brace, 1938), pp. 71–78.
44. R. E. Mueller, "On Supplementing Human Faculties" (Letter to the Editor), *Science*, 130:298 (August 7, 1959).
45. H. Hydén, *Proceedings of the Fourth International Congress of Biological Chemistry* (London, Pergamon Press, 1958), Vol. 3, p. 88.
46. Brillouin, *op. cit.*, p. 29.
47. Shannon, "The Mathematical Theory of Communication," *op. cit.*; Fucks, *op. cit.*
48. Kurt Gödel, "Über formal unentscheidbare Sätze der Principia Mathematik und verwandter Systeme I," *Monatschefte für Mathematik und Physik*, 38:173–198 (1931); E. Nagel and J. R. Newman, *Godel's Proof* (New York, New York University Press, 1960).

49. Brillouin, *op. cit.*, p. 34.
50. Fucks, *op. cit.*
51. L. Hiller, Jr., and L. Isaacson, *Experimental Music* (New York, McGraw-Hill, 1959).
52. David Hawkins, "The Creativity of Science," in H. Brown, ed., *Science and the Creative Spirit* (Toronto, University of Toronto Press, 1958), pp. 127–163.

Chapter 3: The Creativity of Art

1. Susanne K. Langer, *Feeling and Form* (New York, Scribners, 1953).
2. *Ibid.*
3. Albert Hofstadter, *Truth and Art* (New York, Columbia University Press, 1965).
4. Benjamin Whorf, "Science and Linguistics," *The Technology Press Review*, Vol. XLII, No. 6 (April, 1940); G. H. Mead, *Mind, Self, and Society, from the Standpoint of a Social Behaviorist* (Chicago, University of Chicago Press, 1934).
5. Teilhard de Chardin, *The Phenomenon of Man* (New York, Harper & Brothers, 1959).
6. Peter Berlinrut, Roosevelt, New Jersey, private communication.
7. Marshall McLuhan, *The Mechanical Bride* (New York, The Vanguard Press, 1951); Norman O. Brown, *Life Against Death* (New York, Random House, 1955).
8. Arthur Koestler, *The Act of Creation* (London, Hutchinson, 1964).
9. E. H. Gombrich, *Art and Illusion* (New York, Pantheon, 1961).
10. Abraham Moles, *Information Theory and Esthetic Perception*, trans. by J. Cohen (Urbana, University of Illinois Press, 1966).
11. Leonard B. Meyer, *Emotion and Meaning in Music* (Chicago, University of Chicago Press, 1956).
12. William Empson, *Seven Types of Ambiguity* (New York, Meridian, 1955).
13. W. Grey Walter, *The Living Brain* (New York, W. W. Norton, 1953).
14. Max Wertheimer, *Productive Thinking* (New York, Harper & Brothers, 1959).
15. McLuhan, *op. cit.*
16. Brown, *op. cit.*, p. 61.

Chapter 4: The Communication of Art

1. Fletcher Pratt, *Secret and Urgent* (Indianapolis, Bobbs-Merrill, 1939).
2. Leonardo da Vinci, *Treatise on Painting*, A. Philip McMahon, ed. (Princeton, Princeton University Press, 1956).
3. Alexander Cozzens, "A New Method of Assisting the Invention in Drawing Original Compositions of Landscape," 1785, in Paul Oppé, *Alexander and John Robert Cozzens* (London, n.p., 1952).
4. Ben Shahn, *The Shape of Content* (Cambridge, Harvard University Press, 1957).

5. Ben Shahn, private communication.
6. Robert Graves, *The Greek Myths* (Baltimore, Penguin Books, 1955).
7. Marcel Jean, *The History of Surrealist Paintings* (Paris, Grove Press, Editions du Seuil, 1950).
8. Edward Albee, *Who's Afraid of Virginia Woolf* (New York, Atheneum, 1962).
9. Paul Tannenbaum, "Letter to the Editor," Theater Section, *The New York Times*, July 24, 1966.
10. Françoise Gilot and Carolton Lake, *Life with Picasso* (New York, Mc-Graw-Hill, 1964).
11. D. J. Henahan, "Serious Music: In Serious Trouble," *Holiday*, 39:106–8 (March, 1966).
12. The tenor Clarence Moore, Roosevelt, New Jersey, stimulated this suggestion.
13. Marshall McLuhan, *Understanding Media: The Extensions of Man* (New York, McGraw-Hill, 1964), p. 282.
14. Northrop Frye, "Language of Poetry," in Edmund Carpenter and Marshall McLuhan, eds., *Explorations in Communication* (Boston, Beacon Press, 1960).
15. Jean, *op. cit.*
16. James Joyce, *A Portrait of the Artist as a Young Man* (New York, Penguin Signet Book, 1948), p. 168.
17. Maurice Grosser, *The Painter's Eye* (New York, Mentor, 1955).
18. E. H. Gombrich, *Art and Illusion* (New York, Pantheon, 1961); Rudolph Arnheim, *Art and Visual Perception* (Los Angeles, University of California Press, 1954).
19. André Malraux, *Voices of Silence* (Garden City, Doubleday, 1953).

Chapter 5: Music as a Message

1. D. Stevens and A. Robertson, *The Pelican History of Music*, Vol. 1, (Baltimore, Penguin Books, 1960), p. 16.
2. *Ibid.*, pp. 100–1.
3. Paul Hindemith, *A Composer's World* (New York, Doubleday, 1961), p. 6.
4. J. J. Fux, *Steps to Parnassus* (New York, W. W. Norton, 1943).
5. H. L. F. Helmholtz, *On the Sensations of Tone* (New York, Dover, 1954).
6. Paul Hindemith, *The Craft of Musical Composition*, Vol. 1 (London, Schott, 1945).
7. Hindemith, *A Composer's World, op. cit.*, p. 20–25.
8. Leonard B. Meyer, *Emotion and Meaning in Music* (Chicago, University of Chicago Press, 1956).
9. Susanne K. Langer, *Feeling and Form* (New York, Scribners, 1953).
10. Meyer, *op. cit.*
11. Theodore Reik, *The Haunting Melody* (New York, Farrar, Straus and Young, 1953).

12. Albert Hofstadter, *Truth and Art* (New York, Columbia University Press, 1965).

13. Abraham Moles, *Information Theory and Esthetic Perception*, trans. by J. Cohen (Urbana, University of Illinois Press, 1966), p. 104.

14. *Ibid.*, p. 105.

15. Langer, *op. cit.*, chapter 1.

16. Moles, *op. cit.*, p. 192.

17. *Ibid.*, p. 197.

18. Georg Von Békésy, *Experiments in Hearing*, trans. by E. G. Wever (New York, McGraw-Hill, 1960), p. 332; C. J. Hirsch, "Some Aspects of Binaural Sound," *Spectrum* (February, 1967).

19. A. B. Wood, *A Textbook of Sound* (London, George Bell, 1930).

20. Dayton C. Miller, *The Science of Musical Tones* (New York, Macmillan, 1926).

21. Theodore Reik, *Dogma and Compulsion* (New York, International Universities Press, 1951); *The Unknown Murder* (New York, Prentice-Hall, 1945).

22. Gunther Schuller, *Seven Studies After Paul Klee*, RCA Victor LM-2879.

23. H. F. Olsen and H. Belar, "The Electronic Music Synthesizer," *Journal of the Acoustical Society of America*, 27:595 (1955); Olsen, Belar, and J. Timmons, "The Composition of Electronic Music," *ibid.*, 32:311 (1960).

24. *The Sounds and Music of the RCA Electronic Music Synthesizer*, RCA Victor LM-1922.

25. Erich Fromm, *Escape from Freedom* (New York, Farrar, 1941).

26. Theobald Boehm, *The Flute and Flute Playing*, D. C. Miller, ed. (Cleveland, Case School, 1922).

27. Mel Powell, "Electronic Music and Musical Newness," *American Scholar*, Vol. 35, No. 2 (Spring, 1966).

28. Von Békésy, *op. cit.*, p. 272.

29. Colin Cherry, "A History of the Theory of Information," paper read to the Royal Society, 1951.

30. Marshall McLuhan, *The Gutenberg Galaxy* (Toronto, University of Toronto Press, 1962); William M. Ivins, Jr., *Prints and Visual Communication* (Cambridge, Harvard University Press, 1953).

31. André Malraux, *The Voices of Silence* (Garden City, Doubleday, 1953).

32. *Panorama of Music Concrete*, Vol. I, London OTL-93090; Vol. II, London DTL-93121.

33. K. Stockhausen, *Gesang der Junglinge*, Studie I, II, DG-16133.

34. L. Hiller, Jr., and L. Isaacson, *Experimental Music* (New York, McGraw-Hill, 1959).

35. Composers Recording Inc. (CRI) has devoted many records to contemporary electronic music.

36. Dr. H. Olsen, RCA Research Laboratories, Princeton, New Jersey, private communication.

37. Mario Davidovsky, *Three Synchronisms for Instruments and Electronic Sounds*, CRI SD-204.
38. H. Klein, "Old and New, Good and Bad," *The New York Times*, Section X, May 8, 1966, p. 21.
39. Rudolph Arnheim, *Art and Visual Perception* (Los Angeles, University of California Press, 1954).
40. Langer, *op. cit.*
41. Leo Tolstoy, *What Is Art?* (London, Oxford University Press, 1959).
42. Salomon Bochner, *The Role of Mathematics in the Rise of Science* (Princeton, Princeton University Press, 1966).
43. Paul Hindemith, *A Composer's World, op. cit.*, p. 9.
44. A. Moszkowski, *Einstein* (Hamburg, Hoffmann, 1921).

Chapter 6: Visual Communication

1. Eugène Délacroix, *The Journal of Eugène Délacroix*, II. Wellington, ed. (London, Phaidon Press, 1951).
2. E. H. Gombrich, *Art and Illusion* (New York, Pantheon, 1961).
3. E. Gilson, *Painting and Reality* (New York, Pantheon, 1957).
4. Susanne K. Langer, *Problems of Art* (New York, Scribners, 1957).
5. Ortega y Gasset, *The Dehumanization of Art* (New York, Doubleday, 1956).
6. Rudolph Arnheim, *Art and Visual Perception* (Los Angeles, University of California Press, 1954).
7. *Ibid.*, p. 441.
8. Walter Pitts and W. S. McCulloch, "How We Know Universals: The Perception of Auditory and Visual Forms," *Bulletin of Mathematical Biophysics*, IX:127–47 (1947).
9. Susanne K. Langer, *Philosophical Sketches* (New York, Mentor, 1964), p. 67–68.
10. Arnheim, *op. cit.*, p. 164.
11. John Dewey, *Art as Experience* (New York, Minton, Balch, 1934).
12. Norbert Wiener, *Cybernetics* (New York, John Wiley, 1948), p. 180.
13. Herman Hesse, *The Bead Game* (New York, Knopf, 1951).
14. Leonard B. Meyer, *Emotion and Meaning in Music* (Chicago, University of Chicago Press, 1956), p. 35.
15. Arnheim, *op. cit.*, p. 9.
16. Edwin H. Land, "Experiments in Color Vision," *Scientific American* (May, 1959), p. 84.
17. William James, *Psychology* (New York, Dover, 1950), Vol. II, p. 457.
18. Harold Speed, *The Practice and Science of Drawing* (Seely Services and Co., 1939).
19. Marshall McLuhan, *The Mechanical Bride* (New York, The Vanguard Press, 1951).
20. Kenneth Clark, "The Blot and the Diagram," *Encounter*, Vol. XX, No. I (January, 1963).
21. Kenneth Clark, *The Nude* (New York, Pantheon, 1956).

22. The Editors, "The Future of Urban Environment," *Progressive Architecture* (October, 1964), p. 168.
23. Marshall McLuhan, *Understanding Media: The Extensions of Man* (New York, McGraw-Hill, 1964).
24. W. C. Seitz, *The Responsive Eye* (New York, The Museum of Modern Art, 1965).
25. Gombrich, *op. cit.*
26. G. M. Wyburn and others, *Human Senses and Perception* (London, Oliver and Boyd, 1964).
27. W. Grey Walter, *The Living Brain* (New York, W. W. Norton, 1953).
28. Marcel Jean, *The History of Surrealist Painting* (Paris, Grove Press, Editions du Seuil, 1950), p. 253.
29. *Ibid.*, p. 101.
30. Arnheim, *op. cit.*, p. 339–55.
31. Land, *op. cit.*
32. 1955, Lotte Jacobi Gallery, New York (now located in Deering, New Hampshire).
33. Lillian Lieber, *The Education of T. C. Mits* (New York, W. W. Norton, 1944).
34. Aristotle, *De Sensu* (Cambridge, The University Press, 1906).
35. *Encyclopaedia Britannica*, 14th ed., London-New York, Vol. 6, p. 64.
36. Aurelia Bataglia, then another Disney animator, private communication.
37. Arthur Knight, *The Liveliest Art* (New York, Mentor, 1957), p. 100–2.
38. Jean, *op. cit.*
39. R. E. Lewis and N. McLaren, "Synthetic Sound on Film," *Journal of the Society of Motion Picture Engineers*, 50:233 (1948).
40. P. H. Emerson, *Naturalistic Photography* (London, n.p., 1889).
41. Lewis Mumford, *Techniques and Civilization* (New York, Harcourt, 1934).
42. Waldo Frank, ed., *America and Alfred Stieglitz* (New York, The Literary Guild, 1934), p. 116.
43. Gyorgy Kepes, *The New Landscape in Art and Science* (Chicago, Paul Theobald, 1962).
44. Frank, *op. cit.*, p. 116.
45. David M. Pratt, "Painting, Music and Sunshine," (Letter to the Editor) *The Scientific Monthly* (October, 1955).

Chapter 7: Vivifying with Words

1. Charles Morris, *Signs, Language and Behavior* (New York, Prentice-Hall, 1946).
2. Noam Chomsky, *Syntactic Structures* (s'-Gravenhague, Mouton and Co., 1957).
3. Sidney Lanier, *The Science of English Verse* (New York, Scribners, 1898).
4. E. H. Gombrich, "Meditations on a Hobby Horse," in L. L. Whyte, ed., *Aspects of Form* (Bloomington, Inidana University Press, 1951), p. 316.

5. Arthur Koestler, *The Act of Creation* (London, Hutchinson, 1964).

6. Edmund Carpenter and Marshall McLuhan, eds., *Explorations in Communication* (Boston, Beacon Press, 1960), p. 181.

7. William Empson, *Seven Types of Ambiguity* (New York, Meridian, 1955).

8. Emily Dickinson, *Complete Poems* (Cambridge, Harvard University Press, 1955).

9. T. S. Eliot, *Complete Poems* (New York, Harcourt, 1952).

10. John Ciardi, *How Does a Poem Mean?* (Boston, Houghton Mifflin, 1960).

11. Albert Hofstadter, *Truth and Art* (New York, Columbia University Press, 1965), p. 73–85.

12. Robert Scholes, "George Is My Name," *The New York Times Book Review*, August 7, 1966, p. 22.

13. WNDT, Channel 13, New York, Discussion of *Finnegan's Wake*, May 15, 1966.

14. Robert Warshow, *The Immediate Experience* (New York, Doubleday, 1962).

15. John Wilson, "Film Literacy in Africa," *Canadian Communications*, Vol. 1, No. 4 (Spring, 1961), p. 7–14.

16. Simon O. Lesser, *Fiction and the Unconscious* (Boston, Beacon Press, 1957).

17. *Ibid.*

18. *Ibid.*, p. 15.

19. Erich Fromm, *The Art of Loving* (New York, Harper & Brothers, 1956).

20. Aldous Huxley, *Literature and Science* (New York, Harper & Row, 1963).

21. Carpenter and McLuhan, *op. cit.*

22. Marshall McLuhan, *The Gutenberg Galaxy* (Toronto, University of Toronto Press, 1962), p. 142.

23. Edmund Carpenter, "The New Languages," in Carpenter and McLuhan, *op. cit.*, p. 170–71.

24. Denis Diderot, *The Paradox of Acting* (London, Chatto & Windus, 1883).

25. Leonard B. Meyer, *Emotion and Meaning in Music* (Chicago, University of Chicago Press, 1956), p. 197.

26. Brander Matthews, ed., *Papers on Acting* (New York, Hill and Wang, 1958), p. 122.

27. Lecture-demonstration given in Roosevelt, New Jersey, January, 1966, for SNCC.

28. Marjorie Batchelder, *Rod Puppets and the Human Theater* (Columbus, Ohio State University Press, 1947).

29. Bertolt Brecht, *Brecht on Theater* (London, Methuen, 1964).

30. E. Gordon Craig, *On the Art of the Theater* (London, W. Heinemann, 1914).

31. Hanns Sachs, *The Creative Unconscious* (Cambridge, Massachusetts, Sci-Art Publishers, 1951).

32. Broadcast interview with Marshall McLuhan, WNBC, April 24, 1966.

33. Batchelder, *op. cit.*

34. Peter Arnott, *Plays Without People* (Bloomington, Indiana University Press, 1964).

35. Sachs, *op. cit.*, p. 181.

36. Alexandre Bakshy, "The Lesson of the Puppet," *Theater Arts Monthly*, 12:486 (July, 1928).

37. Marcel Jean, *The History of Surrealist Painting* (Paris, Grove Press, Editions du Seuil, 1950), p. 66.

38. APA production of an adaptation by Erwin Piscator, Alfred Newmann, and Guntrum Prufer of Leo Tolstoy's novel *War and Peace*, presented at the Phoenix and Lyceum theaters, New York City, seasons 1965–67; artistic director, Ellis Rabb.

39. Arthur Schopenhauer, *The Works of Schopenhauer*, W. Durant, ed. (New York, Simon and Schuster, 1931).

Chapter 8: The Computer Apprentice

1. E. A. Poe, "Maelzel's Chess Player," *The Works of Edgar Allan Poe* (New York, Scribners, 1894–1895).

2. A. Bernstein and M. de V. Roberts, "Computers vs. Chess-Player," *Scientific American*, 198:22 (June, 1958); "Computer Chess Won by Stanford," *The New York Times*, Section I, November 27, 1966, p. 50.

3. James T. Culbertson, *The Minds of Robots* (Urbana, University of Illinois Press, 1963).

4. Ulric Neisser, "The Imitation of Man by Machines," *Science*, 18:194 (January, 1965).

5. *Ibid.*

6. Norbert Wiener, *Cybernetics* (New York, John Wiley, 1948).

7. W. A. Mozart, *The Dice Composer*, K. anh. 294a, A. Laszlo, ed. (Hollywood, Guild Publications of California, Inc., n.d.).

8. L. Hiller, Jr., and L. Isaacson, *Experimental Music* (New York, McGraw-Hill, 1959).

9. Gyorgy Kepes, *The New Landscape in Art and Science* (Chicago, Paul Theobald, 1962).

10. Bela Julesz, "Texture and Visual Perception," *Scientific American*, 212:2 (February, 1965).

11. Börje Langefors, "Automated Design," *International Science and Technology*, 26:90 (February, 1964).

12. Victor H. Yngve, "Computer Programs for Translation," *Scientific American*, 206:40 (June, 1962).

13. D. Climenson and others, "Automatic Syntax Analysis," *American Documentation* (June, 1962), p. 68.

14. Sol Yurick, author of *The Warriors* (New York, Holt, Rinehart, and Winston, 1965), and *Fertig* (New York, Phoenix Press, 1966).

15. R. E. Mueller, "On Supplementing Human Faculties," (Letter to the Editor) *Science*, 130:298 (August 7, 1959).
16. Culbertson, *op. cit.*

Chapter 9: The Modern Artist

1. Marion Milner, *On Not Being Able to Paint* (New York, International Universities Press, 1957).
2. Günter Grass, *The Plebians Rehearse an Uprising*, trans. by Ralph Manheim (Harcourt, Brace & World, 1966).
3. *Victor Vasarely* (Neuchatel, Switzerland, Editions du Griffon, 1966).
4. Marshall McLuhan, *The Mechanical Bride* (New York, The Vanguard Press, 1951).
5. WNDT, "McLuhan on McLuhanism," *Sunday Showcase*, May 15, 1966.
6. Edmund Wilson, "André Malraux: Museum Without Walls," in *The Bit Between My Teeth* (New York, Farrar, Straus and Giroux, 1965), p. 145.
7. Marshall McLuhan, *Understanding Media: The Extensions of Man* (New York, McGraw-Hill, 1964).
8. M. Esslin, "Now All Artists Are Surrealists," *The New York Times Magazine*, May 22, 1966, p. 32.
9. Jacques Maritain, *Creative Intuition in Art and Poetry* (New York, Meridian, 1955).
10. Jacques Barzun, *The Energies of Art* (New York, Harper & Brothers, 1956).

Chapter 10: The Artistic Vision

1. Karl R. Popper, *The Logic of Scientific Discovery* (New York, Basic Books, 1959).
2. Mario Bunge, *The Myth of Simplicity* (Englewood Cliffs, New Jersey, Prentice-Hall, 1963).
3. Mario Bunge, ed., *The Critical Approach to Science and Philosophy* (London, Collier-Macmillan, 1964).
4. C. P. Snow, *The Two Cultures: And a Second Look* (New York, Mentor, 1963).
5. Martin Johnson, *Art and Scientific Thought* (London, Faber & Faber, 1945).
6. L. L. Whyte, ed., *Aspects of Form* (Bloomington, Indiana University Press, 1951), p. 3.
7. Jacob Landau, "Yes-No, Art-Technology," *Wilson Library Bulletin* (September, 1966), p. 42.
8. Robert Preusser, "Vision in Engineering," *International Science and Technology*, 46:61 (October, 1965).
9. Marshall McLuhan, *The Gutenberg Galaxy* (Toronto, University of Toronto Press, 1962).

10. Theodore Reik, *The Haunting Melody* (New York, Farrar, Straus and Young, 1953).

11. William James, *The Varieties of Religious Experience* (New Hyde Park, New York, University Books, 1963); Erik Erikson, *Young Man Luther* (New York, W. W. Norton, 1958); Weston La Barre, *The Peyote Cult* (Hamden, Connecticut, The Shoestring Press, 1964); David Solomon, ed., *LSD—The Consciousness Expanding Drug*, introduction by Timothy Leary (New York, Putnam, 1964).

12. Robert Graves, "Journey to Paradise," *Holiday*, 32:36–37, (August, 1962).

13. Marion Milner, *On Not Being Able to Paint* (New York, International Universities Press, 1957); Albert Camus, *The Fall* (New York, Knopf, 1957).

14. Norbert Wiener, *Cybernetics* (New York, John Wiley, 1948).

15. Abraham Moles, *La Création Scientifique* (Geneva, 1957), quoted in Jacques Barzun, *Science: The Glorious Entertainment* (New York, Harper & Row, 1964), p. 93.

16. Herbert Butterfield, *The Origins of Modern Science* (London, Bell, 1949).

17. Michael Polanyi, *The Tacit Dimensions* (New York, Doubleday, 1966); *Personal Knowledge* (London, Routledge and Kegan Paul, 1958).

18. Morse Peckham, *Man's Rage for Chaos* (Philadelphia, Chilton, 1965).

19. Rudolph Arnheim, *Art and Visual Perception* (Los Angeles, University of California Press, 1954).

20. Eugene Kaellis, "Society for Holistic Biology," (Letter to the Editor), *Science*, 140:1362 (June, 1963).

21. Mary B. Hesse, *Models and Analogies in Science* (Notre Dame, University of Notre Dame Press, 1966).

22. Susanne K. Langer, *Feeling and Form* (New York, Scribners, 1953).

23. L. Hiller and J. Beauchamp, "Research in Music with Electronics," *Science*, 150:161 (October 8, 1965).

24. Milner, *op. cit.*, p. 139–40.

25. H. G. Cassidy, *The Sciences and the Arts* (New York, Harper & Brothers, 1962).

26. Bunge, *The Myth of Simplicity, op. cit.*

27. Broadcast interview with Marshall McLuhan, WNBC, April 24, 1966.

28. S. I. Hayakawa, *Language in Action* (New York, Harcourt, Brace, 1941).

29. Arthur Koestler, *The Act of Creation* (London, Hutchinson, 1964).

30. *Ibid.*, p. 177.

31. J. Bronowsky, *Science and Human Values* (New York, Harper & Row, 1959); "The Machinery of Nature," *Encounter* (November, 1965), p. 53.

32. S. Giedion, *Mechanization Takes Command* (New York, Oxford University Press, 1948).

33. Marshall McLuhan, *op. cit.*, p. 183.

34. J. C. Maxwell, *The Scientific Papers of James Clerk Maxwell* (New York, Dover, 1952); I. Newton, *The Mathematical Principles of Natural Philosophy* (New York, Philosophical Library, 1964).
35. R. E. Mueller, *Inventivity* (New York, John Day, 1964).
36. David Boehm, *Causality and Chance in Modern Physics* (Princeton, Van Nostrand, 1957).
37. J. W. N. Sullivan, *The Limitations of Science* (New York, Mentor, 1933), p. 144.
38. Jacques Barzun, *The Energies of Art* (New York, Vintage Books, 1962), p. 339.

INDEX